AMERICAN BOOK COMPANY'S

PASSING THE
OHIO
GRADUATION TEST
IN
MATHEMATICS
REVISED EDITION

COLLEEN PINTOZZI
ERICA DAY
ALAN FUQUA

AMERICAN BOOK COMPANY
P O BOX 2638
WOODSTOCK, GEORGIA 30188-1383
TOLL FREE: 1 (888) 264-5877   PHONE: 770-928-2834   FAX 770-928-7483
WEB SITE: www.americanbookcompany.com

ACKNOWLEDGMENTS

In preparing this book, the authors would like to acknowledge the editorial assistance of the following individuals: Dr. Frank Pintozzi, Devin Pintozzi, Mary Reagan, Callie Aubrey, and Marsha Klosowski. Also, thank you to Mary Stoddard for graphics. We would also like to express our appreciation to Dr. Tim Teitloff of Kennesaw State University for writing the following sections of Chapter 20 (Patterns and Problem Solving): Inductive Reasoning and Patterns, and Finding a Rule for Patterns. Finally, we would like to thank my many students whose needs and questions inspired us to write this text.

TABLE OF CONTENTS

OHIO MATHEMATICS

Preface

PASSING THE OHIO GRADUATION TEST will help students preparing for the mathematics portion of the test. This book will also assist students who have failed the mathematics test, and who want to review concepts, skills, and strategies before taking the test again. **The materials in this book are based on the objectives and content descriptions for the Ohio Graduation Test in Mathematics published by the Ohio Department of Education.** This book contains several sections. These sections are as follows: 1) General information about the test; 2) A Diagnostic Test; 3) Chapters that teach the concepts and skills emphasized on the test; 4) Two Practice Tests. Answers to the tests and exercises are in a separate manual.

We welcome comments and suggestions about the book. Please contact the author at

American Book Company
PO Box 2638
Woodstock, GA 30188-1383
Toll Free: 1 (888) 264-5877
Phone: (770) 928-2834
Fax: (770) 928-7483
Web Site: www.americanbookcompany.com

ABOUT THE AUTHORS

Colleen Pintozzi has taught mathematics at the middle school, junior high, senior high, and adult level for 22 years. She holds a B.S. degree from Wright State University in Dayton, Ohio and has done graduate work at Wright State University, Duke University, and the University of North Carolina at Chapel Hill. She is the author of seven mathematics books including such best-sellers as *Basics Made Easy: Mathematics Review, Passing the Georgia High School Graduation Test in Mathematics, Writing, and English Language Arts, Passing the TCAP Competency Test in Mathematics, Passing the LEAP 21 Graduation Exit Exam,* and *Passing the ISTEP 7&8 & GQE in Mathematics.*

Erica Day is working on a Bachelor of Science Degree in Mathematics at Kennesaw State University, Kennesaw, GA. She is a senior and has been on the Dean's List for her entire undergraduate career. She has also tutored all levels of mathematics, ranging from high school algebra and geometry to university-level statistics and linear algebra. She is currently participating in a mathematics internship for American Book Company, where she does writing and editing.

Alan Fuqua graduated from the Georgia Institute of Technology with a Bachelor of Chemical Engineering degree. He has over fifteen years of industrial experience in the manufacture of inorganic chemicals, including implementing lean manufacturing principles and training employees. He has extensive experience applying statistical models and Six Sigma principles to process improvement and cost savings. He is currently working as a math writer for the American Book Company while he finishes his degree in Secondary Math Education at Kennesaw State University.

PREPARING FOR THE OHIO GRADUATION TEST IN MATHEMATICS

INTRODUCTION

If you are a student in an Ohio school district, you must pass the **Ohio Graduation Test (OGT) in Mathematics** to receive a high school diploma. Students who enter 10th grade after July 1, 2004 must pass all five subject areas, reading, writing, mathematics, science, and social studies, of the OGT in order to graduate.

In this book, you'll prepare for the **Ohio Graduation Test in Mathematics**. The questions and answers that follow will provide you with general information about this test.

In this book, you'll take a **Diagnostic Test** to determine your strengths and areas for improvement. In the chapters, you'll learn and practice the skills and strategies that are important in preparing for this test. The last sections contain two practice tests that will provide further preparation for the actual **OGT in Mathematics**.

What Is on the Ohio Graduation Test in Mathematics?

The mathematics portion of the **OGT** is administered as one test. The test consists of 32 multiple-choice questions, 5 short answer questions, and 1 extended response questions. Calculators are allowed.

Why Must I Pass the Ohio Graduation Test in Mathematics?

You are required to pass this test for several reasons. First, the state of Ohio, your future employers, and your community need an educated workforce. Secondly, today's high school graduates will need to adapt to rapidly changing technology throughout their lives. Employees without basic mathematics skills in computation, measurement, algebra, and geometry will be unable to compete in the workplace. Without these skills, there's a great chance they will not only be unemployed but unemployable. Thirdly, by demonstrating your mathematics ability, you can show what you have learned in school and apply this knowledge to new situations and experiences.

How Much Time Do I Have To Take the Test?

The test will be timed at approximately 2 hours and 30 minutes.

Ohio Graduation Test Mathematics Review Sheet

Area (A) Formulas

parallelogram: $A = bh$

rectangle: $A = lw$

trapezoid: $A = \frac{1}{2}h(b_1 + b_2)$

triangle: $A = \frac{1}{2}bh$

Circle Formulas

$C = 2\pi r \quad \pi \cong 3.14 \text{ or } \frac{22}{7}$

$A = \pi r^2$

Volume (V) Formulas

cone: $V = \frac{1}{3}\pi r^2 h$

cylinder: $V = \pi r^2 h$

pyramid: $V = \frac{1}{3}Bh \quad B = \text{area of base}$

rectangular prism: $V = lwh$

right prism: $V = Bh \quad B = \text{area of base}$

sphere: $V = \frac{4}{3}\pi r^3$

Combinations

$_nC_r = C(n,r) = \dfrac{n!}{r!(n-r)!}$

Permutations

$_nP_r = P(n,r) = \dfrac{n!}{(n-r)!}$

Distance Formula

$d = \sqrt{(x_1 - x_2)^2 + (y_1 - y_2)^2}$

Quadratic Formula

$x = \dfrac{^-b \pm \sqrt{b^2 - 4ac}}{2a}$

Trigonometry

$\sin A = \dfrac{opposite}{hypotenuse}$

$\cos A = \dfrac{adjacent}{hypotenuse}$

$\tan A = \dfrac{opposite}{adjacent}$

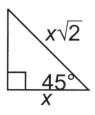 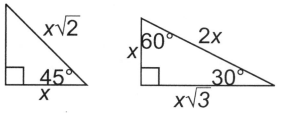

Ohio
Diagnostic Test

1. Which of the following sets contains equivalent numbers?

   A $\frac{9}{25}$ 0.35   35%

   B. $\frac{5}{16}$ 0.315 $31\frac{1}{2}$%

   C. $\frac{3}{8}$ 0.375 $37\frac{1}{2}$%

   D. $\frac{4}{5}$ 0.08   80%

   1E

2. Find the product of 7.5×10^{16} and 2.0×10^{4}. Write the answer in proper scientific notation without using a calculator?

   1I

3. For every 4 fish that Alice has in her pond, she must have five plants for them. If she only has 75 plants, what is the total number of fish she can have?

   A.   60
   B.   94
   C.   135
   D.   169

   1G

4. Simplify: $\sqrt{9}$

   A.   3

   B.   4

   C.   18

   D.   81

   1H

5. Simplify: $12 + (5 \times 2)^{2} \times 14$

   A.   152

   B.   1412

   C.   1568

   D.   16,184

   1C

6. A recipe for 32 ounces of lemonade calls for 4 ounces of lemon juice. Janet wants to make 120 ounces of lemonade. Which proportion below should she use to find the amount of lemon juice needed?

   A. $\frac{32}{120} = \frac{x}{4}$

   B. $\frac{x}{32} = \frac{4}{120}$

   C. $\frac{32}{4} = \frac{x}{120}$

   D. $\frac{4}{32} = \frac{x}{120}$

   1G

7. The price of a skateboard increased from $32.80 to $39.00. What is the approximate percentage of increase?

   A.   6%
   B.   8%
   C.   16%
   D.   19%

   1G

8. Below is shown a solid object constructed with cubes. Which of the following diagrams represents the side view of this object?

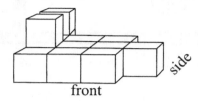

front   side

A.

B.

C.

D.

3E

9. A cylinder with radius 3 inches and height 10 inches is filled with liquid. The liquid is poured into a cylinder with radius 5 inches. What is the height of the liquid in the second cylinder?

A. 1.5 inches
B. 2.8 inches
C. 3.6 inches
D. 6 inches

2D

10. Harrison steps outside his house to see the hot air balloon pass by. He raises his eyes at a 35° angle to view the balloon. If the balloon is 5,000 feet above the ground, how far is it from Harrison.
HINT: Harrison's eye level is 5.2 feet from the ground.

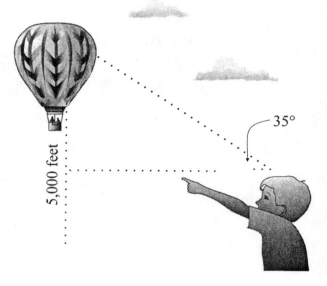

5,000 feet

35°

A. 6100 feet
B. 8700 feet
C. 7100 feet
D. 2900 feet

3I

11. Consider the area of a square with sides of 20 inches each and the area of a circle with diameter 20 inches. Approximately how much smaller is the circle than the square?

A. 86 square inches
B. 136 square inches
C. 214 square inches
D. 228 square inches

2C

12.

TIME IN MINUTES	NUMBER OF PEOPLE AT THE ART SHOW
0	12
10	22
20	32
30	42

Which of the graphs below represents the data in the table?

A.
People at Art Show
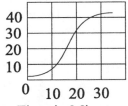

B.
People at Art Show
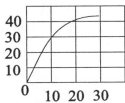

C.
People at Art Show
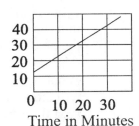

D.
People at Art Show
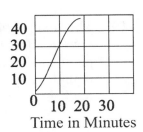

5B

13. Charles plots the point (−4, 3) on a coordinate grid. He then reflects this point over the *y*-axis and translates it down 4 units.

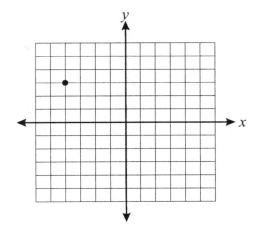

What are the coordinates of the new point?

A.   (−4, −1)
B.   (−4, 1)
C.   (4, −1)
D.   (4, 1)

3F

14. In a game using two numbered cubes, what is the probability of *not* rolling the same number on both cubes in three consecutive rolls?

A. $\frac{125}{256}$

B. $\frac{125}{216}$

C. $\frac{27}{64}$

D. $\frac{16}{27}$

5J

15. Ann is enlarging a triangular design. Triangle *ABC* is to be enlarged with a scale factor of 2 centered at the origin.

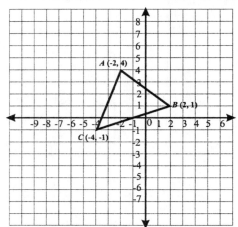

Explain in words how the coordinates of the vertices of the new enlarged triangle can be determined from the original coordinates of points *A*, *B*, and *C*.

Sketch the enlarged triangle, and label the vertices with appropriate coordinates.

3F

16. Aaron is making 100 circular signs, each with a diameter of 30 inches. The weight of the material from which the signs are made is 0.1 ounce per square inch. Which of the following is most nearly the weight of all 100 signs?

A.   70 pounds
B.   450 pounds
C.   700 pounds
D.   1750 pounds

2C

17. There are 8 people at a party and each person shakes hands with each other person. How many handshakes is that?

A.   28
B.   32
C.   56
D.   64

5H

18. Dawn made a spinning game wheel for the math and science exhibit.

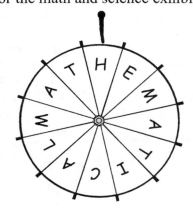

Assume that the wheel is a fair wheel. That is, all 12 segment outcomes are equally likely.

What is the theoretical probability that the wheel will stop on a vowel on the next spin?

What is the probability that the wheel will stop on a vowel on each of the next three spins?

5I

19. The weights of 8 puppies are 10 pounds, 10 pounds, 11 pounds, 8 pounds, 11 pounds, 13 pounds, 6 pounds, 11 pounds. What are the mean, median, and mode of these weights?

	mean	median	mode
A.	9.5	10.5	10.0
B.	10.5	10.0	11.0
C.	10.0	11.0	10.5
D.	10.0	10.5	11.0

5D

20. In a game using two numbered cubes and rolling them twice, what is the probability of rolling 12 on both rolls?

  A $\frac{1}{12}$

  B. $\frac{1}{72}$

  C. $\frac{1}{1296}$

  D. $\frac{1}{1728}$

5J

21. What are the roots of the quadratic equation below?

$$x^2 - 2x - 24$$

  A. (−8, 6)
  B. (−6, 4)
  C. (−6, −4)
  D. (−8, 3)

4G

22. The graph shows the percentage of a family's net income spent in various categories.

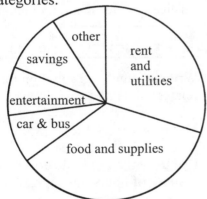

If the family's annual net income is $26,723, approximately how much is spent on rent and utilities in one year?

  A $9,000
  B. $11,000
  C. $14,000
  D. $17,000

5A

23. Which of the following charts would be most useful in predicting height as a function of finger length?

A.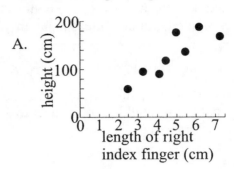

B.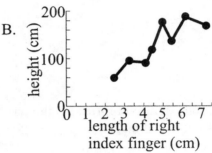

C.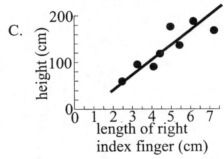

D.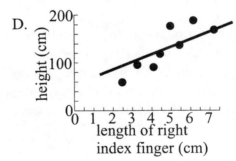

5E

5

24. Jacob has had a new job for 6 weeks and has received a bonus in his paycheck each week. He has not been told how the amount of the bonus is computed, but he notices a pattern.

Week	1	2	3	4	5	6	7
Bonus	$11	$12	$14	$17	$21	$26	

Based on the pattern in the table above, what bonus could Jacob expect to receive in week 7?

A. $29
B. $30
C. $31
D. $32

4A

25. Which equation represents the pattern shown in the table?

x	−3	−2	−1	0	1	2	3
y	−30	−8	0	0	−2	0	12

A. $y = x^3 - x^2 - 2x$
B. $y = x^3 + x^2 - 2x$
C. $y = x^3 - 2x^2 - 3x$
D. $y = x^3 - 4x$

4C

26. The formula $F = \frac{9}{5}C + 32$ relates degrees Celsius (°C) to degrees Fahrenheit (°F). If the temperature rose 45°C, this would be equivalent to an increase of how many degrees Fahrenheit?

A. 25°F
B. 77°F
C. 81°F
D. 113°F

4D

27. Debra is making a string of 92 beads for her great grandmother's 92nd birthday. She is using six colors of beads: Red, Orange Yellow, Green, Blue, and Violet. The six colors are arranged in the repeating pattern shown below.

ⓇⓄⓎⒼⒷⓋⓇⓄⓎⒼⒷⓋⓇⓄⓎ

What will be the color of the last bead (the 92nd bead) on the string?

Show the calculation and explain the logic of the solution.

4A

28. There are a total of 24 cats and dogs at the animal shelter. There are 3 times as many dogs as cats. How many cats are there?

A. 6
B. 8
C. 16
D. 18

4D

29. The sign below is posted over the service counter in a repair shop.

Hours	1	2	3	4	5	6
Cost	$35	$60	$85	$110	$135	$160

Write an algebraic equation that relates hours and cost.

You receive a bill for $585.

Use the equation to determine the number of hours this represents.

4C, 4F

6

30. A building lot is 72 feet wide by 96 feet long. If the length of the lot on a landscape designer's drawing is 4 inches, what will the width of the lot be on the drawing?

    A. 3 inches
    B. 4 inches
    C. 5 inches
    D. 6 inches

    2D

31. If $y = 6$ and $x = 4$, what is the value of y when $x = 8$ if this represents an indirect variation?

    A. 4

    B. 12

    C. 3

    D. 8

    4I

32. Which of these will provide the best estimate of the area of this circle?

    9.7 cm

    A. $3^2 \times (10 \div 2)$

    B. $3 \times (10 \div 2)^2$

    C. 3×10^2

    D. $(3 \times 10)^2$

    2E

33. The graph represents the equation $2y = 3x - 6$.

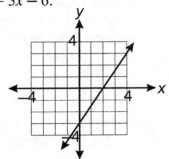

If the constant term changes from -6 to 4, what will the graph look like?

A.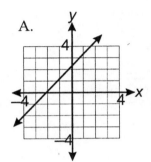

B.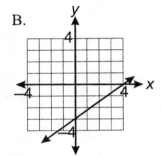

C.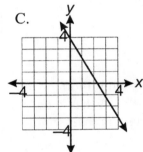

D.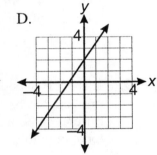

4E

34. Brent and Andrew are training, preparing to someday swim the English Channel. They swam across Blue Lake from Eagle Point to Clark's Resort. Approximately how far did they swim?

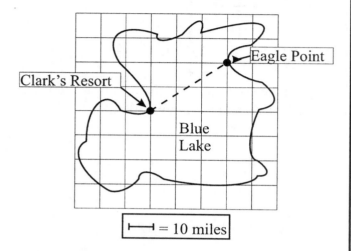

$\longmapsto$ = 10 miles

   A. 20 miles
   B. 30 miles
   C. 40 miles
   D. 50 miles

3G

35. It is 65°F outside, but tomorrow it is predicted to be 81°F. What is the difference between the temperature today and tomorrow?

   A. −16°F
   B. 6°F
   C. 16°F
   D. Cannot be determined

2F

36. Sally is seven years old and goes to the store with her mother every Saturday morning. Every time they go, she notices that her mother gives the check out clerk money before they leave the store. Sally concluded that everyone has to give money in exchange for things they want to take out of the store. This is an example of

   A. deductive reasoning.
   B. inductive reasoning.
   C. analytical reasoning.
   D. none of the above.

3H

37. If you double the radius of a circle, how much does the area increase?

2D

38. In the triangles below, $\triangle ACE$ is similar to $\triangle BCD$. What is the measure of $\overline{AE}$?

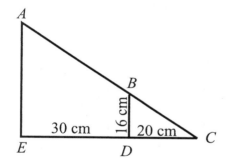

   A. 70 cm
   B. 60 cm
   C. 24 cm
   D. 40 cm

3B

EVALUATION CHART
DIAGNOSTIC MATHEMATICS TEST

Directions: On the following chart, circle the question numbers that you answered incorrectly, and evaluate the results. Then turn to the appropriate topics (listed by chapters), read the explanations, and complete the exercises. Review the other chapters as needed. Finally, complete the Practice Mathematics Tests to further review for the Ohio Graduation Test in Mathematics.

	QUESTIONS	PAGES
Chapter 1: Numbers and Number Systems	5	11 – 19
Chapter 2: Exponents	2, 4	20 – 30
Chapter 3: Fractions and Decimals		31 – 40
Chapter 4: Percents	1, 7	41 – 51
Chapter 5: Word Problems	35	52 – 60
Chapter 6: Measurement		61 – 66
Chapter 7: Ratios, Proportions, and Scale Drawings	3, 6, 30	67 – 73
Chapter 8: Introduction to Graphing		74 – 86
Chapter 9: Introduction to Algebra	28	87 – 96
Chapter 10: Solving Equations and Inequalities	26, 31	97 – 117
Chapter 11: Graphing and Writing Equations and Inequalities	21, 25, 33	118 – 137
Chapter 12: Applications of Graphs	12, 29	138 – 149

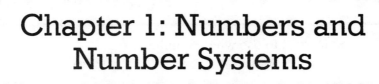 

Chapter 1: Numbers and Number Systems

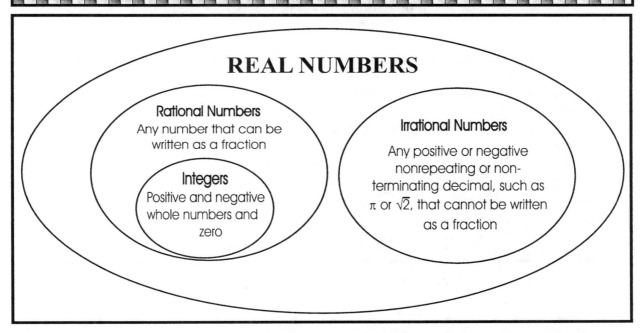

REAL NUMBERS

Rational Numbers
Any number that can be written as a fraction

Integers
Positive and negative whole numbers and zero

Irrational Numbers
Any positive or negative nonrepeating or non-terminating decimal, such as π or $\sqrt{2}$, that cannot be written as a fraction

Real numbers include all positive and negative numbers and zero. Included in the set of real numbers are positive and negative fractions, decimals, and rational and irrational numbers.

Use the diagram above and your calculator to answer the following questions.

1. Using your calculator, find the square root of 7. Does it repeat? Does it end? Is it a rational or an irrational number?
2. Find $\sqrt{25}$. Is it rational or irrational? Is it an integer?
3. Is an integer an irrational number?
4. Is an integer a real number?
5. Is $\frac{1}{8}$ a real number? Is it rational or irrational?

Identify the following numbers as rational (R) or irrational (I).

6. 5π
7. $\sqrt{8}$
8. $\frac{1}{3}$
9. -7.2
10. $-\frac{3}{4}$

11. $\frac{\sqrt{2}}{2}$
12. $9 + \pi$
13. 1.0004
14. $-\frac{4}{5}$
15. $1.1\overline{8}$

16. $\sqrt{81}$
17. $\frac{\pi}{4}$
18. $-\sqrt{36}$
19. $17\frac{1}{2}$
20. $-\frac{5}{3}$

INTEGERS

In elementary school, you learned to use whole numbers.

Whole numbers = { 0, 1, 2, 3, 4, 5 . . . }

For most things in life, whole numbers are all we need to use. However, when a checking account falls below zero or the temperature falls below zero, we need a way to express that. Mathematicians have decided that a negative sign, which looks exactly like a subtraction sign, would be used in front of a number to show that the number is below zero. All the negative whole numbers and positive whole numbers plus zero make up the set of integers.

Integers = { . . . −4, −3, −2, −1, 0, 1, 2, 3, 4 . . . }

ABSOLUTE VALUE

The absolute value of a number is the distance the number is from zero on the number line.

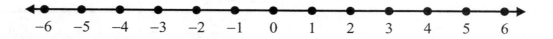

The absolute value of 6 is written | 6 |. | 6 | = 6
The absolute value of −6 is written | −6 |. | −6 | = 6

Both 6 and −6 are the same distance, 6 spaces, from zero, so their absolute value is the same, 6.

EXAMPLES:

| −4 | = 4   − | −4 | = −4 | −9 | + 5 = 9 + 5 = 14

| 9 | − | 8 | = 9 − 8 = 1 | 6 | − | −6 | = 6 − 6 = 0 | −5 | + | −2 | = 5 + 2 = 7

Simplify the following absolute value problems.

1. | 9 | = _____   6. | −2 | = _____   11. | −2 | + | 6 | = _____

2.   − | 5 | = _____   7.   − | −3 | = _____   12. | 10 | + | 8 | = _____

3. | −25 | = _____   8. | −4 | − | 3 | = _____   13. | −2 | + | 4 | = _____

4.   − | −12 | = _____   9. | −8 | − | −4 | = _____   14. | −3 | + | −4 | = _____

5.   − | 64 | = _____   10. | 5 | + | −4 | = _____   15. | 7 | − | −5 | = _____

RULES FOR ADDING INTEGERS WITH THE SAME SIGNS

To add integers without using the number line, use these simple rules:

> 1. **Add the numbers together.**
> 2. **Give the answer the same sign.**

EXAMPLE 1: $(-2) + (-5) =$ _____   Both integers are negative. To find the answer, add the numbers together $(2 + 5)$, and give the answer a negative sign.

$(-2) + (-5) = (-7)$

EXAMPLE 2: $3 + 4 =$ _____   Both integers are positive, so the answer is positive.

$3 + 4 = 7$ **NOTE:** Sometimes positive signs are placed in front of positive numbers. For example $3 + 4 = 7$ may be written $(+3) + (+4) = +7$. Positive signs in front of positive numbers are optional. If a number has no sign, it is considered positive.

Solve the problems below using the rules for adding integers with the same signs.

1. $(-18) + (-4) =$ _____
2. $(-12) + (-3) =$ _____
3. $(-2) + (-7) =$ _____
4. $(+22) + (+11) =$ _____
5. $(-7) + (-6) =$ _____
6. $(-9) + (-8) =$ _____
7. $8 + 4 =$ _____
8. $(-4) + (-7) =$ _____
9. $(-15) + (-5) =$ _____
10. $(+7) + (+4) =$ _____
11. $(-7) + (-20) =$ _____
12. $(-18) + (-16) =$ _____
13. $25 + 32 =$ _____
14. $(-15) + (-3) =$ _____
15. $(9) + (9) =$ _____

Solve the following integer word problems.

16. A submarine was 1500 feet below sea level. The captain gave an order to come up 800 feet closer to the surface. How far below sea level was the submarine then?

17. The countdown for the space launch was at 25 minutes before blastoff. Ten minutes later, what was the countdown?

18. It is 2° above 0 tonight. By morning, the temperature will have dropped 12 degrees. How cold will it be then?

19. The highest point in Africa is Mount Killimanjaro at 19,340 ft. The lowest point is the Qattara Depression at −440 ft. What is the difference between the two points?

20. Aristotle was born in 384 BC and died in 322 BC. How old was he when he died?

RULES FOR ADDING INTEGERS WITH OPPOSITE SIGNS

> 1. Ignore the signs and find the difference.
> 2. Give the answer the sign of the larger number.

EXAMPLE 1: $(-4) + 6 =$ _____

To find the difference, take the larger number minus the smaller number. $6 - 4 = 2$. Looking back at the original problem, the larger number, 6, is positive, so the answer is positive.

$(-4) + 6 = 2$

EXAMPLE 2: $3 + (-7) =$ _____

Find the difference. $7 - 3 = 4$. Looking at the problem, the larger number, 7, is a negative number, so the answer is negative.

$3 + (-7) = (-4)$

Solve the problems below, using the rules of adding integers with opposite signs.

1. $(-4) + 8 =$ _____
2. $-10 + 12 =$ _____
3. $9 + (-3) =$ _____
4. $(+3) + (-3) =$ _____
5. $5 + (-2) =$ _____
6. $(-18) + 9 =$ _____
7. $25 + (-30) =$ _____

8. $+8 + (-7) =$ _____
9. $(-5) + (+12) =$ _____
10. $-14 + (+7) =$ _____
11. $7 + (-8) =$ _____
12. $(-30) + 15 =$ _____
13. $100 + (-65) =$ _____
14. $85 + (-14) =$ _____

15. $6 + (-12) =$ _____
16. $(-11) + 1 =$ _____
17. $3 + (-13) =$ _____
18. $(-12) + 8 =$ _____
19. $52 + (-9) =$ _____
20. $(-39) + 8 =$ _____
21. $(+14) + (-16) =$ _____

Solve the mixed addition problems below, using the rules for adding integers.

22. $-7 + 8 =$ _____
23. $5 + 6 =$ _____
24. $(-2) + (-6) =$ _____
25. $3 + (-5) =$ _____
26. $(-7) + (-9) =$ _____
27. $14 + 9 =$ _____
28. $(-15) + 6 =$ _____

29. $8 + (-5) =$ _____
30. $(-6) + 13 =$ _____
31. $(-9) + (-12) =$ _____
32. $(-7) + (+12) =$ _____
33. $+8 + (-9) =$ _____
34. $(-13) + (-18) =$ _____
35. $46 + (-52) =$ _____

36. $(-7) + (+10) =$ _____
37. $(+4) + 11 =$ _____
38. $11 + 6 =$ _____
39. $-4 + (-10) =$ _____
40. $(+6) + (+2) =$ _____
41. $1 + (-17) =$ _____
42. $(-42) + 6 =$ _____

RULES FOR SUBTRACTING INTEGERS

One of the simplest ways to subtract integers is to change the problem to an addition problem, and follow the rules you already know.

> 1. **Change the subtraction sign to addition.**
> 2. **Change the sign of the second number to the opposite sign.**

EXAMPLE 1: $-6 - (-2) =$ _____   Change the subtraction sign to addition and -2 to 2. $-6 - (-2) = (-6) + 2$

$(-6) + 2 = (-4)$

EXAMPLE 2: $5 - 6 =$ _____   Change the subtraction sign to addition and 6 to -6. $5 - 6 = 5 + (-6)$

$5 + (-6) = (-1)$

Solve the problems using the rules above.

1. $(-3) - 8 =$ _____
2. $5 - (-9) =$ _____
3. $8 - (-5) =$ _____
4. $(-2) - (-6) =$ _____
5. $8 - (-9) =$ _____
6. $(-4) - (-1) =$ _____

7. $(-5) - (-13) =$ _____
8. $6 - (-7) =$ _____
9. $8 - (-6) =$ _____
10. $(-2) - (-2) =$ _____
11. $(-3) - 7 =$ _____
12. $(-4) - 8 =$ _____

13. $(-7) - 4 =$ _____
14. $1 - (-9) =$ _____
15. $(-5) - 12 =$ _____
16. $(-1) - 9 =$ _____
17. $6 - (-7) =$ _____
18. $(-8) - (-12) =$ _____

Solve the addition and subtraction problems below.

19. $4 - (-2) =$ _____
20. $(-3) + 7 =$ _____
21. $(-4) + 14 =$ _____
22. $(-1) - 5 =$ _____
23. $(-1) + (-4) =$ _____
24. $(-12) + (-2) =$ _____
25. $0 - (-6) =$ _____
26. $2 - (-5) =$ _____

27. $(-5) + 3 =$ _____
28. $(-6) + 7 =$ _____
29. $(-4) + 8 =$ _____
30. $(-4) - 11 =$ _____
31. $(-5) + 8 =$ _____
32. $(-3) - (-3) =$ _____
33. $(-8) + 9 =$ _____
34. $0 + (-10) =$ _____

35. $30 + (-15) =$ _____
36. $-40 - (-5) =$ _____
37. $25 - 50 =$ _____
38. $-13 + 12 =$ _____
39. $(-21) - (-1) =$ _____
40. $62 - (-3) =$ _____
41. $(-16) + (-2) =$ _____
42. $(-25) + 5 =$ _____

15

MULTIPLYING INTEGERS

You are probably used to seeing multiplication written with a "×" sign, but multiplication can be written two other ways. A "•" between numbers means the same as "×", and parentheses ( ) around a number without a "×" or a "•" also means to multiply.

EXAMPLES: $2 \times 3 = 6$ or $2 \cdot 3 = 6$ or $(2)(3) = 6$

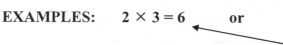

All of these mean the same thing.

DIVIDING INTEGERS

Division is commonly indicated two ways: with a "÷" or in the form of a fraction.

EXAMPLE: $6 \div 3 = 2$ means the same thing as $\dfrac{6}{3} = 2$

RULES FOR MULTIPLYING AND DIVIDING INTEGERS

> 1. **If the numbers have the same sign, the answer is positive.**
> 2. **If the numbers have different signs, the answer is negative.**

EXAMPLES: $6 \times 8 = 48$ $(-6) \times 8 = (-48)$ $(-6) \times (-8) = 48$

              $48 \div 6 = 8$ $(-48) \div 6 = (-8)$ $(-48) \div (-6) = 8$

Solve the problems below using the rules for multiplying and dividing integers with opposite signs.

1. $(-4) \div 2 =$ _____

2. $12 \div (-3) =$ _____

3. $\dfrac{(-14)}{(-2)} =$ _____

4. $-15 \div 3 =$ _____

5. $(-3) \times (-7) =$ _____

6. $(-1) \cdot (5) =$ _____

7. $-1 \times (-4) =$ _____

8. $(3)(2) =$ _____

9. $2(-5) =$ _____

10. $3 \times (-7) =$ _____

11. $(-12) \cdot (-2) =$ _____

12. $\dfrac{(-18)}{(-6)} =$ _____

13. $21 \div (-7) =$ _____

14. $-5 \times 3 =$ _____

15. $(-6)(7) =$ _____

16. $\dfrac{(-3)}{(-3)} =$ _____

17. $(-5) \times 8 =$ _____

18. $\dfrac{-12}{6} =$ _____

19. $8(-4) =$ _____

20. $1 \cdot (-8) =$ _____

21. $(-7) \cdot (-4) =$ _____

22. $(-2) \div (-2) =$ _____

23. $\dfrac{18}{(-6)} =$ _____

24. $5(-3) =$ _____

16

MIXED INTEGER PRACTICE

1. $(-6) + 13 =$ _____
2. $(-3) + (-9) =$ _____
3. $(-4) \times 4 =$ _____
4. $(-18) \div 3 =$ _____
5. $(-1) - 5 =$ _____
6. $(-1) \times (-4) =$ _____
7. $3 + (-5) =$ _____
8. $6 + (-5) =$ _____
9. $(-9) - (-12) =$ _____

10. $2 + (-5) =$ _____
11. $\dfrac{(-24)}{(-6)} =$ _____
12. $(-5) + 3 =$ _____
13. $(-6) - 7 =$ _____
14. $(-33) \div (-11) =$ _____
15. $(-21)(-3) =$ _____
16. $(-7) + (-14) =$ _____
17. $(-5) - 8 =$ _____
18. $1(-8) =$ _____

19. $(-2) \cdot (-2) =$ _____
20. $8 + (-6) =$ _____
21. $\dfrac{-14}{7} =$ _____
22. $(+7) \cdot (-2) =$ _____
23. $(10)(4) =$ _____
24. $24 \div (-4) =$ _____
25. $6(-5) =$ _____
26. $\dfrac{12}{(-3)} =$ _____
27. $36 \div 12 =$ _____

INTEGER WORD PROBLEMS

Solve the following word problems.

1. If it is 2° outside and the temperature will drop 15° tonight, how cold will it get?

2. What is the difference in elevation between Mount McKinley (20,320 ft) and Death Valley (−282 ft)?

3. It is −24° tonight, but the weather reporter predicted it will be 16° warmer tomorrow. What will the temperature be tomorrow?

4. The average temperature of the earth's stratosphere is −70°F. The average temperature on the earth's surface is 57°F. How much warmer is the average temperature on the surface of the earth than in the stratosphere?

5. The elevation of the Dead Sea is −1,286 feet. (The Dead Sea is below sea level.) Mt. McKinley has an elevation of 20,320 feet. What is the difference in the elevation between the Dead Sea and Mt. McKinley?

6. A submarine dives 462 feet beneath the surface of the ocean. It then climbs up 257 feet. What depth is the submarine now?

7. Eratosthenes was born about 274 BC. Sir Isaac Newton was born in 1642 AD. About how many years apart were they born?

8. The average daily low temperature in International Falls, Minnesota during the month of January is −9°F. The average high is 14°F. What is the temperature difference between the average low and the average high?

ORDER OF OPERATIONS

In long math problems with $+$, $-$, $\times$, $\div$, ( ), and exponents in them, you have to know what to do first. Without following the same rules, you could get different answers. If you will memorize the silly sentence, Please Excuse My Dear Aunt Sally, you can memorize the order you must follow.

Please	**"P"** stands for parentheses. You must get rid of parentheses first. Examples: $3(1+4) = 3(5) = 15$ $6(10-6) = 6(4) = 24$
Excuse	**"E"** stands for exponents. You must eliminate exponents next. Example: $4^2 = 4 \times 4 = 16$
My Dear	**"M"** stands for multiply. **"D"** stands for divide. Start on the left of the equation and perform all multiplications and divisions in the order in which they appear.
Aunt Sally	**"A"** stands for add. **"S"** stands for subtract. Start on the left and perform all additions and subtractions in the order they appear.

EXAMPLE: $12 \div 2(6-3) + 3^2 - 1$

Please	Eliminate **parentheses**. $6 - 3 = 3$ so now we have	$12 \div 2(3) + 3^2 - 1$
Excuse	Eliminate **exponents**. $3^2 = 9$ so now we have	$12 \div 2(3) + 9 - 1$
My Dear	**Multiply** and **divide** next in order from left to right.	$12 \div 2 = 6$ then $6(3) = 18$
Aunt Sally	Last, we **add** and **subtract** in order from left to right.	$18 + 9 - 1 = 26$

Simplify the following problems.

1. $6 + 9 \times 2 - 4$ = _____

2. $3(4+2) - 6^2$ = _____

3. $3(6-3) - 2^3$ = _____

4. $49 \div 7 - 3 \times 3$ = _____

5. $10 \times 4 - (7-2)$ = _____

6. $2 \times 3 \div 6 \times 4$ = _____

7. $4^3 \div 8(4+2)$ = _____

8. $7 + 8(14-6) \div 4$ = _____

9. $(2 + 8 - 12) \times 4$ = _____

10. $4(8-13) \times 4$ = _____

11. $8 + 4^2 \times 2 - 6$ = _____

12. $3^2(4+6) + 3$ = _____

13. $(12-6) + 27 \div 3^2$ = _____

14. $82^0 - 1 + 4 \div 2^2$ = _____

15. $1 - (2-3) + 8$ = _____

16. $12 - 4(7-2)$ = _____

17. $18 \div (6+3) - 12$ = _____

18. $10^2 + 3^3 - 2 \times 3$ = _____

19. $4^2 + (7+2) \div 3$ = _____

20. $7 \times 4 - 9 \div 3$ = _____

CHAPTER 1 REVIEW

Simplify the following problems.

1. $(-7) \times (-4) =$ _____
2. $15^0 =$ _____
3. $7 - (-8) =$ _____
4. $9 \div (-3) =$ _____
5. $\sqrt{100} =$ _____
6. $-9 - 7 =$ _____
7. $(-10) \cdot (4) =$ _____
8. $\sqrt{49} =$ _____
9. $(-3)^3 =$ _____
10. $4 + (-4) =$ _____

11. $\dfrac{(-16)}{4} =$ _____
12. $(7)(-7) =$ _____
13. $-5 + (-2) =$ _____
14. $(-12) \div (-3) =$ _____
15. $(-2) \times 6 =$ _____
16. $-4 + (-10) =$ _____
17. $5 - (-5) =$ _____
18. $(9)(-1) =$ _____
19. $\dfrac{(-20)}{(-5)} =$ _____
20. $14 - 25 =$ _____

21. $|-4| + |5| =$ _____
22. $18 - |-6| =$ _____
23. $|-14| + |9| =$ _____
24. $|-2| - |-9| =$ _____
25. $|5| - |-8| =$ _____
26. $|-2| + |7| =$ _____
27. $|12| - |-6| =$ _____
28. $|-3| + 9 =$ _____
29. $|10| - |6| =$ _____
30. $14 - |5| =$ _____

Simplify the following problems using the correct order of operations.

31. $2^3 + (2^2)(5 - 7) =$ _____

32. $10 \div (-1 - 4) + 2 =$ _____

33. $5 + (2)(4 - 1) \div 3 =$ _____

34. $5 - 5^2 + (2 - 4) =$ _____

35. $\dfrac{10 + 5^2 - 3}{2^2 + 2(5 - 3)} =$ _____

36. $1 - (3^2 - 1) \div 2 =$ _____

37. $\dfrac{5(3 - 6) + 3^2}{4(2 + 1) - 6} =$ _____

38. $-4(6 + 4) \div (-2) + 1 =$ _____

39. $12 \div (7 - 4) - 2 =$ _____

40. $2^3 + (5)(3 - 5) =$ _____

Chapter 2: Exponents

UNDERSTANDING EXPONENTS

Sometimes it is necessary to multiply a number by itself one or more times. For example, in a math problem, you may need to multiply 3×3 or $5 \times 5 \times 5 \times 5$. Mathematicians have come up with a shorter way of writing out this kind of multiplication. Instead of writing 3×3, you can write 3^2; also, instead of $5 \times 5 \times 5 \times 5$, 5^4 means the same thing. The first number is the **base**. The small, raised number is called the **exponent**. The exponent tells how many times the base should be multiplied by itself.

EXAMPLE 1: 6^3 ← exponent, base ←   **This means multiply 6 three times: $6 \times 6 \times 6$.**

You also need to know two special properties of exponents:

> 1. Any base number raised to the exponent of 1 equals the base number.
> 2. Any base number raised to the exponent of 0 equals 1.

EXAMPLE 2: $4^1 = 4$ $10^1 = 10$ $25^1 = 25$
                         $4^0 = 1$ $10^0 = 1$ $25^0 = 1$

Rewrite the following problems using _exponents_.

Example: $2 \times 2 \times 2 = 2^3$

1. $4 \times 4 \times 4 = $ _____
2. $5 \times 5 \times 5 \times 5 = $ _____
3. $11 \times 11 = $ _____
4. $8 \times 8 = $ _____
5. $17 \times 17 \times 17 = $ _____
6. $12 \times 12 = $ _____
7. $1 \times 1 \times 1 \times 1 \times 1 = $ _____
8. $7 \times 7 \times 7 \times 7 \times 7 \times 7 = $ _____
9. $100 \times 100 \times 100 = $ _____

Use your calculator to figure what number each number with an exponent represents.

Example: $2^3 = 2 \times 2 \times 2 = 8$

10. $2^5 = $ _____
11. $10^2 = $ _____
12. $8^3 = $ _____
13. $3^4 = $ _____
14. $25^1 = $ _____
15. $10^5 = $ _____
16. $15^0 = $ _____
17. $9^2 = $ _____
18. $3^3 = $ _____

Express each of the following numbers as a number with an exponent.

Example: $4 = 2 \times 2 = 2^2$

19. $32 = $ _____
20. $64 = $ _____ or _____
21. $1000 = $ _____
22. $27 = $ _____
23. $81 = $ _____ or _____
24. $121 = $ _____
25. $16 = $ _____ or _____
26. $8 = $ _____
27. $49 = $ _____

MULTIPLICATION WITH EXPONENTS

Rule 1:   To multiply two expressions with the same base, add the exponents together and keep the base the same.

EXAMPLE: $2^3 \times 2^5 = 2^{3+5} = 2^8$

Rule 2:   If a power is raised to another power, multiply the exponents together and keep the base the same.

EXAMPLE: $(2^3)^2 = 2^{3\times2} = 2^6$

Rule 3:   If a product in parentheses is raised to a power, then each factor is raised to the power when parentheses are eliminated.

EXAMPLE 1: $(2 \times 4)^2 = 2^2 \times 4^2 = 4 \times 16 = 64$

EXAMPLE 2: $(3a)^3 = 3^3 \times a^3 = 27a^3$

EXAMPLE 3: $(7b^5)^2 = 7^2 b^{10} = 49b^{10}$

Simplify each of the expressions below.

1. $(5^3)^2$

2. $6^3 \times 6^5$

3. $4^3 \times 4^3$

4. $(7^5)^2$

5. $(6^2)^5$

6. $2^5 \times 2^3$

7. $(4 \times 5)^2$

8. $(3^4)^0$

9. $(3^3)^2$

10. $2^5 \times 2^5$

11. $(3 \times 3)^2$

12. $(2a)^4$

13. $(3^2)^4$

14. $4^5 \times 4^3$

15. $(3 \times 2)^4$

16. $(5^2)^2$

17. $(6 \times 4)^2$

18. $(9a^5)^3$

19. $4^3 \times 4^4$

20. $(6b^5)^2$

21. $(5^2)^3$

22. $3^7 \times 3^3$

23. $(3a)^2$

24. $(3^4)^2$

25. $(4^4)^2$

26. $(2b^3)^4$

27. $(5a^2)^5$

28. $(8a^3)^2$

29. $(9^2)^2$

30. $10^5 \times 10^4$

31. $(3 \times 5)^2$

32. $(7^3)^2$

DIVISION WITH EXPONENTS

Rule 1: Expressions can also have negative exponents. Negative exponents do not indicate negative numbers. They indicate reciprocals.

EXAMPLE 1: $2^{-3} = \dfrac{1}{2^3} = \dfrac{1}{8}$

EXAMPLE 2: $3a^{-5} = 3 \times \dfrac{1}{a^5} = \dfrac{3}{a^5}$

Rule 2: When dividing expressions with exponents that have the same base, subtract the exponents.

EXAMPLE 1: $\dfrac{3^5}{3^3} = 3^{5-3} = 3^2 = 9$

EXAMPLE 2: $\dfrac{3^5}{3^8} = 3^{5-8} = 3^{-3} = \dfrac{1}{3^3} = \dfrac{1}{27}$ Expressions in simplified form have only positive exponents.

Rule 3: If a fraction is raised to a power, then both the numerator and denominator are raised to the same power.

EXAMPLE 1: $\left(\dfrac{3}{4}\right)^3 = \dfrac{3^3}{4^3} = \dfrac{27}{64}$

EXAMPLE 2: $(2x)^{-2} = \dfrac{1}{(2x)^2} = \dfrac{1}{4x^2}$

Reduce the following expressions to their simplest form. All exponents should be positive.

1. $5x^{-4}$

2. $\dfrac{2^2}{2^4}$

3. $\left(\dfrac{2}{3}\right)^2$

4. $6a^{-2}$

5. $(6a)^{-2}$

6. $\left(\dfrac{7}{8}\right)^3$

7. $\dfrac{3^4}{3^3}$

8. $(5a)^{-2}$

9. $\dfrac{3^6}{3^3}$

10. $\dfrac{(x^2)^3}{x^4}$

11. $\dfrac{(3y)^3}{3^2 y}$

12. $\dfrac{(3a^2)^3}{a^4}$

13. $(2x^2)^{-5}$

14. $2x^{-2}$

15. $(a^3)^{-2}$

16. $(2^{-2})^3$

17. $\left(\dfrac{1}{2}\right)^2$

18. $4y^{-5}$

19. $(4y)^{-5}$

20. 3^{-2}

SQUARE ROOT

Just as working with exponents is related to multiplication, so finding square roots is related to division. In fact, the sign for finding the square root of a number looks similar to a division sign. The best way to learn about square roots is to look at examples.

EXAMPLES: This is a square root problem: $\sqrt{64}$

It is asking, "What is the square root of 64?"

It means, "What number multiplied by itself equals 64?"

The answer is 8. $8 \times 8 = 64$.

Look at the square roots of the following numbers.

$\sqrt{36}$ $6 \times 6 = 36$ so $\sqrt{36} = 6$ $\sqrt{144}$ $12 \times 12 = 144$ so $\sqrt{144} = 12$

Find the square roots of the following numbers.

1. $\sqrt{49}$ _____
2. $\sqrt{81}$ _____
3. $\sqrt{25}$ _____
4. $\sqrt{16}$ _____

5. $\sqrt{121}$ _____
6. $\sqrt{100}$ _____
7. $\sqrt{169}$ _____
8. $\sqrt{4}$ _____

9. $\sqrt{900}$ _____
10. $\sqrt{64}$ _____
11. $\sqrt{9}$ _____
12. $\sqrt{400}$ _____

SIMPLIFYING SQUARE ROOTS

Square roots can sometimes be simplified even if the number under the square root is not a perfect square. One of the rules of roots is that if a and b are two positive real numbers, then it is always true that $\sqrt{a \cdot b} = \sqrt{a} \cdot \sqrt{b}$. You can use this rule to simplify square roots.

EXAMPLE 1: $\sqrt{100} = \sqrt{4 \cdot 25} = \sqrt{4} \cdot \sqrt{25} = 2 \cdot 5 = 10$

EXAMPLE 2: $\sqrt{200} = \sqrt{100 \cdot 2} = 10\sqrt{2}$ ⬅ Means 10 multiplied by the square root of 2

EXAMPLE 3: $\sqrt{160} = \sqrt{10 \cdot 16} = 4\sqrt{10}$

Simplify.

1. $\sqrt{98}$ _____
2. $\sqrt{600}$ _____
3. $\sqrt{50}$ _____
4. $\sqrt{27}$ _____

5. $\sqrt{8}$ _____
6. $\sqrt{63}$ _____
7. $\sqrt{48}$ _____
8. $\sqrt{75}$ _____

9. $\sqrt{54}$ _____
10. $\sqrt{40}$ _____
11. $\sqrt{72}$ _____
12. $\sqrt{80}$ _____

13. $\sqrt{90}$ _____
14. $\sqrt{175}$ _____
15. $\sqrt{18}$ _____
16. $\sqrt{20}$ _____

ADDING AND SUBTRACTING ROOTS

You can add and subtract terms with square roots only if the number under the square root sign is the same.

EXAMPLE 1: $2\sqrt{2} + 3\sqrt{2} = 5\sqrt{2}$
EXAMPLE 2: $12\sqrt{7} - 3\sqrt{7} = 9\sqrt{7}$

Or, look at the following examples where you can simplify the square roots and then add or subtract.

EXAMPLE 3: $2\sqrt{25} + \sqrt{36}$
Step 1: Simplify. You know that $\sqrt{25} = 5$, and $\sqrt{36} = 6$, so the problem simplifies to $2(5) + 6$

Step 2: Solve: $2(5) + 6 = 10 + 6 = 16$

EXAMPLE 4: $2\sqrt{72} - 3\sqrt{2}$

Step 1: Simplify what you know. $\sqrt{72} = \sqrt{36 \cdot 2} = 6\sqrt{2}$
Step 2: Substitute $6\sqrt{2}$ for $\sqrt{72}$ and simplify
$2(6)\sqrt{2} - 3\sqrt{2} = 12\sqrt{2} - 3\sqrt{2} = 9\sqrt{2}$

Simplify the following addition and subtraction problems.

1. $3\sqrt{5} + 9\sqrt{5}$

2. $3\sqrt{25} + 4\sqrt{16}$

3. $4\sqrt{8} + 2\sqrt{2}$

4. $3\sqrt{32} - 2\sqrt{2}$

5. $\sqrt{25} - \sqrt{49}$

6. $2\sqrt{5} + 4\sqrt{20}$

7. $5\sqrt{8} - 3\sqrt{72}$

8. $\sqrt{27} + 3\sqrt{27}$

9. $3\sqrt{20} - 4\sqrt{45}$

10. $4\sqrt{45} - \sqrt{125}$

11. $2\sqrt{28} + 2\sqrt{7}$

12. $\sqrt{64} + \sqrt{81}$

13. $5\sqrt{54} - 2\sqrt{24}$

14. $\sqrt{32} + 2\sqrt{50}$

15. $2\sqrt{7} + 4\sqrt{63}$

16. $8\sqrt{2} + \sqrt{8}$

17. $2\sqrt{8} - 4\sqrt{32}$

18. $\sqrt{36} + \sqrt{100}$

19. $\sqrt{9} + \sqrt{25}$

20. $\sqrt{64} - \sqrt{36}$

21. $\sqrt{75} + \sqrt{108}$

22. $\sqrt{81} + \sqrt{100}$

23. $\sqrt{192} - \sqrt{75}$

24. $3\sqrt{5} + \sqrt{245}$

MULTIPLYING ROOTS

You can also multiply square roots. To multiply square roots, you just multiply the numbers under the square root sign and then simplify. Look at the examples below.

EXAMPLE 1: $\quad \sqrt{2} \times \sqrt{6}$

Step 1: $\quad \sqrt{2} \times \sqrt{6} = \sqrt{2 \times 6} = \sqrt{12}$ $\quad$ Multiply the numbers under the square root sign.

Step 2: $\quad \sqrt{12} = \sqrt{4 \times 3} = 2\sqrt{3}$ $\quad$ Simplify.

EXAMPLE 2: $\quad 3\sqrt{3} \times 5\sqrt{6}$

Step 1: $\quad (3 \times 5)\sqrt{3 \times 6} = 15\sqrt{18}$ $\quad$ Multiply the numbers in front of the square root, and multiply the numbers under the square root sign.

Step 2: $\quad 15\sqrt{18} = 15\sqrt{3 \times 9}$ $\quad$ Simplify.
$\quad 15 \times 3\sqrt{3} = 45\sqrt{3}$

EXAMPLE 3: $\quad \sqrt{14} \times \sqrt{42}$ $\quad$ For this more complicated multiplication problem, use the rule of roots that you learned in the section called 'Simplifying Square Roots,' $\sqrt{a \cdot b} = \sqrt{a} \cdot \sqrt{b}$.

Step 1: $\quad \sqrt{14} = \sqrt{7} \times \sqrt{2}$ and $\quad$ Instead of multiplying 14 by 42, divide these
$\quad \sqrt{42} = \sqrt{2} \times \sqrt{3} \times \sqrt{7}$ $\quad$ numbers into their roots.

$\quad \sqrt{14} \times \sqrt{42} = \sqrt{7} \times \sqrt{2} \times \sqrt{2} \times \sqrt{3} \times \sqrt{7}$

Step 2: $\quad$ Since you know that $\sqrt{7} \times \sqrt{7} = 7$ and $\sqrt{2} \times \sqrt{2} = 2$, the problem simplifies to $(7 \times 2)\sqrt{3} = 14\sqrt{3}$

Simplify the following multiplication problems.

1. $\sqrt{5} \times \sqrt{7}$

2. $\sqrt{32} \times \sqrt{2}$

3. $\sqrt{10} \times \sqrt{14}$

4. $2\sqrt{3} \times 3\sqrt{6}$

5. $4\sqrt{2} \times 2\sqrt{10}$

6. $\sqrt{5} \times 3\sqrt{15}$

7. $\sqrt{45} \times \sqrt{27}$

8. $5\sqrt{21} \times \sqrt{7}$

9. $\sqrt{42} \times \sqrt{21}$

10. $4\sqrt{3} \times 2\sqrt{12}$

11. $\sqrt{56} \times \sqrt{24}$

12. $\sqrt{11} \times 2\sqrt{33}$

13. $\sqrt{13} \times \sqrt{26}$

14. $2\sqrt{2} \times 5\sqrt{5}$

15. $\sqrt{6} \times \sqrt{12}$

RATIONALIZING THE DENOMINATOR

When dividing a number or a square root by another square root, you cannot leave the square root sign in the denominator (the bottom number) of a fraction. You must simplify the problem (rationalize) so that the square root is not in the denominator. Look at the examples below.

EXAMPLE 1: $\dfrac{\sqrt{2}}{\sqrt{5}}$

Step 1: $\dfrac{\sqrt{2}}{\sqrt{5}} \times \dfrac{\sqrt{5}}{\sqrt{5}}$ ⟵ The fraction $\dfrac{\sqrt{5}}{\sqrt{5}}$ is equal to 1, and multiplying by 1 does not change the value of a number

Step 2: $\dfrac{\sqrt{2 \times 5}}{5} = \dfrac{\sqrt{10}}{5}$ Multiply and simplify. Since $\sqrt{5} \times \sqrt{5}$ equals 5, you no longer have a square root in the denominator.

EXAMPLE 2: $\dfrac{6\sqrt{2}}{2\sqrt{10}}$ In this problem, the numbers outside of the square root will also simplify.

Step 1: $\dfrac{6}{2} = 3$ so you have $\dfrac{3\sqrt{2}}{\sqrt{10}}$

Step 2: $\dfrac{3\sqrt{2}}{\sqrt{10}} \times \dfrac{\sqrt{10}}{\sqrt{10}} = \dfrac{3\sqrt{2 \times 10}}{10} = \dfrac{3\sqrt{20}}{10}$

Step 3: $\dfrac{3\sqrt{20}}{10}$ will further simplify because $\sqrt{20} = 2\sqrt{5}$ so you then have $\dfrac{3 \times 2\sqrt{5}}{10}$ which reduces to $\dfrac{3 \times \overset{1}{2}\sqrt{5}}{\underset{5}{10}}$ or $\dfrac{3\sqrt{5}}{5}$

Simplify the following division problems.

1. $\dfrac{9\sqrt{3}}{\sqrt{5}}$

2. $\dfrac{16}{\sqrt{8}}$

3. $\dfrac{24\sqrt{10}}{12\sqrt{3}}$

4. $\dfrac{\sqrt{121}}{\sqrt{6}}$

5. $\dfrac{\sqrt{40}}{\sqrt{90}}$

6. $\dfrac{33\sqrt{15}}{11\sqrt{2}}$

7. $\dfrac{\sqrt{32}}{\sqrt{12}}$

8. $\dfrac{\sqrt{11}}{\sqrt{5}}$

9. $\dfrac{\sqrt{2}}{\sqrt{6}}$

10. $\dfrac{2\sqrt{7}}{\sqrt{14}}$

11. $\dfrac{5\sqrt{2}}{4\sqrt{8}}$

12. $\dfrac{4\sqrt{21}}{7\sqrt{7}}$

13. $\dfrac{9\sqrt{22}}{2\sqrt{2}}$

14. $\dfrac{\sqrt{35}}{2\sqrt{14}}$

15. $\dfrac{\sqrt{40}}{\sqrt{15}}$

SCIENTIFIC NOTATION

Mathematicians use **scientific notation** to express very large and very small numbers. **Scientific notation** expresses a number in the following form:

$$x.xx \times 10^x$$

only one digit before the decimal

remaining digits not ending in zeros after the decimal

multiplied by a multiple of ten

USING SCIENTIFIC NOTATION FOR LARGE NUMBERS

Scientific notation simplifies very large numbers that have many zeros. For example, Pluto averages a distance of 5,900,000,000 kilometers from the sun. In scientific notation, a decimal is inserted after the first digit (5.); the rest of the digits are copied except for the zeros at the end (5.9), and the result is multiplied by 10^9. The exponent = the total number of digits in the original number minus 1 or the number of spaces the decimal point moved.

$5,900,000,000 = 5.9 \times 10^9$ The following are more examples:

EXAMPLES: $32,560,000,000 = 3.256 \times 10^{10}$ $5,060,000 = 5.06 \times 10^6$

decimal moves 10 spaces to the left   decimal moves 6 spaces to the left

---

Convert the following numbers to scientific notation.

1.   4,230,000,000 = _____

2.   64,300,000 = _____

3.   951,000,000,000 = _____

4.   12,300 = _____

5.   20,350,000,000 = _____

6.   9,000 = _____

7.   450,000,000,000 = _____

8.   6,200 = _____

9.   87,000,000 = _____

10.   105,000,000 = _____

11.   1,083,000,000,000 = _____

12.   304,000 = _____

To convert a number written in scientific notation back to conventional form, reverse the steps.

EXAMPLE: $4.02 \times 10^5 = 4.02000 = 402,000$ Move the decimal 5 spaces to the right and add zeros.

Convert the following numbers from scientific notation to conventional numbers.

13. 6.85×10^8 = _____

14. 1.3×10^{10} = _____

15. 4.908×10^4 = _____

16. 7.102×10^6 = _____

17. 2.5×10^3 = _____

18. 9.114×10^5 = _____

19. 5.87×10^7 = _____

20. 8.047×10^8 = _____

21. 3.81×10^5 = _____

22. 9.5×10^{12} = _____

23. 1.504×10^6 = _____

24. 7.3×10^9 = _____

USING SCIENTIFIC NOTATION FOR SMALL NUMBERS

Scientific notation also simplifies very small numbers that have many zeros. For example, the diameter of a helium atom is 0.000000000244 meters. It can be written in scientific notation as 2.44×10^{-10}. The first number is always greater than 0, and the first number is always followed by a decimal point. The negative exponent indicates how many digits the decimal point moved to the right. The exponent is negative when the original number is less than 1. To convert small numbers to scientific notation, follow the examples below.

EXAMPLES: $0.00058 = 5.8 \times 10^{-4}$ $0.00003059 = 3.059 \times 10^{-5}$

decimal point moves 4 spaces to the right   negative exponent indicates the original number is less than 1.   decimal moves 5 spaces to the right

---

Convert the following numbers to scientific notation.

1. $0.00000254 =$ _____

2. $0.00000000508 =$ _____

3. $0.000008004 =$ _____

4. $0.00047 =$ _____

5. $0.000000005478 =$ _____

6. $0.00000059 =$ _____

7. $0.00000004712 =$ _____

8. $0.00025 =$ _____

9. $0.0000000501 =$ _____

10. $0.0000006 =$ _____

11. $0.0000000000875 =$ _____

12. $0.00004 =$ _____

Now convert small numbers written in scientific notation back to conventional form.

EXAMPLE: $3.08 \times 10^{-5} = 00003.08 = 0.0000308$ Move the decimal 5 spaces to the left, and add zeros.

Convert the following numbers from scientific notation to conventional numbers.

13. $1.18 \times 10^{-7} =$ _____

14. $2.3 \times 10^{-5} =$ _____

15. $6.205 \times 10^{-9} =$ _____

16. $4.1 \times 10^{-6} =$ _____

17. $7.632 \times 10^{-4} =$ _____

18. $5.48 \times 10^{-10} =$ _____

19. $2.75 \times 10^{-8} =$ _____

20. $4.07 \times 10^{-7} =$ _____

21. $5.2 \times 10^{-3} =$ _____

22. $7.01 \times 10^{-6} =$ _____

23. $4.4 \times 10^{-5} =$ _____

24. $3.43 \times 10^{-2} =$ _____

ORDERING NUMBERS IN SCIENTIFIC NOTATION

When you compare numbers such as 500 and 500,000, it is easy to see that the more 0's there are, the larger the number. By converting these two numbers to scientific notation, $500 = 5 \times 10^2$ and $500,000 = 5 \times 10^5$, you can see that the larger the exponent, the larger the number expressed in scientific notation. The farther to the left you move the decimal point, the larger the number. The farther to the right you move the decimal point, the smaller the number. Thus 3.45×10^{-5} is smaller than 3.45×10^{-4}. On the Ohio Graduation Test, you may be asked to order numbers in scientific notation from greatest to least or least to greatest.

EXAMPLE 1: Consider the median distance from the sun of the following 3 planets: Planet A is 7.783×10^8 km from the sun. Planet B is 1.082×10^8 km from the sun. Planet C is 5.899×10^9 km from the sun. Put the planets in order of distance from the sun starting with the planet closest to the sun.

Step 1: Look at the exponents. Planets A and B have the smallest exponents, so they are closer to the sun than Planet C.

Step 2: Compare the decimal numbers. 1.082 is smaller than 7.783, so Planet B is the closest to the sun, followed by Planet A and then Planet C.

EXAMPLE 2: The radii of 3 atoms are as follows: Atom 1 measures 1.8×10^{-8}, Atom 2 measures 1.97×10^{-8}, and Atom 3 measures 5.3×10^{-7}. Put the atoms in order of the measure of their radii from greatest to smallest.

Step 1: Look at the negative exponents. The closer the exponent is to 0, the larger the number. 10^{-7} is larger than 10^{-8}, so Atom 3 is the largest.

Step 2: Compare the decimal numbers. 1.97 is larger than 1.8, so atom 2 is the next largest and Atom 1 is the smallest.

For problems 1–6 below, put each number in scientific notation in order from smallest to largest.

1. 2.54×10^{-7} 1.082×10^8 1.97×10^{-8} 1.504×10^6

2. 4.4×10^{-5} 4.04×10^{-6} 4.14×10^{-5} 4.4×10^{-6}

3. 5.2×10^{-3} 5.632×10^{-4} 5.01×10^{-6} 5.4×10^{-5}

4. 10^5 10^{-3} 10^6 10^{-8} 10^7 10^{-5}

5. 1.3×10^{10} 1.102×10^6 1.81×10^5 1.047×10^8

6. 0.206×10^{-4} 2.5×10^{-3} 2.102×10^{-6} 2.114×10^{-5}

CHAPTER 2 REVIEW

Rewrite the following problems using exponents.

1. $3 \times 3 \times 3 \times 3$ _____

2. $5 \times 5 \times 5$ _____

3. $10 \times 10 \times 10 \times 10 \times 10$ _____

4. 25×25 _____

Evaluate each expression.

5. $2^2 =$ _____

6. $5^3 =$ _____

7. $12^1 =$ _____

10. $15^0 =$ _____

11. $10^4 =$ _____

12. $7^2 =$ _____

Simplify the following expressions. Reduce to simplest form, and make all exponents positive.

13. $5^2 \times 5^3$

14. $(4^4)^5$

15. $(4y^3)^3$

16. $6x^{-3}$

17. $(3a^2)^{-2}$

18. $(b^3)^{-4}$

19. $\dfrac{4^6}{4^4}$

20. $\left(\dfrac{3}{5}\right)^2$

21. $\dfrac{(3a^2)^3}{a^3}$

22. $(2x)^{-4}$

Simplify the following square root expressions.

23. $2\sqrt{5} + 6\sqrt{5}$

24. $5\sqrt{3} + \sqrt{12}$

25. $4\sqrt{7} - \sqrt{28}$

26. $9\sqrt{5} - 5\sqrt{5}$

27. $\sqrt{6} \times \sqrt{3}$

28. $\sqrt{18} \times 2\sqrt{3}$

29. $\dfrac{3\sqrt{5}}{\sqrt{15}}$

30. $\dfrac{\sqrt{10}}{\sqrt{5}}$

Convert the following numbers to scientific notation.

31. $5{,}340{,}000 =$ _____

32. $0.00000005874 =$ _____

33. $1{,}451 =$ _____

34. $0.0000041 =$ _____

35. $0.0004178 =$ _____

36. $105{,}000 =$ _____

37. $705{,}000{,}000 =$ _____

38. $0.0000747 =$ _____

39. $0.08 =$ _____

Convert the following numbers from scientific notation to conventional numbers.

40. $5.204 \times 10^{-5} =$ _____

41. $1.02 \times 10^7 =$ _____

42. $8.1 \times 10^5 =$ _____

43. $2.0078 \times 10^{-4} =$ _____

44. Put the following planets in order of distance from the sun.

Planet A 2.27×10^8 m

Planet B 1.427×10^9 m

Planet C 5.899×10^9 m

Planet D 1.496×10^8 m

45. Put the following particles in order from smallest to largest.

Particle A 6.645×10^{-25} g

Particle B 6.63×10^{-24} g

Particle C 6.0645×10^{-25} g

Particle D 6.1645×10^{-24} g

Chapter 3
Fractions and Decimals

GREATEST COMMON FACTOR

To reduce fractions to their simplest form, you must be able to find the greatest common factor.

EXAMPLE: Find the greatest common factor (GCF) of 16 and 24.

To find the **greatest common factor (GCF)** of two numbers, first list the factors of each number.

The factors of 16 are: 1, 2, 4, 8, and 16.
The factors of 24 are: 1, 2, 3, 4, 6, 8, 12, and 24.

What is the **largest** number they both have in common?   **8**
8 is the **greatest** (largest number) **common factor**.

Find all the factors and the greatest common factor (GCF) of each pair of numbers below.

	Pairs	Factors	GCF		Pairs	Factors	GCF
1.	10			6.	6		
	15				42		
2.	12			7.	14		
	16				63		
3.	18			8.	9		
	36				51		
4.	27			9.	18		
	45				45		
5.	32			10.	12		
	40				20		

Solve the following word problems.

1. Dan's glass company wants to ship out 2 orders for glasses, one for 48 and one for 60 glasses. He wants to use full boxes of the same size to ship each order. What is the greatest number of glasses he can put in each box? How many total boxes will he ship for the two orders?

2. Sarah makes hand-made beads to be used in necklaces. She has orders for 72, 88, and 104 beads. She wants to make up bags of the same number of beads to fill each order. What is the greatest number of beads she can put in each bag?

LEAST COMMON MULTIPLE

Find the least common multiple (LCM) of 6 and 10.

To find the **least common multiple (LCM)** of two numbers, first list the multiples of each number. The multiples of a number are 1 times the number, 2 times the number, 3 times the number, and so on.

The multiples of 6 are: 6, 12, 18, 24, 30 …

The multiples of 10 are: 10, 20, 30, 40, 50…

What is the smallest multiple they both have in common?   **30**
30 is the **least** (smallest number) **common multiple** of 6 and 10.

Find the least common multiple (LCM) of each pair of numbers below.

	Pairs	Multiples	LCM		Pairs	Multiples	LCM
1.	6	6, 12, 18, 24, 30	30	6.	6		
	15	15, 30			7		
2.	12			7.	4		
	16				18		
3.	18			8.	7		
	36				5		
4.	7			9.	30		
	3				45		
5.	12			10.	3		
	8				8		

Solve the following word problems.

1. A timer beeps every 18 seconds. Another timer beeps every 48 seconds. If they both start beeping at the same time, how long will it be before the next time they beep together?

2. One student sounds the cymbals every 3 seconds. Another student rings the bell every 8 seconds. If they both start playing at the same time, how long will it be before they play the cymbal and bell at the same time?

3. Greg sneezes every 6 minutes. Elaine coughs every 8 minutes. How often will they sneeze and cough at the same time?

REDUCING PROPER FRACTIONS

EXAMPLE: Reduce $\frac{4}{8}$ to lowest terms.

Step 1: First you need to find the greatest common factor of 4 and 8. Think: What is the largest number that can be divided into 4 and 8 without a remainder?

These must be the same number. $\searrow$ $?\overline{)4}$ 4 and 8 can both be divided by 4.
$?\overline{)8}$

Step 2: Divide the top and bottom of the fraction by the same number.

$$\frac{4 \div 4}{8 \div 4} = \frac{1}{2} \qquad \text{Therefore, } \frac{4}{8} = \frac{1}{2}$$

NOTE: $\frac{4}{8}$ is equivalent to $\frac{1}{2}$. Two fractions are equivalent if they are the same when written in lowest terms.

Reduce the following fractions to lowest terms.

1. $\frac{2}{8} =$ _____

2. $\frac{12}{15} =$ _____

3. $\frac{9}{27} =$ _____

4. $\frac{12}{42} =$ _____

5. $\frac{3}{21} =$ _____

6. $\frac{27}{54} =$ _____

7. $\frac{14}{22} =$ _____

8. $\frac{9}{21} =$ _____

9. $\frac{4}{14} =$ _____

10. $\frac{6}{26} =$ _____

11. $\frac{30}{45} =$ _____

12. $\frac{16}{64} =$ _____

13. $\frac{10}{25} =$ _____

14. $\frac{3}{12} =$ _____

15. $\frac{15}{30} =$ _____

16. $\frac{12}{36} =$ _____

17. $\frac{13}{39} =$ _____

18. $\frac{28}{49} =$ _____

19. $\frac{8}{18} =$ _____

20. $\frac{14}{21} =$ _____

21. $\frac{2}{12} =$ _____

22. $\frac{5}{15} =$ _____

23. $\frac{9}{15} =$ _____

24. $\frac{24}{48} =$ _____

25. $\frac{3}{18} =$ _____

26. $\frac{6}{27} =$ _____

27. $\frac{4}{18} =$ _____

28. $\frac{8}{28} =$ _____

29. $\frac{14}{42} =$ _____

30. $\frac{18}{36} =$ _____

COMPARING THE RELATIVE MAGNITUDE OF FRACTIONS

This section involves comparing the relative magnitude of fractions using the greater than (>), less than (<), and equal to (=) signs.

EXAMPLE 1: Compare $\dfrac{3}{4}$ and $\dfrac{5}{8}$.

Step 1: Find the lowest common denominator. The lowest common denominator is 8.

Step 2: Change fourths to eighths by multiplying three fourths by two halves, $\dfrac{2}{2} \times \dfrac{3}{4} = \dfrac{6}{8}$.

Step 3: $\dfrac{6}{8} > \dfrac{5}{8}$

EXAMPLE 2: Compare the mixed numbers $1\dfrac{3}{5}$ and $1\dfrac{2}{3}$.

Step 1: Change the mixed numbers to improper fractions (explained in a previous lesson).

$$1\dfrac{3}{5} = \dfrac{8}{5} \quad \text{and} \quad 1\dfrac{2}{3} = \dfrac{5}{3}$$

Step 2: Find the lowest common denominator for the improper fractions. The lowest common denominator is 15.

Step 3: Change fifths to fifteenths and thirds to fifteenths, $\dfrac{3 \times 8}{3 \times 5} = \dfrac{24}{15}$ and $\dfrac{5 \times 5}{5 \times 3} = \dfrac{25}{15}$.

Step 4: $\dfrac{24}{15} < \dfrac{25}{15}$ **therefore** $1\dfrac{3}{5} < 1\dfrac{2}{3}$.

Fill in the box with the correct sign.

1. $\dfrac{7}{9} \square \dfrac{7}{8}$ 2. $\dfrac{6}{7} \square \dfrac{5}{6}$ 3. $\dfrac{4}{6} \square \dfrac{5}{7}$ 4. $\dfrac{3}{10} \square \dfrac{4}{13}$

5. $\dfrac{5}{8} \square \dfrac{4}{11}$ 6. $\dfrac{5}{8} \square \dfrac{4}{7}$ 7. $\dfrac{9}{10} \square \dfrac{8}{13}$ 8. $\dfrac{2}{13} \square \dfrac{1}{10}$

9. $\dfrac{4}{9} \square \dfrac{3}{5}$ 10. $\dfrac{2}{6} \square \dfrac{4}{5}$ 11. $\dfrac{7}{12} \square \dfrac{6}{11}$ 12. $\dfrac{3}{11} \square \dfrac{5}{12}$

34

FRACTION WORD PROBLEMS

Solve and reduce answers to lowest terms.

1. Sal works for a movie theater and sells candy by the pound. Her first customer bought $1\frac{1}{3}$ pounds of candy, the second bought $\frac{3}{4}$ of a pound, and the third bought $\frac{4}{5}$ of a pound. How many pounds did she sell to the first three customers?

2. Beth has a bread machine that makes a loaf of bread that weighs $1\frac{1}{2}$ pounds. If she makes a loaf of bread for each of her three sisters, how many pounds of bread will she make?

3. A farmer hauled in 120 bales of hay. Each of his cows ate $1\frac{1}{4}$ bales. How many cows did the farmer feed?

4. John was competing in a 1000 meter race. He had to pull out of the race after running $\frac{3}{4}$ of it. How many meters did he run?

5. Tad needs to measure where the free-throw line should be in front of his basketball goal. He knows his feet are $1\frac{1}{8}$ feet long and the free-throw line should be 15 feet from the backboard. How many toe-to-toe steps does Tad need to take to mark off 15 feet?

6. A chemical plant takes in $5\frac{1}{2}$ million gallons of water from a local river and discharges $3\frac{2}{3}$ million back into the river. How much water does not go back into the river?

7. In January, Jeff filled his car with $11\frac{1}{2}$ gallons of gas the first week, $13\frac{1}{3}$ gallons the second week, $12\frac{1}{4}$ gallons the third week, and $10\frac{1}{5}$ gallons the forth week of January. How many gallons of gas did he buy in January?

8. Martin makes sandwiches for his family. He has $8\frac{1}{4}$ ounces of sandwich meat. If he divides the meat equally to make $4\frac{1}{2}$ sandwiches, how much meat will each sandwich have?

9. The company water cooler started with $4\frac{1}{3}$ gallons of water. Employees drank $3\frac{3}{4}$ gallons. How many gallons were left in the cooler?

10. Jay, Amy, and Todd are all in the band. On a particular song, Jay clangs a bell every 12 seconds. Amy clangs the symbols every 20 seconds and Todd beats the drum every 16 seconds. If they all start at the same time, how many seconds will it be until they play their instruments at the same time?

ROUNDING DECIMALS

EXAMPLE:

$$\underset{\substack{\text{Hundred}\\ \text{Ten}\\ \text{Ones}\\ \text{Tenth}\\ \text{Hundredth}\\ \text{Thousandth}\\ \text{Ten Thousandth}}}{\textbf{5 6 8.4 5 8 7}}$$

Consider the number 568.4587 shown with the place values labeled to the left. To round to a given place value, first find the place value in the decimal. Then look to the digit on the right. If the digit on the right is 5 or greater, INCREASE BY ONE the place value you are rounding to. All the digits to the right of the given place value are dropped if the place value is after the decimal point. If the digit on the right is LESS THAN 5, leave the place value the same. All the digits to the right of the given place value are dropped if the place value you are rounding to is after the decimal point.

Round the number 568.4587 to the nearest:

tenth   568.5
hundredth   568.46
thousandth   568.459

Note: The decimal point is never moved when rounding.

Round to the nearest tenth.

1.	32.89	56.821	0.156	2.846
2.	23.068	23.805	0.209	46.098
3.	0.219	48.541	3.456	10.058

Round to the nearest hundredth.

4.	0.841	21.567	65.987	0.567
5.	32.108	1.705	0.8406	10.576
6.	8.2047	6.0358	0.8738	56.841

Round to the nearest thousandth.

7.	0.0259	4.2689	24.0068	8.0506
8.	3.1045	10.0569	1.8009	6.5073
9.	5.6004	78.6015	17.6038	21.0084

ORDERING DECIMALS

EXAMPLE: Order the following decimals from greatest to least.

.3, .029, .208, .34

Step 1: Arrange numbers with decimal points directly under each other.

.3
.029
.208
.34

Step 2: Fill in with 0's so they all have the same number of places after the decimal point.

.300
Read the numbers as if the   .029   **Least**
decimal points weren't there.   .208
.340   **Greatest**

Answer: .34, .3, .208, .029

Order each set of decimals below from greatest to least.

1. .075, .705, .7, .75

2. .5, .56, .65, .06

3. .9, .09, .099, .95

4. .6, .59, .06, .66

5. .3, .303, .03, .33

6. .02, .25, .205, .5

7. .004, .44, .045, .4

8. .59, .905, .509, .099

9. .1, .01, .11, .111

10. .87, .078, .78, .8

11. .41, .45, .409, .49

12. .754, .7, .74, .75

13. .63, .069, .07, .06

14. .23, .275, .208, .027

Order each set of decimals below from least to greatest.

15. .055, .5, .59, .05

16. .7, .732, .74, .72

17. .04, .48, .048, .408

18. .9, .905, .95, .09

19. .19, .09, .9, .1

20. .21, .02, .021, .2

21. .038, .3, .04, .38

22. .695, .59, .065, .69

23. .08, .88, .808, .008

24. .015, .05, .105, .15

25. .4, .407, .47, .047

26. .632, .63, .603, .62

27. .02, .022, .222, .20

28. .541, .54, .504, .5

DETERMINING CHANGE

EXAMPLE: **Jamie bought 2 T-shirts for $13.95 each and paid $1.68 sales tax. How much change should Jamie get from a $50.00 bill?**

Step 1: Find the total cost of items and tax.

$$\begin{array}{r} \$13.95 \\ 13.95 \\ +\ 1.68 \\ \hline \$29.58 \end{array}$$

Step 2: Subtract the total cost from the amount of money given.

$$\begin{array}{r} \$50.00 \\ -\ 29.58 \\ \hline \$20.42 \end{array}$$

Change

Find the correct change for each of the following problems.

1. Kenya bought a leather belt for $22.89 and a pair of earrings for $4.69. She paid $1.38 sales tax. What was her change from $30.00?

2. Mark spent a total of $78.42 on party supplies. What was his change from a $100.00 bill?

3. The Daniels spent $42.98 at a steak restaurant. How much change did they receive from $50.00?

4. Myra bought a sweater for $49.95 and a dress for $85.89. She paid $9.51 in sales tax. What was her change from $150.00?

5. Roland bought a calculator for $22.78 and an extra battery for $5.69. He paid $1.56 sales tax. What was his change from $40.00?

6. For lunch, Daul purchased 2 hotdogs for $1.09 each, a bag of chips for $0.89, and a large drink for $1.39. He paid $0.18 sales tax. What was his change from $10.00?

7. Geri bought a dining room set for $2,265.99. She paid $135.96 sales tax. What was her change from $2500.00?

8. Juan purchased a bag of dog food for $5.89, a leash for $11.88, and a dog collar for $4.75. The sales tax on the purchase was $1.13. How much change did he get back from $25.00?

9. Celina bought a blouse for $15.46 and a shirt for $23.58. She paid $3.12 sales tax. What was her change from $50.00?

10. Jackie paid for four houseplants that cost $4.95 each. She paid $1.19 sales tax. How much change did she receive from $30.00?

11. Bo spent a total of $13.59 on school supplies. How much change did he receive from $14.00?

12. Fran bought 4 packs of candy on sale for 2 for $0.99 and 2 sodas for $0.65 each. She paid $0.13 sales tax. What was her change from a $5.00 bill?

DECIMAL WORD PROBLEMS

1. Micah can have his oil changed in his car for $19.99, or he can buy the oil and filter and change it himself for $8.79. How much would he save by changing the oil himself?

   _____

2. Megan bought 5 boxes of cookies for $3.75 each. How much did she spend?

   _____

3. Will subscribes to a monthly auto magazine. His one year subscription costs $29.97. If he pays for the subscription in 3 equal installments, how much is each payment?

   _____

4. Pat purchases 2.5 pounds of hamburger at $0.98 per pound. What is the total cost of the hamburger?

   _____

5. The White family took $650 cash with them on vacation. At the end of their vacation, they had $4.67 left. How much cash did they spend on vacation?

   _____

6. Acer Middle School spent $1443.20 on 55 math books. How much did each book cost?

   _____

7. The Junior Beta Club needs to raise $1513.75 to go to a national convention. If they decide to sell candy bars at $1.25 each, how many will they need to sell to meet their goal?

   _____

8. Fleta owns a candy store. On Monday, she sold 6.5 pounds of chocolate, 8.34 pounds of jelly beans, 4.9 pounds of sour snaps, and 5.64 pounds of yogurt-covered raisins. How many pounds of candy did she sell total?

   _____

9. Randal purchased a rare coin collection for $1803.95. He sold it at auction for $2700. How much money did he make on the coins?

   _____

10. A leather jacket that normally sells for $259.99 is on sale now for $197.88. How much can you save if you buy it now?

    _____

11. At the movies, Gigi buys 0.6 pounds of candy priced at $2.10 per pound. How much did she spend on candy?

    _____

12. George has $6.00 to buy candy. If each candy bar costs $.60, how many bars can he buy?

    _____

CHAPTER 3 REVIEW

Simplify.

1. $\dfrac{15}{6}$ _____

2. $\dfrac{24}{4}$ _____

3. $\dfrac{20}{15}$ _____

4. $\dfrac{14}{3}$ _____

Reduce.

5. $\dfrac{9}{27}$ _____

6. $\dfrac{4}{16}$ _____

7. $\dfrac{8}{12}$ _____

8. $\dfrac{12}{18}$ _____

Change to an improper fraction.

9. $5\dfrac{1}{10}$ _____

10. 7 _____

11. $3\dfrac{3}{5}$ _____

12. $6\dfrac{2}{3}$ _____

Use > and < to compare the following.

13. 2.123 ☐ $.21234$

14. $.1025$ ☐ $.125$

15. Carter's Junior High track team ran the first leg of a 400 meter relay race in 10.23 seconds, the second leg in 11.4 seconds, the third leg in 10.77 seconds, and the last leg in 9.9 seconds. How long did it take for them to complete the race?

_____

16. Mrs. Tate brought $5\dfrac{1}{2}$ pounds of candy to divide among her 22 students. If the candy was divided equally, how many pounds of candy did each student receive?

_____

17. Elenita used $1\dfrac{1}{4}$ yards of material to recover one dining room chair. How much material would she need to recover all eight chairs?

_____

18. The square tiles in Mr. Cooke's math classroom measure $2\dfrac{1}{3}$ feet across. The students counted that the classroom was $5\dfrac{2}{3}$ tiles wide. How wide is Mr. Cooke's classroom?

_____

19. Allie practiced the piano 3 hours last week and practiced her clarinet 5 hours. What is the ratio of the time she practiced the piano to her total instrument practice time?

_____

20. Alejandro ran 3 miles every day for 7 days. What is the ratio of his daily run to his mileage run for the 7 day week?

_____

Chapter 4
Percents

CHANGING PERCENTS TO DECIMALS
AND DECIMALS TO PERCENTS

Change the following percents to **decimal** numbers.

Directions: Move the **decimal** point two places to the left, and drop the **percent** sign. If there is no decimal point written, it is after the number and before the percent sign. Sometimes you will need to add a "0". (See 5% below.)

EXAMPLES: 14% = 0.14   5% = 0.05   100% = 1   103% = 1.03
(decimal point)⤴

Change the following percents to decimal numbers.

1. 18% = _____	8. 119% = _____	15. 5% = _____
2. 23% = _____	9. 2% = _____	16. 25% = _____
3. 9% = _____	10. 55% = _____	17. 410% = _____
4. 63% = _____	11. 80% = _____	18. 1% = _____
5. 4% = _____	12. 17% = _____	19. 50% = _____
6. 45% = _____	13. 66% = _____	20. 99% = _____
7. 2% = _____	14. 13% = _____	21. 107% = _____

Change the following decimal numbers to percents.

Directions: To change a **decimal** number to a **percent**, move the **decimal** point two places to the right, and add a **percent** sign. You may need to add a "0". (See 0.8 below.)

EXAMPLES: 0.62 = 62%   0.07 = 7%   0.8 = 80%   0.166 = 16.6%   1.54 = 154%

Change the following decimal numbers to percents.

22. 0.15 = _____	29. 0.044 = _____	36. 0.042 = _____
23. 0.62 = _____	30. 0.58 = _____	37. 0.375 = _____
24. 1.53 = _____	31. 0.86 = _____	38. 5.09 = _____
25. 0.22 = _____	32. 0.29 = _____	39. 0.75 = _____
26. 0.35 = _____	33. 0.06 = _____	40. 0.3 = _____
27. 0.375 = _____	34. 0.48 = _____	41. 2.9 = _____
28. 0.648 = _____	35. 3.089 = _____	42. 0.06 = _____

CHANGING PERCENTS TO FRACTIONS
AND FRACTIONS TO PERCENTS

EXAMPLE: Change 15% to a fraction.

Step 1: Copy the number without the percent sign. **15** is the top number of the fraction.

Step 2: The bottom number of the fraction is 100.

$$15\% = \frac{15}{100}$$

Step 3: Reduce the fraction. $\frac{15}{100} = \frac{3}{20}$

Change the following percents to fractions and reduce.

1. 50%	6. 63%	11. 25%	16. 40%
2. 13%	7. 75%	12. 5%	17. 99%
3. 22%	8. 91%	13. 16%	18. 30%
4. 95%	9. 18%	14. 1%	19. 15%
5. 52%	10. 3%	15. 79%	20. 84%

EXAMPLE: Change $\frac{7}{8}$ to a percent.

Step 1: Divide 7 by 8. Add as many 0's as necessary.

```
        .875
    8)7.000
    - 6 4
      ----
       60
     - 56
      ----
       40
     - 40
      ----
        0
```

Step 2: Change the decimal answer, .875, to a percent by moving the decimal point 2 places to the right.

$$\frac{7}{8} = .875 = 87.5\%$$

Change the following fractions to percents.

1. $\frac{1}{5}$	4. $\frac{3}{8}$	7. $\frac{1}{10}$	10. $\frac{3}{4}$	13. $\frac{1}{16}$	16. $\frac{3}{4}$
2. $\frac{5}{8}$	5. $\frac{3}{16}$	8. $\frac{4}{5}$	11. $\frac{1}{8}$	14. $\frac{1}{4}$	17. $\frac{2}{5}$
3. $\frac{7}{16}$	6. $\frac{19}{100}$	9. $\frac{15}{16}$	12. $\frac{5}{16}$	15. $\frac{4}{100}$	18. $\frac{16}{25}$

CHANGING RATIOS TO PERCENTS

EXAMPLE: The ratio of girls to boys in the class is 9 to 11. What percent of the class are girls?

Step 1: We need to change the ratio to a fraction. Copy down the part of the ratio that are girls. Girls are mentioned first, so the **top** number of the fraction will be 9.

Step 2: The bottom number of the fraction is the sum of both numbers of the ratio. $9 + 11 = 20$. The bottom number of the fraction is 20.

Step 3: Change the fraction $\frac{9}{20}$ to a percent. $9 \div 20 = .45$ or 45%

Change the following ratios to percents.

1. The ratio of students who walk to school to students who take the bus is 3 to 5. What percent of the students take the bus?

2. The survey showed that pizza is preferred to peanut butter sandwiches 7 to 3. What percent of those surveyed prefer pizza?

3. The ratio of black rabbits to white rabbits in a pet store is 7 to 3. What percent of the rabbits are white?

4. Nicholas collected 11 empty orange drink cans and 9 empty cola cans for his school's recycling program. What percent of the cans were cola cans?

5. The principal of Eastside High School presented perfect attendance awards to 25 boys and 50 girls. What percent of those who received awards were girls?

6. Volunteers at the Palm Coast Homeless Shelter are planning a Thanksgiving dinner for its residents. The residents include 12 adults and 28 children. What percent of the residents are children?

7. In one popular Lake Erie restaurant, 14 customers ate crab dinners and 16 customers ate shrimp dinners. What percent of the customers ate crab dinners?

8. At Joliet High School, for every 4 students who like classical music, 11 do not. What percent of the students like classical?

9. The ratio of red gumballs to yellow gumballs in a gumball machine is 12 to 5. What percent of the gumballs are red?

10. Frederick and Isabell stayed up to watch a meteor shower. Looking different directions, Frederick counted 9 and Isabel counted 14 shooting stars. Of the shooting stars they both sighted, what percent did Frederick see?

FINDING THE PERCENT OF THE TOTAL

EXAMPLE: There were 75 customers at Bill's gas station this morning. Thirty-two percent used a credit card to make their purchase. How many customers used credit cards this morning at Bill's?

Step 1:   Change 32% to a decimal.   32% = .32

Step 2:   Multiply by the total number mentioned.

$$
\begin{array}{r}
.32 \\
\times\ 75 \\
\hline
160 \\
224 \\
\hline
24.00
\end{array}
$$

24 customers used credit cards.

Find the percent of the total in the problems below.

1. Eighty-five percent of Mrs. Coomer's math class passed her final exam. There were 40 students in her class. How many passed?

2. Fifteen percent of a bag of chocolate candies have a red coating on them. How many red pieces are in a bag of 60 candies?

3. Sixty-eight percent of Valley Creek School students attended this year's homecoming dance. There are 675 students. How many attended the dance?

4. Out of the 4,500 people who attended the rock concert, forty-six percent purchased a T-shirt. How many people bought T-shirts?

5. Nina sold ninety-five percent of her 500 cookies at the bake sale. How many cookies did she sell?

6. Twelve percent of yesterday's customers purchased premium grade gasoline from GasCo. If GasCo had 200 customers, how many purchased premium grade gasoline?

7. The Candy Shack sold 138 pounds of candy on Tuesday. Fifty-two percent of the candy was jelly beans. How many pounds of jelly beans were sold Tuesday?

8. A fund-raiser at the school raised $617.50. Ninety-four percent went to local charities. How much money went to charities?

9. Out of a company's $6.5 million profit, eight percent will be paid to shareholders as dividends. How much will be paid out in dividends?

10. Ted's Toys sold seventy-five percent of its stock of stuffed bean animals on Saturday. If Ted's Toys had 620 originally in stock, how many were sold on Saturday?

TIPS AND COMMISSIONS

Vocabulary

Tip: A **tip** is money given to someone doing a service for you such as a waiter, waitress, porter, cab driver, beautician, etc.

Commission: In many businesses, sales people are paid on **commission** - a percent of the total sales they make.

Problems requiring you to figure a tip, commission, or percent of a total are all done in the same way.

EXAMPLE: Ramon made a 4% commission on an $8,000 pickup truck he sold. How much was his commission?

TOTAL COST	**$8,000**
× RATE OF COMMISSION	**× 0.04**
COMMISSION	**$320.00**

Solve each of the following problems.

1. Whitney makes 12% commission on all her sales. This month she sold $9,000 worth of merchandise. What was her commission?

   _____

2. Marcus gives 25% of his income to his parents to help cover expenses. He earns $340 per week. How much money does he give his parents?

   _____

3. Jan pays $640 per month for rent. If the rate of inflation is 5%, how much can Jan expect to pay monthly next year?

   _____

4. The total bill at Jake's Catfish Place came to $35.80. Jim wanted to leave a 15% tip. How much money will he leave for the tip?

   _____

5. Rami makes $2,400 per month and puts 6% in a savings plan. How much does he save per month?

   _____

6. Cristina makes $2,550 per month. Her boss promised her a 7% raise. How much more will she make per month?

   _____

7. Out of 150 math students, 86% passed. How many students passed math class?

   _____

8. Marta sells Sue Ann Cosmetics and gets 20% commission on all her sales. Last month, she sold $560.00 worth of cosmetics. How much was her commission?

   _____

FINDING THE AMOUNT OF DISCOUNT

Sale prices are sometimes marked 30% off, or better yet, 50% off. A 30% DISCOUNT means you will pay 30% less than the original price. How much money you save is also known as the amount of the DISCOUNT. Read the example below to learn to figure the amount of a discount.

EXAMPLE: A $179.00 chair is on sale for 30% off. How much can I save if I buy it now?

Step 1: Change 30% to a decimal. 30% = .30

Step 2: Multiply the original price by the discount.

ORIGINAL PRICE	$179.00
× **% DISCOUNT**	× .30
SAVINGS	$ 53.70

Practice finding the amount of the discount. Round off answers to the nearest penny.

1. Tubby Tires is offering a 25% discount on tires purchased on Tuesday. How much can you save if you buy tires on Tuesday regularly priced at $225.00 any other day of the week? _____

2. The regular price for a garden rake is $10.97 at Sly's Super Store. This week, Sly is offering a 30% discount. How much is the discount on the rake? _____

3. Christine bought a sweater regularly priced at $26.80 with a coupon for 20% off any sweater. How much did she save? _____

4. The software that Marge needs for her computer is priced at $69.85. If she waits until a store offers it at 20% off, how much will she save? _____

5. Ty purchased jeans that were priced $23.97. He received a 15% employee discount. How much did he save? _____

6. The Bakery Company offers a 60% discount on all bread made the day before. How much can you save on a $2.40 loaf made today if you wait until tomorrow to buy it? _____

7. A furniture store advertises a 40% off liquidation sale on all items. How much would the discount be on a $2530 dining room set? _____

8. Becky bought a $4.00 nail polish on sale for 30% off. What was the dollar amount of the discount? _____

9. How much is the discount on a $350 racing bike marked 15% off? _____

10. Raymond receives a 2% discount from his credit card company on all purchases made with the credit card. What is his discount on $1575.50 worth of purchases? _____

FINDING THE DISCOUNTED SALE PRICE

To find the discounted sale price, you must go one step further than shown on the previous page. Read the example below to learn how to figure **discount** prices.

EXAMPLE: A $74.00 chair is on sale for 25% off. How much can I save if I buy it now?

Step 1: Change 25% to a decimal.   25% = .25

Step 2: Multiply the original price by the discount.

ORIGINAL PRICE	$74.00
× **% DISCOUNT**	× .25
SAVINGS	$18.50

Step 3: Subtract the savings amount from the original price to find the sale price.

ORIGINAL PRICE	$74.00
− **SAVINGS**	− 18.50
SALE PRICE	$55.50

Figure the sale price of the items below. The first one is done for you.

ITEM	PRICE	% OFF	MULTIPLY	SUBTRACT	SALE PRICE
1. pen	$1.50	20%	1.50 × .2 = $0.30	1.50 − 0.30 = 1.20	$1.20
2. recliner	$325	25%			
3. juicer	$55	15%			
4. blanket	$14	10%			
5. earrings	$2.40	20%			
6. figurine	$8	15%			
7. boots	$159	35%			
8. calculator	$80	30%			
9. candle	$6.20	50%			
10. camera	$445	20%			
11. VCR	$235	25%			
12. video game	$25	10%			

SALES TAX

EXAMPLE: The total price of a sofa is $560.00 + 6% sales tax. How much is the sales tax? What is the total cost?

Step 1: You will need to change 6% to a decimal.   6% = .06

Step 2: Simply multiply the cost, $560, by the tax rate, 6%. 560 × .06 = 33.6
The answer will be $33.60. (You need to add a 0 to the answer. When dealing with money, there needs to be two places after the decimal point).

COST	$560
× **6% TAX**	× .06
SALES TAX	$33.60

Step 3: Add the sales tax amount, $33.60, to the cost of the item sold, $560. This is the total cost.

COST	$560.00
SALES TAX	+ 33.60
TOTAL COST	$593.60

NOTE: When the answer to the question involves money, you always need to round off the answer to the nearest hundredth (2 places after the decimal point). Sometimes you will need to add a zero.

Figure the total costs in the problems below. The first one is done for you.

ITEM	PRICE	% SALES TAX	MULTIPLY	ADD PRICE PLUS TAX	TOTAL
1. jeans	$42	7%	$42 × 0.07 = $2.94	42 + 2.94 = 44.94	$44.94
2. truck	$17,495	6%			
3. film	$5.89	8%			
4. T-shirt	$12	5%			
5. football	$36.40	4%			
6. soda	$1.78	5%			
7. 4 tires	$105.80	10%			
8. clock	$18	6%			
9. burger	$2.34	5%			
10. software	$89.95	8%			

FINDING THE PERCENT

EXAMPLE: 15 is what percent of 60?

Step 1: To solve these problems, simply divide the smaller amount by the larger amount. You will need to add a decimal point and two 0's.

$$
\begin{array}{r}
.25 \\
60\overline{)15.00} \\
-12\ 0 \\
\hline
3\ 00 \\
-3\ 00 \\
\hline
0
\end{array}
$$

Step 2: Change the answer, .25, to a percent by moving the decimal point two places to the right. .25 = 25%   15 is 25% of 60.

Remember: **To change a decimal to a percent, you will sometimes have to add a zero when moving the decimal point two places to the right.**

Find the following percents.

1. What percent of 50 is 16?

2. 20 is what percent of 80?

3. 9 is what percent of 100?

4. 19 is what percent of 95?

5. Ruth made 200 cookies for the picnic. Only 25 were left at the end of the day. What percent of the cookies was left?

6. Pat made 116 bird houses to sell at the county fair. The first day he sold 29. What percent of the bird houses did he sell?

7. Eileen planted 90 sweet corn seeds, but only 18 plants came up. What percent of the seeds germinated?

8. Tomika invests $36 of her $240 paycheck in a retirement account. What percent of her pay is she investing?

9. Ray sold a house for $115,000, and his commission was $9,200. What percent commission did he make?

10. Peter was making $16.00 per hour. After one year, he received a $2.00 per hour raise. What percent of a raise did he get?

11. Calvin budgets $235 per month for food. If his salary is $940 per month, what percent of his salary does he budget for food?

12. Katie earned $45 on commission for her sales totaling $225. What percent was her commission?

13. Among the students taking band this year, 2 out of 5 are freshmen. What percent of the band are freshmen?

14. Of the donuts we have left to sell, the ratio of chocolate donuts to non-chocolate is 3 to 5. What percent of the donuts left to sell are chocolate?

15. The school bought 340 new history books for 400 students. What percent of the students got new history books?

16. Of the 48 dogs enrolled in obedience school, 36 successfully completed training. What percent of the dogs completed training?

17. The results of a student survey show that hamburgers are preferred to hotdogs by a ratio of 17 to 25. What percent of the students prefer hamburgers?

COMPARING THE RELATIVE MAGNITUDE OF NUMBERS

When comparing the relative magnitude of numbers, the greater than (>), less than (<), and the equal to (=) signs are the ones most frequently used. The simplest way to compare numbers that are in different notations, like percent, decimals, and fractions, is to change all of them to one notation. Decimals are the easiest to compare.

EXAMPLE 1:   Which is larger: $1\frac{1}{4}$ or 1.3?

Answer: Change $1\frac{1}{4}$ to a decimal. $\frac{1}{4} = .25$, so $1\frac{1}{4} = 1.25$.
1.3 is larger than 1.25, so $1.3 > 1\frac{1}{4}$.

EXAMPLE 2:   Which is smaller: 60% or $\frac{2}{3}$?

Answer: Change both to decimals.
$60\% = .6$ and $\frac{2}{3} = .\overline{66}$
.6 is smaller than $.\overline{66}$, so $60\% < \frac{2}{3}$

Fill in each box with the correct sign.

1. 23.4 ☐ $23\frac{1}{2}$

2. 17% ☐ .17

3. $\frac{3}{8}$ ☐ 37.5%

4. 25% ☐ $\frac{2}{10}$

5. 234% ☐ 23.4

6. $\frac{1}{7}$ ☐ 14%

7. 13.95 ☐ $13\frac{8}{9}$

8. 4.0 ☐ 40%

9. 25% ☐ $\frac{3}{2}$

10. $\frac{12}{4}$ ☐ 300%

11. 6% ☐ $\frac{1}{16}$

12. 1.33 ☐ $\frac{4}{3}$

13. .8 ☐ $\frac{4}{5}$

14. 75% ☐ $\frac{3}{4}$

15. $\frac{5}{8}$ ☐ 62%

Compare the sums, differences, products, and quotients below. Fill in each box with the correct sign.

1. $(32+15)$ ☐ $(65-17)$

2. $(45-13)$ ☐ $(31+9)$

3. $(24 \div 4)$ ☐ $(24 \div 6)$

4. $(48 \div 6)$ ☐ (4×3)

5. (4×3) ☐ $(48 \div 6)$

6. (18×4) ☐ (5×17)

7. $[(1+3)+5]$ ☐ $[(5+(3+1)]$

8. $[(1+(3+5)]$ ☐ $[(5-3)+1]$

9. $(25 \div 5)$ ☐ (5×5)

CHAPTER 4 REVIEW

Change the following percents to decimals.

1. 45%   _____
2. 219%   _____
3. 22%   _____
4. 1.25%   _____

Change the following decimals to percents.

5. 0.52   _____
6. 0.64   _____
7. 1.09   _____
8. 0.625   _____

Change the following percents to fractions.

9. 25%   _____
10. 3%   _____
11. 68%   _____
12. 102%   _____

Change the following fractions to percents.

13. $\frac{9}{10}$ _____
14. $\frac{5}{16}$ _____
15. $\frac{1}{8}$ _____
16. $\frac{1}{4}$ _____

17. Celeste makes 6% commission on her sales. If her sales for a week total $4580, what is her commission?

    _____

18. Peeler's Jewelry is offering a 30% off sale on all bracelets. How much will you save if you buy a $45.00 bracelet during the sale?

    _____

19. Uncle Howard left his only niece 56% of his assets according to his will. If his assets totaled $564,000 when he died, how much did his niece inherit?

    _____

20. How much would an employee pay for a $724.00 stereo if the employee got a 15% discount?

    _____

21. Misha bought a CD for $14.95. If sales tax was 7%, how much did she pay total?

    _____

22. The Pep band made $640 during a fundraiser. The band spent $400 of the money on new uniforms. What percent of the total did they spend on uniforms?

    _____

23. Patton, Patton, and Clark, a law firm, won a malpractice law suit for $4,500,000. Sixty-eight percent went to the law firm. How much did the law firm make?

    _____

24. Jeneane earned $340.20 commission by selling $5670 worth of products. What percent commission did she earn?

    _____

25. At Jefferson High School, the ratio of band members to non-band members is 2 to 5. What percent of the students are band members?

    _____

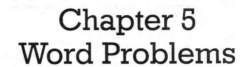

Chapter 5
Word Problems

ROUNDING WHOLE NUMBERS

EXAMPLE:

Ten Thousand	Thousand	Hundred	Ten	Ones
4	8,	5	3	8

Consider the number 48,538 shown at the left with the place values labeled. To round to a given place value, first find the place in the number. Then look to the digit on the right. If the digit on the right is 5 or greater, INCREASE BY ONE the place to which the number is being rounded. All the digits to the right of the given place value become 0's. If the digit on the right is LESS THAN 5, leave that place value the same, and change the digits on the right to 0's.

EXAMPLE: Round the number 48,538 to the nearest:

ten	48,540
hundred	48,500
thousand	49,000
ten thousand	50,000

Round to the nearest ten.

1.	478	654	3,240	1,878
2.	4,565	7,305	1,432	8,799

Round to the nearest hundred.

3.	4,566	7,821	6,587	10,746
4.	789	430	55,123	7,297
5.	45,149	550	11,500	14,278

Round to the nearest thousand.

6.	66,150	78,951	41,299	5,870
7.	40,112	38,711	20,099	4,299
8.	32,889	112,240	905,887	54,800

Round to the nearest ten thousand.

9.	14,876	154,681	109,901	65,789
10.	154,730	78,354	506,056	137,196

WORD PROBLEMS

Most of the problems on the Ohio Graduation Test in Mathematics will be word problems. The problems below will require adding, subtracting, multiplying, and dividing to solve. Read each problem carefully.

1. If Jacob averages 15 points per basketball game, how many points will he score in a season with 12 games?

2. A cashier can ring up 12 items per minute. How long will it take the cashier to ring up a customer's purchase of 72 items?

3. Mrs. Randolph has 26 students in 1st period, 32 students in 2nd period, 27 students in 3rd period, and 30 students in 4th period. What is the total number of students Mrs. Randolph teaches?

4. When Blake started on his trip, his odometer read 109,875. At the end of his trip it read 110,480. How many miles did he travel?

5. The Beta Club is raising money by selling boxes of candy. It sold 152 boxes on Monday, 236 boxes on Tuesday, 107 boxes on Wednesday, and 93 boxes on Thursday. How many total boxes did the Beta Club sell?

6. Jonah won 1056 tickets in the arcade. He purchased a pair of binoculars for 964 tickets. How many tickets does he have left?

7. A school cafeteria has 52 tables. If each table seats 14 people, how many people can be seated in the cafeteria?

8. Leadville, Colorado is 14,286 feet above sea level. Denver, Colorado is 5,280 feet above sea level. What is the difference in elevation between these two cities?

9. The local bakery made 288 donuts on Friday morning. How many dozen donuts did they make?

10. Mattie ate 14 chocolate-covered raisins. Her big brother ate 5 times as many. How many chocolate-covered raisins did her brother eat?

11. Concession stand sales for a football game totaled $1563. The actual cost for the food and beverages was $395. How much profit did the concession stand make?

12. An orange grove worker can harvest 480 oranges per hour by hand. How many oranges can the worker harvest in an 8 hour day?

TWO-STEP WORD PROBLEMS

1. There are 25 miniature chocolate bars in a bag. There are 20 bags in a carton. Damon needs to order 10,000 miniature chocolate bars. How many cartons will he need to order?

2. LeAnn needs 2,400 boxes for her business. The boxes she needs come in bundles of 50 that weigh 45 pounds per bundle. What will be the total weight of the 2,400 boxes she needs?

3. Seth uses 20 nails to make a birdhouse. He wants to make 60 birdhouses to sell at the county fair. There are 30 nails in a box. How many boxes will he need?

4. There are 12 computer disks in a box. There are 10 boxes in a carton. John ordered 16 cartons. How many disks is he getting?

5. The Do-Nut Factory packs 13 doughnuts in each baker's dozen box. They also sell cartons of doughnuts which have 6 baker's dozen boxes. Duncan needs to feed 780 people. Assuming each person eats only 1 doughnut, how many cartons will he need to buy from the Do-Nut Factory?

6. Brittany has 2 dogs, a Saint Bernard and a Golden Retriever. The Saint Bernard eats twice as much as the Golden Retriever. The retriever eats 5 pounds of food in 6 days. How many pounds of food do the two dogs eat in 30 days?

7. Each of the 4 engines on a jet uses 500 gallons of fuel per hour. How many gallons of fuel are needed for a 5 hour flight with enough extra fuel for an additional 2 hours as a safety precaution?

8. The Farmer's Dairy has 1620 pounds of butter to package. They are packaging the butter in five-pound tubs to distribute to restaurants. If they put 12 tubs in a case, how many cases of butter can they fill?

9. Tom has 155 head of cattle. Each animal eats 8 pounds of grain per day. How many pounds of grain does Tom need to feed his cattle for 10 days?

10. When you grind 3 cups of grain, you get 5 cups of flour. How many cups of grain must you grind to get 40 cups of flour?

TIME OF TRAVEL

EXAMPLE: Katrina drove 384 miles at an average of 64 miles per hour. How many hours did she travel?

Solution: Divide the number of miles by the miles per hour. $\dfrac{384 \text{ miles}}{64 \text{ miles/hour}} = 6 \text{ hours}$

Find the hours of travel in each problem below.

1. Bobbi drove 342 miles at an average speed of 57 miles per hour. How many hours did she drive?   _____

2. Jan set her speed control at 55 miles per hour and drove for 165 miles. How many hours did she drive?   _____

3. John traveled 2,092 miles in a jet that flew an average of 523 miles per hour. How long was he in the air?   _____

4. How long will it take a bus averaging 54 miles per hour to travel 378 miles?   _____

5. Kyle drove his motorcycle in a 225 mile race, and he averaged 75 miles per hour. How long did it take for him to complete the race?   _____

6. Stacy drove 576 miles at an average speed of 48 miles an hour. How many hours did she drive?   _____

7. Kendra flew 250 miles in a glider and averaged 125 miles per hour in speed. How many hours did she fly?   _____

8. Travis traveled 496 miles at an average speed of 62 miles per hour. How long did he travel?   _____

9. Wanda rode her bicycle an average of 15 miles an hour for 60 miles. How many hours did she ride?   _____

10. Rami drove 184 miles at an average speed of 46 miles per hour. How many hours did he drive?   _____

11. A train traveled at a constant 85 miles per hour for 425 miles. How many hours did the train travel?   _____

12. How long was Amy on the road if she drove 195 miles at an average of 65 miles per hour?   _____

RATE

EXAMPLE: Laurie traveled 312 miles in 6 hours. What was her average rate of speed?

Solution: Divide the number of miles by the number of hours. $\frac{312 \text{ miles}}{6 \text{ hours}} = 52 \text{ miles/hour}$

Laurie's average rate of speed was 52 miles per hour (or 52 mph).

Find the average rate of speed in each problem below.

1. A race car went 500 miles in 4 hours. What was its average rate of speed?

   _____

2. Carrie drove 124 miles in 2 hours. What was her average speed?

   _____

3. After 7 hours of driving, Chad had gone 364 miles. What was his average speed?

   _____

4. Anna drove 360 miles in 8 hours. What was her average speed?

   _____

5. After 3 hours of driving, Paul had gone 183 miles. What was his average speed?

   _____

6. Nicole ran 25 miles in 5 hours. What was her average speed?

   _____

7. A train traveled 492 miles in 6 hours. What was its average rate of speed?

   _____

8. A commercial jet traveled 1,572 miles in 3 hours. What was its average speed?

   _____

9. Jillian drove 195 miles in 3 hours. What was her average speed?

   _____

10. Greg drove 8 hours from his home to a city 336 miles away. At what average speed did he travel?

    _____

11. Caleb drove 64 miles in one hour. What was his average speed in miles per hour?

    _____

12. After 9 hours of driving, Kate had traveled 405 miles. What speed did she average?

    _____

MORE RATES

On the previous page, rate was discussed in terms of miles per hour. Rate can be any distance over time such as feet per second, kilometers per minute, inches per hour, and so on. Rate can be how fast something is done. For example, a brick layer may lay 80 bricks per hour. A copy machine may make 100 copies per minute. A person doing data entry may type 65 words per minute. Finding the rate is the same as finding the speed.

EXAMPLE: Nathan entered his snail in a race. His snail went 18 feet in 6 minutes. How fast did his snail move?

Solution: Rate is the same as $\frac{\text{distance}}{\text{time}}$. The time is six minutes. Rate needs to be expressed in terms of one minute, one hour, one day, and so on. You need to find out how far the snail went in one minute. $\frac{18 \text{ feet}}{6 \text{ minutes}} = \frac{3 \text{ feet}}{1 \text{ minute}}$

Nathan's snail went an average of 3 feet per minute or 3 ft/min.

Find the average rate or speed for each of the following problems.

1. Tewanda read a 2000 word news article in 8 minutes. How fast did she read the news article?

_____

2. Chandler rides his bike to school every day. He travels 2560 feet in 640 seconds. How many feet does he travel per second?

_____

3. Mr. Molier is figuring out the semester averages for his history students. He can figure the average for 20 students in an hour. How long does it take him to figure the average for each student?

_____

4. In 1908, John Hurlinger of Austria walked 1400 kilometers from Vienna to Paris on his hands. The journey took 55 days. What was his average speed per day?

_____

5. Spectators at the Super Circus were amazed to watch a canon shoot a clown 212 feet into a net in 4 seconds. How many feet per second did the clown travel?

_____

6. Marcus Page, star receiver for the Big Bulls, was awarded a 5 year contract for 105 million dollars. How much would his annual rate of pay be?

_____

7. Duke Delaney scored 28 points during the 4 quarters of the basketball playoffs. What was his average score per quarter?

_____

8. The new McDonald's in Moscow serves 11,208 customers during a 24 hour period. What is the average number of customers served per hour?

_____

DISTANCE

EXAMPLE: Jessie traveled for 7 hours at an average rate of 58 miles per hour. How far did she travel?

Solution: Multiply the number of hours by the average rate of speed.
7 hours × 58 miles/hour = 406 miles

Find the distance in each of the following problems.

1. Myra traveled for 9 hours at an average rate of 45 miles per hour. How far did she travel?

   _____

2. A tour bus drove 4 hours, averaging 58 miles per hour. How many miles did it travel?

   _____

3. Tina drove for 7 hours at an average speed of 53 miles per hour. How far did she travel?

   _____

4. Dustin raced for 3 hours, averaging 176 miles per hour. How many miles did he race?

   _____

5. Kris drove 5 hours and averaged 49 miles per hour. How far did she travel?

   _____

6. Oliver drove at an average of 93 miles per hour for 3 hours. How far did he travel?

   _____

7. A commercial airplane traveled 514 miles per hour for 2 hours. How far did it fly?

   _____

8. A train traveled at 125 miles per hour for 4 hours. How many miles did it travel?

   _____

9. Carl drove a constant 65 miles an hour for 3 hours. How many miles did he drive?

   _____

10. Jasmine drove for 5 hours, averaging 40 miles per hour. How many miles did she drive?

    _____

11. Roger flew his glider for 2 hours at 87 miles per hour. How many miles did his glider fly?

    _____

12. Beth traveled at a constant 65 miles per hour for 4 hours. How far did she travel?

    _____

58

FINDING A PROFIT

EXAMPLE: Tory decided to make doghouses to sell at the hardware store near his home to make money for college. He spent $37 on materials for each doghouse. He sold each doghouse for $60 and gave $5.00 to the hardware store for each doghouse he sold in return for space to display his doghouses. How many doghouses will he have to sell if he wants to earn $1,000 for college?

Step 1: Take the selling price and subtract all the expenses for each doghouse to find the profit on each doghouse. $60 - 37 - 5 =$ **$18 profit on each doghouse.**

Step 2: Take the amount he wants to make and divide by the profit on each doghouse to find out how many he has to sell to make $1,000. $1000 \div 18 = 55.5$. **He will need to sell 56 doghouses to make $1,000.**

Find the profit for each of the following questions.

1. Troy bought a worm farm and decided to raise worms to make money. The worm farm cost $110.00 and came with 200 worms and 500 worm capsules, each containing about 4 baby worms. He figures he can sell the worms to bait shops for $1.25 per dozen. How many dozen worms will he have to sell to begin to make a profit? Worms eat table scraps, so there are no food expenses.

2. Sharon had a black Labrador retriever with an excellent pedigree which she decided to breed so she could sell the puppies to earn money. Her parents said they would loan her the money she needed to cover her expenses until the puppies were sold. She borrowed $500 for stud fees, $150.00 for vet fees, and $80 for food. Her dog had 8 healthy puppies which she sold for $400.00 each. She paid $25.00 for each puppy for shots and $60.00 for puppy chow, and $25.00 for a heat lamp for the dog house. The ad in the paper cost $12.00/week, and she was happy they all sold in 1 week. After she paid back her parents for all the expenses, how much profit did she make on the puppies?

3. White County High School's band needed new uniforms. They decided to sell candy bars to raise money. The candy bar company sent them 1,000 candy bars and a bill for $850.00. The band members sold the bars for $1.50 each. How much was their profit from candy bar sales when all of the bars were sold?

4. Randy and Jeff were brothers who decided to go into business together mowing lawns. Their parents told them they could use the family truck but would need to buy their own equipment since the family lawn mower was barely working. They bought two lawn mowers for $150.00 each and had 300 flyers made for 12¢ each. They agreed to work together on every job and split the money evenly. After distributing flyers to all the homes around them, they waited for the calls. They soon had so much business they could hardly keep up. They charged $30 for $\frac{1}{4}$ acre lots and $60 for $\frac{1}{2}$ acre lots. They had to buy a trimmer for $30 and a hedge trimmer for $20. A receipt book and appointment book came to $12. How many $\frac{1}{4}$ acre lots will they have to cut to earn $500 each after they pay their expenses? They estimate they spent about $1.00 on gas for each lawn.

CHAPTER 5 REVIEW

1. The animal keeper feeds Mischief, the monkey, 5 pounds of bananas per day. The gorilla eats 4 times as many bananas as the monkey. How many pounds of bananas does the animal keeper need to feed both animals for a week?

2. You and 4 friends are going to split a restaurant bill evenly. The total bill is $46.80. How much are each of you going to pay?

3. The Bing family's odometer read 65453 before driving to Disney World for vacation. After their vacation, the odometer read 66245. How many miles did they drive during their vacation?

4. Jonathan can assemble 47 widgets per hour. How many can he assemble in an 8 hour day?

5. Jacob drove 252 miles, and his average speed was 42 miles per hour. How many hours did he drive?

6. The Jones family traveled 300 miles in 5 hours. What was their average speed?

7. Alisha climbed a mountain that was 4,760 feet high in 14 hours. What was her average speed per hour?

8. Xandra bought a mechanical pencil for $2.38, 3 pens for $0.89 each, and a pack of graph paper for $3.42. She paid $0.42 tax. What was her change from a ten dollar bill?

9. Charlie makes $13.45 per hour repairing lawn mowers part-time. If he works 15 hours, how much is his gross pay?

10. Gene works for his father sanding wooden rocking chairs. He earns $6.35 per chair. How many chairs does he need to sand in order to buy a portable radio/CD player for $146.05?

11. Margo's Mint Shop has a machine that produces 4.35 pounds of mints per hour. How many pounds of mints are produced in each 8 hour shift if the machine is constantly running?

12. Carter's Junior High track team ran the first leg of a 400 meter relay race in 10.23 seconds, the second leg in 11.4 seconds, the third leg in 10.77 seconds, and the last leg in 9.9 seconds. How long did it take for them to complete the race?

13. Brent drives to and from school Monday through Friday. He lives 10.8 miles from school. His car gets 22 miles per gallon, and he is paying $1.42 per gallon at the gas pump for gas right now. How much does it cost for gasoline to drive to and from school for 2 weeks?

14. Doug is a plumber. He charges $63 per hour for labor plus $50 per service call. He went to Mary's house to fix a pipe. The job took him 2.5 hours to complete. The materials cost $12.00. How much profit did he make?

15. Sprayberry High School decided to sell boxes of oranges to earn money for new football uniforms. They ordered a truckload of 500 boxes of oranges from a Florida grower for $16.00 per box. They sold 450 boxes for $19.00 per box. On the last day of the sale, they sold the oranges they had left for $17.00 per box. How much profit did they make?

Chapter 6
Measurement

Customary Measurements:

Time	Abbreviations
1 week = 7 days	week = wk
1 day = 24 hours	hour = hr or h
1 hour = 60 minutes	minutes = min
1 minute = 60 seconds	seconds = sec

Length	Abbreviations
1 mile = 5,280 feet	mile = mi
1 yard = 3 feet	yard = yd
1 foot = 12 inches	foot = ft

Volume	Abbreviations
1 gallon = 4 quarts	gallon = gal
1 quart = 2 pints	quart = qt
1 pint = 2 cups	pint = pt
1 cup = 8 ounces	ounce = oz

Weight	Abbreviations
16 ounces = 1 pound	pound = lb
	ounce = oz

EXAMPLE: Simplify: 2 days 34 hr 75 min

Step 1: 75 minutes is more than 1 hour. There are 60 minutes in an hour, so divide 75 by 60.

$$\begin{array}{r} 1 \text{ hr} \\ 60 \overline{)\ 75} \\ -60 \\ \hline 15 \text{ min} \end{array}$$

$$\begin{array}{r} 2 \text{ days } 34 \text{ hr } \cancel{75} \text{ min} \\ + \phantom{2 \text{ days } 34 } 1 \text{ hr } 15 \text{ min} \\ \hline 2 \text{ days } 35 \text{ hr } 15 \text{ min} \end{array}$$

Step 2: 35 hours is more than 1 day. There are 24 hours in a day, so divide 35 hours by 24.

$$\begin{array}{r} 1 \text{ day} \\ 24 \overline{)\ 35} \\ -24 \\ \hline 11 \text{ hr} \end{array}$$

$$\begin{array}{r} 2 \text{ days } \cancel{35} \text{ hr } 15 \text{ min} \\ + 1 \text{ day } 11 \text{ hr} \\ \hline 3 \text{ days } 11 \text{ hr } 15 \text{ min} \end{array}$$

Simplify the following:

1.   3 lb 20 oz

_____

2.   2 cup 12 oz

_____

3.   3 wk 9 days 30 hr

_____

4.   1 pt 1 cup 16 oz

_____

5.   2 hr 84 min 62 sec

_____

6.   1 gal 6 qt 3 pt

_____

7.   3 yd 10 ft 18 in

_____

8.   2 wk 8 days 36 hr

_____

9.   2 ft 18 in

_____

10.   1 lb 33 oz

_____

11.   23 hr 62 min 94 sec

_____

12.   3 days 54 hr 75 min

_____

TWO-STEP TIME PROBLEMS

Example: Theresa and Laura left Huntsville at 10:00 a.m. After $5\frac{1}{2}$ hours of driving, they arrived at their aunt's farm in Pennsylvania. What time was it then?

Step 1:   Compute the time from 10:00 a.m. to noon.
$$
\begin{array}{r}
12:00 \\
\underline{10:00} \\
2:00 \text{ hours}
\end{array}
$$

Step 2:   Subtract these 2 hours from the total driving time to find the answer.
$$
\begin{array}{r}
5:30 \\
\underline{-\ 2:00} \\
3:30 \text{ p.m.}
\end{array}
$$

---

1.   Trevor and Johnny drove $3\frac{3}{4}$ hours from Andalusia to go hunting. They started out at 11:30 a.m. When did they get to their campground?

2.   Holly and Julie drove from their house to Akron to visit a friend. They left at 9:00 a.m. and drove for $5\frac{1}{4}$ hours. What time was it when they arrived?

3   Mary left her home in Adamsville at 10:30 a.m. After driving $4\frac{5}{6}$ hours, she got to her brother's house. What time was it when she got there?

4.   Chuck and Eric make the $4\frac{1}{2}$ hour drive to the beach every weekend during the summer. If they leave home at 11:15 a.m., what time will they get to the beach?

5.   Dana and Tammy drove to their sister's house. They left at 10:30 a.m. and arrived $6\frac{3}{4}$ hours later. What time was it when they arrived?

6.   Jessie left home at 4:50 a.m. to go hunting. He came back home $10\frac{1}{2}$ hours later. What time did he come home?

7.   Johnathan went to work at 6:30 a.m. He got home $8\frac{1}{2}$ hours later. What time did he get home?

8.   Sara Beth went to the mall at 10:45 in the morning. She got home $6\frac{2}{3}$ hours later. What time was it when she got home?

9.   Sandy left home at 11:20 a.m. She returned home $7\frac{1}{2}$ hours later. What time did she return?

10.   Steve and Dad drove $2\frac{1}{6}$ hours from Cincinnati to go camping in the mountains. They left at 12:30 p.m. When did they get to their campground?

11.   Kelsie and Keri left Canton at 7:30 a.m. to vacation in St. Louis. After driving $3\frac{2}{3}$ hours, they took a break. What time was it then?

12.   Alicia left home at 2:30 p.m. to drive to her sister's house in Toledo. It took her $3\frac{1}{4}$ hours. What time did she get there?

THE METRIC SYSTEM

The metric system uses units based on multiples of ten. The basic units of measure in the metric system are the **meter**, the **liter**, and the **gram**. Metric prefixes tell what multiple of ten the basic unit is multiplied by. Below is a chart of metric prefixes and their values. The ones rarely used are shaded.

Prefix	kilo (k)	hecto (h)	deka (da)	unit (m, L, g)	deci (d)	centi (c)	milli (m)
Meaning	1000	100	10	1	0.1	0.01	0.001

Multiply when changing from a greater unit to a smaller one; **divide** when changing from a smaller unit to a larger one. **The chart is set up to help you know how far and which direction to move a decimal point when making conversions from one unit to another.**

UNDERSTANDING METERS

The basic unit of **length** in the metric system is the **meter**. Meter is abbreviated "m".

Metric Unit	Abbreviation	Memory Tip	Equivalents
1 millimeter	mm	Thickness of a dime	10 mm = 1 cm
1 centimeter	cm	Width of the tip of the little finger	100 cm = 1 m
1 meter	m	Distance from the nose to the tip of fingers (a little longer than a yard)	1000 m = 1 km
1 kilometer	km	A little more than half a mile	

UNDERSTANDING LITERS

The basic unit of **liquid volume** in the metric system is the **liter**. Liter is abbreviated "L".

The liter is the volume of a cube measuring 10 cm on each side. A milliliter is the volume of a cube measuring 1 cm on each side. A capital L is used to signify liter, so it is not confused with the number 1.

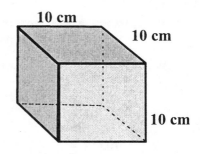

Volume = 1000 cm^3 = 1 Liter
(a little more than a quart)

Volume = 1 cm^3 = 1 mL
(an eyedropper holds 1 mL)

UNDERSTANDING GRAMS

The basic unit of **mass** in the metric system is the **gram**. Gram is abbreviated "g".

A **gram** is the **mass** of **one cubic centimeter** of **water** at 4°C.

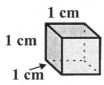

A large paper clip has a mass of about 1 gram (1 g).
A nickel has a mass of 5 grams (5 g).
1000 grams = 1 kilogram (kg) = a little over 2 pounds

1 milligram (mg) = 0.001 gram. This is an extremely small amount and is used in medicine.

An aspirin tablet has a mass of 300 mg.

CONVERTING UNITS WITHIN THE METRIC SYSTEM

Converting units such as kilograms to grams or centimeters to decimeters is easy now that you know how to multiply and divide by multiples of ten.

Prefix	kilo (k)	hecto (h)	deka (da)	unit (m, L, g)	deci (d)	centi (c)	milli (m)
Meaning	1000	100	10	1	0.1	0.01	0.001

EXAMPLE 1: 2 L = _____ mL

2.000 L = 2000 mL

Look at the chart above. To move from liters to milliliters, you move to the right three places. So, to convert the 2 L to mL, move the decimal point three places to the right. You will need to add zeros.

EXAMPLE 2: 5.25 cm = _____ m

005.25 cm = 0.0525 m

To move from centimeters to meters, you need to move two spaces to the left. So, to convert 5.25 cm to m, move the decimal point two spaces to the left. Again, you need to add zeros.

Solve the following problems.

1.   35 mg = _____ g
2.   6 km = _____ m
3.   21.5 mL = _____ L
4.   4.9 mm = _____ cm
5.   5.35 kL = _____ mL
6.   32.1 mg = _____ kg
7.   156.4 m = _____ km

8.   25 mg = _____ cg
9.   17.5 L = _____ mL
10. 4.2 g = _____ kg
11. 0.06 daL = _____ dL
12. 0.417 kg = _____ cg
13. 18.2 cL = _____ L
14. 81.2 dm = _____ cm

15. 72.3 cm = _____ m
16. 0.003 kL = _____ L
17. 5.06 g = _____ mg
18. 1.058 mL = _____ cL
19. 43 hm = _____ km
20. 2.057 m = _____ cm
21. 564.3 g = _____ kg

ESTIMATING METRIC MEASUREMENTS

Choose the best estimates.

1. The height of an average man
    A. 18 cm
    B. 1.8 m
    C. 6 km
    D. 36 mm

2. The volume of a coffee cup
    A. 300 mL
    B. 20 L
    C. 5 L
    D. 1 kL

3. The width of this book
    A. 215 mm
    B. 75 cm
    C. 2 m
    D. 1.5 km

4. The mass of an average man
    A. 5 mg
    B. 15 cg
    C. 25 g
    D. 90 kg

5. The length of a basketball player's foot
    A. 2 m
    B. 1 km
    C. 30 cm
    D. 100 mm

6. The mass of a dime
    A. 3 g
    B. 30 g
    C. 10 cg
    D. 1 kg

7. The width of your hand
    A. 2 km
    B. 0.5 m
    C. 25 cm
    D. 90 mm

8. The length of a basketball court
    A. 1000 mm
    B. 250 cm
    C. 28 m
    D. 2 km

Choose the best units of measure.

9. The distance from Toledo to Steubenville
    A. millimeter
    B. centimeter
    C. meter
    D. kilometer

10. The length of a house key
    A. millimeter
    B. centimeter
    C. meter
    D. kilometer

11. The width of a classroom
    A. millimeter
    B. centimeter
    C. meter
    D. kilometer

12. The length of a piece of chalk
    A. millimeter
    B. centimeter
    C. meter
    D. kilometer

CHAPTER 6 REVIEW

The table below shows the length of four movies shown on a cable TV channel.

	Begin	End
Ghost Town	7:05 p.m.	8:20 p.m.
Get A Life	8:40 p.m.	10:10 p.m.
Mumbo Jumbo	11:55 p.m.	1:35 a.m.
Our Adventure	1:45 p.m.	3:05 p.m.

1. Which movie is the longest?

2. Which movie is the shortest?

Choose the best units of measure for questions 5 and 6.

3. The thickness of a nickel
   A. millimeter
   B. centimeter
   C. meter
   D. kilometer

4. The height of a pine tree
   A. millimeter
   B. centimeter
   C. meter
   D. kilometer

Fill in the blanks below with the appropriate unit of measurement.

5. A box of assorted chocolates might weigh about 1 _____ (English).

6. A compact disc is about 7 _____ (English) across.

7. In Europe, gasoline is sold in _____ (metric).

8. A vitamin C tablet has a mass of 500 _____ (metric).

Fill in the blanks below with the appropriate English or metric conversions.

9. Two gallons equals _____ cups.

10. 4.2 L equals _____ mL.

11. $3\frac{1}{2}$ yards equals _____ inches.

12. 6,800 m equals _____ kilometers.

13. 36 oz. equals _____ pounds.

14. 730 mg equals _____ kg.

Chapter 7: Ratio, Proportions, and Scale Drawings

RATIO PROBLEMS

In some word problems, you may be asked to express answers as a **ratio**. Ratios can look like fractions, they can be written with a colon, or they can be written in word form with "to" between the numbers. Numbers must be written in the order they are requested. In the following problem, 8 cups of sugar are mentioned before 6 cups of strawberries. But in the question part of the problem, you are asked for the ratio of STRAWBERRIES to SUGAR. The amount of strawberries IS THE FIRST WORD MENTIONED, so it must be the **top** number of the fraction. The amount of sugar, THE SECOND WORD MENTIONED, must be the **bottom** number of the fraction.

EXAMPLE: A recipe for jam requires 8 cups of sugar for every 6 cups of strawberries. What is the ratio of strawberries to sugar in this recipe?

First number requested $\quad\quad\quad \dfrac{6}{8}$ **cups strawberries**
Second number requested $\quad\quad\quad \phantom{\dfrac{6}{8}}$ **cups sugar**

Answers may be reduced to lowest terms. $\quad \dfrac{6}{8} = \dfrac{3}{4}$

This ratio is also correctly expressed as 3:4 or 3 to 4.

Practice writing ratios for the following word problems and reduce to lowest terms. DO NOT CHANGE ANSWERS TO MIXED NUMBERS. Ratios should be left in fraction form.

1. Out of the 248 seniors, 112 are boys. What is the ratio of boys to the total number of seniors?

   _____

2. It takes 7 cups of flour to make 2 loaves of bread. What is the ratio of cups of flour to loaves of bread?

   _____

3. A skyscraper that stands 620 feet tall casts a shadow that is 125 feet long. What is the ratio of the shadow to the height of the skyscraper?

   _____

4. The newborn weighs 8 pounds and is 22 inches long. What is the ratio of weight to length?

   _____

5. Jack paid $6.00 for 10 pounds of apples. What is the ratio of the price of apples to the pounds of apples?

   _____

6. Twenty boxes of paper weigh 520 pounds. What is the ratio of boxes to pounds?

   _____

SOLVING PROPORTIONS

Two **ratios (fractions)** that are **equal** to each other are called **proportions**. For example, $\frac{1}{4} = \frac{2}{8}$. Read the following example to see how to find a number missing from a proportion.

EXAMPLE: $\frac{5}{15} = \frac{8}{x}$

Step 1: To find x, you first multiply the two numbers that are diagonal to each other. $\quad$ **15 × 8 = 120** $\qquad \frac{5}{\boxed{15}} = \frac{\boxed{8}}{x}$

Step 2: Then divide the product (120) by the other number in the proportion (5).
120 ÷ 5 = 24

Therefore, $\frac{5}{15} = \frac{8}{24}$ $\quad x = 24$

Practice finding the number missing from the following proportions. First, multiply the two numbers that are diagonal from each other. Then divide by the other number.

1. $\frac{2}{5} = \frac{6}{x}$

2. $\frac{9}{3} = \frac{x}{5}$

3. $\frac{x}{12} = \frac{3}{4}$

4. $\frac{7}{x} = \frac{3}{9}$

5. $\frac{12}{x} = \frac{2}{5}$

6. $\frac{12}{x} = \frac{4}{3}$

7. $\frac{27}{3} = \frac{x}{2}$

8. $\frac{1}{x} = \frac{3}{12}$

9. $\frac{15}{2} = \frac{x}{4}$

10. $\frac{7}{14} = \frac{x}{6}$

11. $\frac{5}{6} = \frac{10}{x}$

12. $\frac{4}{x} = \frac{3}{6}$

13. $\frac{x}{5} = \frac{9}{15}$

14. $\frac{9}{18} = \frac{x}{2}$

15. $\frac{5}{7} = \frac{35}{x}$

16. $\frac{x}{2} = \frac{8}{4}$

17. $\frac{15}{20} = \frac{x}{8}$

18. $\frac{x}{40} = \frac{5}{100}$

19. $\frac{4}{7} = \frac{x}{28}$

20. $\frac{7}{6} = \frac{42}{x}$

21. $\frac{x}{8} = \frac{1}{4}$

RATIO AND PROPORTION WORD PROBLEMS

You can use ratios and proportions to solve problems.

EXAMPLE: A stick one meter long is held perpendicular to the ground and casts a shadow 0.4 meters long. At the same time, an electrical tower casts a shadow 112 meters long. Use ratio and proportion to find the height of the tower.

Step 1: Set up a proportion using the numbers in the problem. Put the shadow lengths on one side of the equation, and put the heights on the other side. The 1 meter height is paired with the 0.4 meter length, so let them both be top numbers. Let the unknown height be x.

$$\frac{\text{shadow length}}{} \quad \frac{\text{object height}}{}$$

$$\frac{0.4}{112} = \frac{1}{x}$$

Step 2: Solve the proportion as you did on the previous page. $112 \times 1 = 112$

$112 \div 0.4 = 280$ **Answer:** The tower height is 280 meters.

Use ratio and proportion to solve the following problems.

1. Rudolph can mow a lawn that measures 1000 square feet in 2 hours. At that rate, how long would it take him to mow a lawn 3500 square feet?

   _____

2. Faye wants to know how tall her school building is. On a sunny day, she measures the shadow of the building to be 6 feet. At the same time, she measures the shadow cast by a 5 foot statue to be 2 feet. How tall is her school building?

   _____

3. Out of every 5 students surveyed, 2 listen to country music. At that rate, how many students in a school of 800 listen to country music?

   _____

4. Bailey, a Labrador Retriever, had a litter of 8 puppies. Four of the puppies were black. At that rate, how many would be black in a litter of 10 puppies?

   _____

5. According to the instructions on a bag of fertilizer, 5 pounds of fertilizer are needed for every 100 square feet of lawn. How many square feet will a 25 pound bag cover?

   _____

6. A race car can travel 2 laps in 5 minutes. How long will it take the race car to complete 100 laps at that rate?

   _____

7. If it takes 7 cups of flour to make 4 loaves of bread, how many loaves of bread can you make from 35 cups of flour?

   _____

8. If 3 pounds of jelly beans cost $6.30, how much would 2 pounds cost?

   _____

9. For the first 4 home football games, the concession stand sold 600 hotdogs. If that ratio stays constant, how many hotdogs will sell for all 10 home games?

   _____

PROPORTIONAL REASONING

Proportional reasoning can be used when a selected number of individuals are tagged in a population in order to estimate the total population.

EXAMPLE: A team of scientists capture, tag, and release 50 deer in a particular national forest. One week later, they capture another 50 deer, and 2 of the deer are ones that were tagged previously. What is the approximate deer population in the national forest?

Solution: Use proportional reasoning to determine the total deer population. Set up a proportion like you did in chapter 3, using the information given. You know that 50 deer out of the total deer population in the forest were tagged. You also know that 2 out of those 50 were recaptured. These two ratios should be equal because they both represent a fraction of the total deer population.

$$\frac{50 \text{ deer tagged}}{x \text{ deer total}} = \frac{2 \text{ tagged deer}}{50 \text{ deer captured}}$$

$2x = 2,500 \quad$ so $\quad x = 1,250$ total deer

Use proportional reasoning to solve the following problems.

1. Dr. Wolf, the biologist, captures 20 fish out of a small lake behind his college. He fastens a marker onto each of these and throws them back into the lake. A week later, he again captures 20 fish. Of these, 2 have markers. How many fish could Dr. Wolf estimate are in the pond?

2. Tawanda drew 20 cards from a box. She marked each one, returned them to the box, and shook the box vigorously. She then drew 20 more cards and found that 5 of them were marked. Estimate how many cards were in the box.

3. Maureen pulls 100 pennies out of her piggy bank, which contains only pennies. She marks each of these, puts them back in the bank, shakes vigorously, and again pulls 100 pennies. She discovers that 2 of them are marked. Estimate how many pennies are in her piggy bank.

4. Mr. Kizer owns a ten acre wooded island in the middle of a lake. He catches 20 squirrels, tags them, and releases them. Several days later, he catches another 20 squirrels. One of the 20 squirrels had a tag. Estimate the number of squirrels living on Mr. Kizer's ten acres.

MAPS AND SCALE DRAWINGS

EXAMPLE 1: On a map drawn to scale, 5 cm represents 30 kilometers. A line segment connecting two cities is 7 cm long. What distance does this line segment represent?

Step 1: Set up a proportion using the numbers in the problem. Keep centimeters on one side of the equation and kilometers on the other. The 5 cm is paired with the 30 kilometers, so let them both be top numbers. Let the unknown distance be x.

$$\frac{\overset{\text{cm}}{5}}{7} = \frac{\overset{\text{km}}{30}}{x}$$

Step 2: Solve the proportion as you have previously. $7 \times 30 = 210$
$210 \div 5 = 42$ **Answer:** 7 cm represents 42 km.

Sometimes the answer to a scale drawing problem will be a fraction or mixed number.

EXAMPLE 2: On a scale drawing, 2 inches represent 30 feet. How many inches long is a line segment that represents 5 feet?

Step 1: Set up the proportion as you did above.

$$\frac{\overset{\text{inches}}{2}}{x} = \frac{\overset{\text{feet}}{30}}{5}$$

Step 2: **First multiply the two numbers that are diagonal from each other. Then divide by the other number.**

$2 \times 5 = 10$ $10 \div 30$ is less than 1, so express the answer as a fraction and reduce.

$10 \div 30 = \frac{10}{30} = \frac{1}{3}$ inch **Answer:** $\frac{1}{3}$ of an inch represents 5 feet.

Set up proportions for each of the following problems and solve.

1. If 2 inches represent 50 miles on a scale drawing, how long would a line segment be that represents 25 miles? _____

2. On a scale drawing, 2 cm represent 15 km. A line segment on the drawing is 3 cm long. What distance does this line segment represent? _____

3. On a map drawn to scale, 5 cm represent 250 km. How many kilometers are represented by a line 6 cm long? _____

4. If 2 inches represent 80 miles on a scale drawing, how long would a line segment be that represents 280 miles? _____

5. On a map drawn to scale, 5 cm represent 200 km. How long would a line segment be that represents 260 km? _____

6. On a scale drawing of a house plan, one inch represents 5 feet. How many feet wide is the bathroom if the width on the drawing is 3 inches? _____

USING A SCALE ON A BLUEPRINT

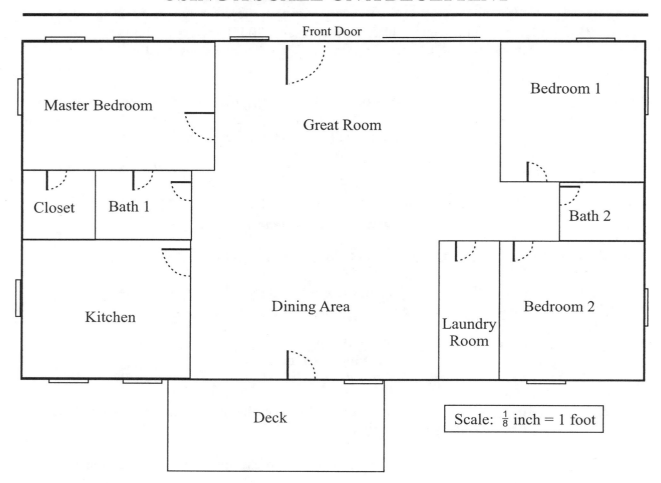

Front Door

Master Bedroom

Great Room

Bedroom 1

Closet

Bath 1

Bath 2

Kitchen

Dining Area

Laundry Room

Bedroom 2

Deck

Scale: $\frac{1}{8}$ inch = 1 foot

Use a ruler to find the measurements of the rooms on the blueprint above. Convert to feet using the scale. The first problem is done for you.

	long wall		short wall	
	ruler measurement	room measurement	ruler measurement	room measurement
1. Kitchen	$1\frac{3}{4}$ inch	14 feet	$1\frac{1}{2}$ inch	12 feet
2. Deck				
3. Closet				
4. Bedroom 1				
5. Bedroom 2				
6. Master Bedroom				
7. Bath 1				
8. Bath 2				

1. Out of 100 coins, 45 are in mint condition. What is the ratio of mint condition coins to the total number of coins?

_____

2. The ratio of boys to girls in the ninth grade is 6:5. If there are 135 girls in the class, how many boys are there?

_____

3. Twenty out of the total 235 seniors graduated with honors. What is the ratio of seniors graduating with honors to the total number of seniors?

_____

4. Aunt Bess uses 3 cups of oatmeal to bake 6 dozen oatmeal cookies. How many cups of oatmeal would she need to bake 15 dozen cookies?

_____

5. On a map, 2 centimeters represent 150 kilometers. If a line between two cities measures 5 centimeters, how many kilometers apart are they?

_____

6. Shondra used six ounces of chocolate chips to make two dozen cookies. At that rate, how many ounces of chocolate chips would she need to make seven dozen cookies?

_____

7. When Rick measures the shadow of a yard stick, it is 5 inches. At the same time, the shadow of the tree he would like to chop down is 45 inches. How tall is the tree in yards?

_____

Solve the following proportions:

8. $\frac{8}{x} = \frac{1}{2}$

9. $\frac{2}{5} = \frac{x}{10}$

10. $\frac{x}{6} = \frac{3}{9}$

11. $\frac{4}{9} = \frac{8}{x}$

12. On a scale drawing of a house floor plan, 1 inch represents 2 feet. The length of the kitchen measures 5 inches on the floor plan. How many feet does that represent?

_____

13. If 4 inches represent 8 feet on a scale drawing, how many feet does 6 inches represent?

_____

14. On a scale drawing, 3 centimeters represent 100 miles. If a line segment between two points measured 5 centimeters, how many miles would it represent?

_____

15. Bob wonders how many ants are in his ant farm. He puts a stick in the container, and when he pulls it out, there are 15 ants on it. He gently sprays these ants with a mixture of water and food coloring, then puts them back into the container. The next day his stick draws 20 ants, 1 of which is green. Estimate how many ants Bob has in his ant farm.

_____

Chapter 8: Introduction to Graphing

GRAPHING ON A NUMBER LINE

Number lines allow you to graph values of positive and negative numbers as well as zero. Any real number, whether it is a fraction, decimal, or integer, can be plotted on a number line. Number lines can be horizontal or vertical. The sections below describe how to plot different types of numbers on a number line.

GRAPHING FRACTIONAL VALUES

EXAMPLE 1: What number does point A represent on the number line below?

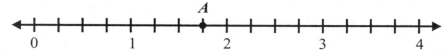

Step 1: Point A is between the numbers 1 and 2, so it is greater than 1 but less than 2. We can express the value of A as a fractional value that falls between 1 and 2. To do so, copy the integer that point A falls between which is closer to zero on the number line. In this case, copy the 1 because 1 is closer to zero on the number line than the 2.

Step 2: Count the number of spaces between each integer. In this case, there are 4 spaces between the 1 and the 2. Put this number as the bottom number in your fraction.

Step 3: Count the number of spaces between the 1 and point A. Point A is 3 spaces away from the number 1. Put this number as the top number in your fraction.

Point A is at $1\frac{3}{4}$ ← The integer that point A falls between that is closest to 0
                    ← The number of spaces between 1 and A
                    ← The number of spaces between 1 and 2

EXAMPLE 2: What number does point B represent on the number line below?

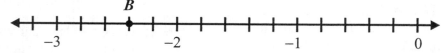

Step 1: Point B is between −2 and −3. Again, we can express the value of B as a fraction that falls between −2 and −3. Copy the integer that point B falls between which is closer to zero. The −2 is closer to zero than −3, so copy −2.

Step 2: In this example, there are 5 spaces between each integer. Five will be the bottom number in the fraction.

Step 3: There are 2 spaces between −2 and point B. Two will be the top number in the fraction.

Point B is at $-2\frac{2}{5}$

Determine and record the value of each point on the number lines below.

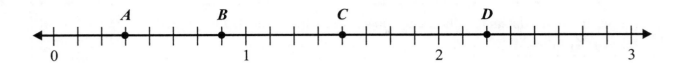

1. $A =$ _____ $B =$ _____ $C =$ _____ $D =$ _____

2. $E =$ _____ $F =$ _____ $G =$ _____ $H =$ _____

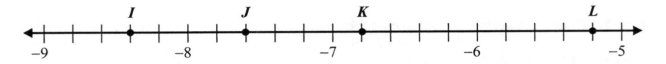

3. $I =$ _____ $J =$ _____ $K =$ _____ $L =$ _____

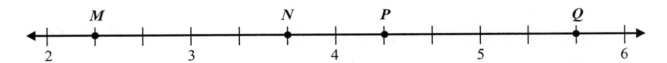

4. $M =$ _____ $N =$ _____ $P =$ _____ $Q =$ _____

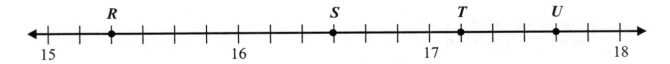

5. $R =$ _____ $S =$ _____ $T =$ _____ $U =$ _____

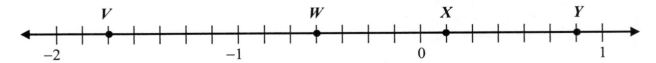

6. $V =$ _____ $W =$ _____ $X =$ _____ $Y =$ _____

RECOGNIZING IMPROPER FRACTIONS, DECIMALS, AND SQUARE ROOT VALUES ON A NUMBER LINE

Improper fractions, decimal values, and square root values can also be plotted on a number line. Study the examples below.

EXAMPLE 1: Where would $\frac{4}{3}$ fall on the number line below?

Step 1: Convert the improper fraction to a mixed number. $\frac{4}{3} = 1\frac{1}{3}$

Step 2: $1\frac{1}{3}$ is $\frac{1}{3}$ of the distance between the numbers 1 and 2. Estimate this distance by dividing the distance between points 1 and 2 into thirds. Plot the point at the first division.

EXAMPLE 2: Plot the value of -1.75 on the number line below.

Step 1: Convert the value -1.75 to a mixed fraction. $-1.75 = -1\frac{3}{4}$

Step 2: $-1\frac{3}{4}$ is $\frac{3}{4}$ of the distance between the numbers -1 and -2. Estimate this distance by dividing the distance between points -1 and -2 into fourths. Plot the point at the third division.

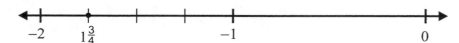

EXAMPLE 3: Plot the value of $\sqrt{3}$ on the number line below.

Step 1: Estimate the value of $\sqrt{3}$ by using the square root of values that you know. $\sqrt{1} = 1$ and $\sqrt{4}$ is 2, so the value of $\sqrt{3}$ is going to be between 1 and 2.

Step 2: To estimate a little closer, try squaring 1.5. $1.5 \times 1.5 = 2.25$, so $\sqrt{3}$ has to be greater than 1.5. If you do further trial and error calculations, you will find that $\sqrt{3}$ is greater than 1.7 ($1.7 \times 1.7 = 2.89$) but less than 1.8 ($1.8 \times 1.8 = 3.24$).

Step 3: Plot $\sqrt{3}$ around 1.75.

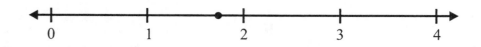

Plot and label the following values on the number lines given below.

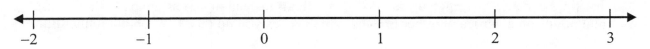

1. $A = \dfrac{5}{4}$ $B = \dfrac{12}{5}$ $C = \dfrac{2}{3}$ $D = -\dfrac{3}{2}$

2. $E = 1.4$ $F = -2.25$ $G = -0.6$ $H = 0.625$

3. $I = \sqrt{2}$ $J = \sqrt{5}$ $K = \sqrt{6}$ $L = \sqrt{8}$

Match the correct value for each point on the number lines below.

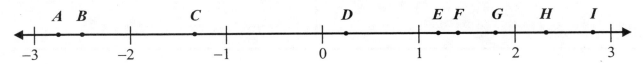

4. $1.8 = \underline{\hspace{1cm}}$ 7. $-\dfrac{5}{2} = \underline{\hspace{1cm}}$ 10. $\sqrt{8} = \underline{\hspace{1cm}}$

5. $\dfrac{7}{3} = \underline{\hspace{1cm}}$ 8. $-2.75 = \underline{\hspace{1cm}}$ 11. $\dfrac{6}{5} = \underline{\hspace{1cm}}$

6. $\sqrt{2} = \underline{\hspace{1cm}}$ 9. $-\dfrac{4}{3} = \underline{\hspace{1cm}}$ 12. $0.25 = \underline{\hspace{1cm}}$

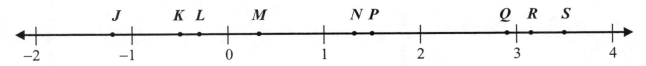

13. $\sqrt{12} = \underline{\hspace{1cm}}$ 16. $\dfrac{1}{3} = \underline{\hspace{1cm}}$ 19. $-\dfrac{6}{5} = \underline{\hspace{1cm}}$

14. $-0.5 = \underline{\hspace{1cm}}$ 17. $1.5 = \underline{\hspace{1cm}}$ 20. $\sqrt{10} = \underline{\hspace{1cm}}$

15. $\dfrac{5}{4} = \underline{\hspace{1cm}}$ 18. $-0.3 = \underline{\hspace{1cm}}$ 21. $2.9 = \underline{\hspace{1cm}}$

PLOTTING POINTS ON A VERTICAL NUMBER LINE

Number lines can also be drawn up and down **(vertical)** instead of across the page **(horizontal)**. You plot points on a vertical number line the same way as you do on a horizontal number line.

Record the value represented by each point on the number lines below.

1. $A = $ _____

2. $B = $ _____

3. $C = $ _____

4. $D = $ _____

5. $E = $ _____

6. $F = $ _____

7. $G = $ _____

8. $H = $ _____

17. $Q = $ _____

18. $R = $ _____

19. $S = $ _____

20. $T = $ _____

21. $U = $ _____

22. $V = $ _____

23. $W = $ _____

24. $X = $ _____

9. $I = $ _____

10. $J = $ _____

11. $K = $ _____

12. $L = $ _____

13. $M = $ _____

14. $N = $ _____

15. $P = $ _____

16. $Q = $ _____

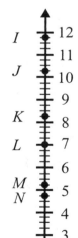

25. $A = $ _____

26. $B = $ _____

27. $C = $ _____

28. $D = $ _____

29. $E = $ _____

30. $F = $ _____

31. $G = $ _____

32. $H = $ _____

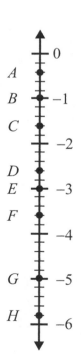

CARTESIAN COORDINATES

A number line allows you to graph points with only one value. A **Cartesian coordinate plane** allows you to graph points with two values. A Cartesian coordinate plane is made up of two number lines. The horizontal number line is called the **x-axis** and the vertical number line is called the **y-axis**. The point where the *x* and *y* axes intersect is called the **origin**. The *x* and *y* axes separate the Cartesian coordinate plane into four quadrants that are labeled I, II, III, and IV. The quadrants are labeled and explained on the graph below. Each point graphed on the plane is designated by an **ordered pair** of coordinates. For example, (2, −1) is an ordered pair of coordinates designated by **point B** on the plane below. The first number, 2, tells you to go over positive two on the *x*-axis. The −1 tells you to then go down negative one on the *y*-axis.

Remember: The first number always tells you how far to go right or left of 0, and the second number always tells you how far to go up or down from 0.

Quadrant II:
The *x*-coordinate is negative, and the *y*-coordinate is positive (−, +).

Quadrant III:
Both coordinates in the ordered pair are negative (−, −).

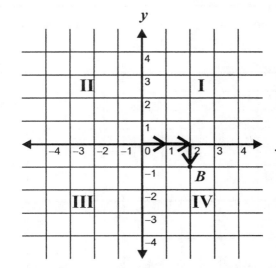

Quadrant I:
Both coordinates in the ordered pair are positive (+, +).

Quadrant IV:
The *x*-coordinate is positive and the *y*-coordinate is negative (+, −).

Plot and label the following points on the Cartesian coordinate plane provided.

A.	(2, 4)	*K.*	(−1, −1)	
B.	(−1, 5)	*L.*	(3, −3)	
C.	(3, −4)	*M.*	(5, 5)	
D.	(−5, −2)	*N.*	(−2, −2)	
E.	(5, 3)	*O.*	(0, 0)	
F.	(−7, −6)	*P.*	(0, 4)	
G.	(−2, 5)	*Q.*	(2, 0)	
H.	(6, −1)	*R.*	(−4, 0)	
I.	(4, −7)	*S.*	(0, −2)	
J.	(6, 2)	*T.*	(5, 1)	

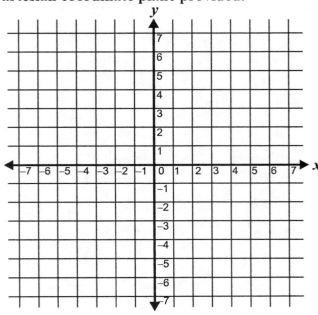

IDENTIFYING ORDERED PAIRS

When identifying **ordered pairs**, count how far left or right of 0 to find the *x*-coordinate and then how far up or down from 0 to find the *y*-coordinate.

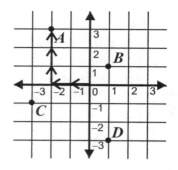

Point A: Left (negative) two and up (positive) three = (−2, 3) in quadrant II

Point B: Right (positive) one and up (positive) one = (1, 1) in quadrant I

Point C: Left (negative) three and down (negative) one = (−3, −1) in quadrant III

Point D: Right (positive) one and down (negative) three = (1, −3) in quadrant IV

Fill in the ordered pair for each point, and tell which quadrant it is in.

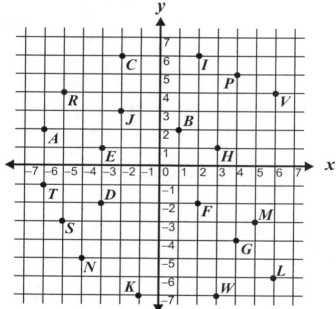

1. point A = (,) quadrant _____   11. point K = (,) quadrant _____
2. point B = (,) quadrant _____   12. point L = (,) quadrant _____
3. point C = (,) quadrant _____   13. point M = (,) quadrant _____
4. point D = (,) quadrant _____   14. point N = (,) quadrant _____
5. point E = (,) quadrant _____   15. point P = (,) quadrant _____
6. point F = (,) quadrant _____   16. point R = (,) quadrant _____
7. point G = (,) quadrant _____   17. point S = (,) quadrant _____
8. point H = (,) quadrant _____   18. point T = (,) quadrant _____
9. point I = (,) quadrant _____   19. point V = (,) quadrant _____
10. point J = (,) quadrant _____   20. point W = (,) quadrant _____

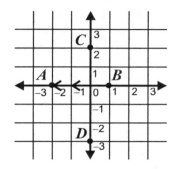

Sometimes, points on a coordinate plane fall on the *x* or *y* axis. If a point falls on the *x*-axis, then the second number of the ordered pair is 0. If a point falls on the *y*-axis, the first number of the ordered pair is 0.

Point *A*: Left (negative) two and up zero = (−2, 0)
Point *B*: Right (positive) one and up zero = (1, 0)
Point *C*: Left/right zero and up (positive) two = (0, 2)
Point *D*: Left/right zero and down (negative) three = (0, −3)

Fill in the ordered pair for each point.

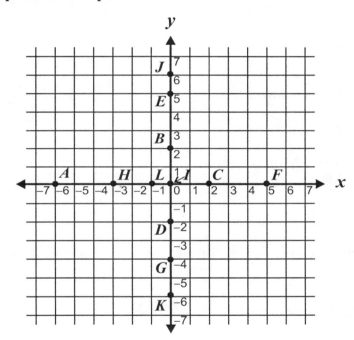

1. point *A* = (,)

2. point *B* = (,)

3. point *C* = (,)

4. point *D* = (,)

5. point *E* = (,)

6. point *F* = (,)

7. point *G* = (,)

8. point *H* = (,)

9. point *I* = (,)

10. point *J* = (,)

11. point *K* = (,)

12. point *L* = (,)

DRAWING GEOMETRIC FIGURES ON A
CARTESIAN COORDINATE PLANE

You can use a **Cartesian coordinate plane** to draw geometric figures by plotting **vertices** and connecting them with line segments.

EXAMPLE 1: What are the coordinates of each vertex of quadrilateral *ABCD* below?

Step 1: To find the coordinates of point *A*, count over −3 on the *x*-axis and up 1 on the *y*-axis.
point *A* = (−3, 1)

Step 2: The coordinates of point *B* are located to the right two units on the *x*-axis and up 3 units on the *y*-axis.
point *B* = (2, 3)

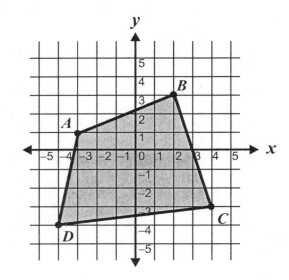

Step 3: Point *C* is located 4 units to the right on the *x*-axis and down −3 on the *y*-axis.
point *C* = (4, −3)

Step 4: Point *D* is −4 units left on the *x*-axis and down −4 units on the *y*-axis.
point *D* = (−4, −4)

EXAMPLE 2: Plot the following points. Then construct and identify the geometric figure that you plotted.

A = (−2, −5), *B* = (−2, 1),
C = (3, 1), *D* = (3, −5)

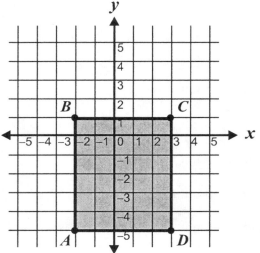

Figure *ABCD* is a rectangle.

Find the coordinates of the geometric figures graphed below.

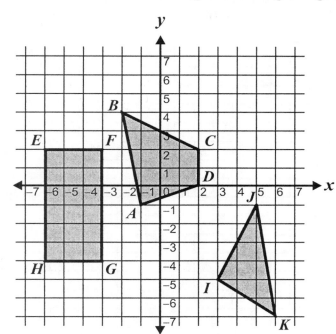

1. quadrilateral *ABCD*

    A = _____

    B = _____

    C = _____

    D = _____

2. rectangle *EFGH*

    E = _____

    F = _____

    G = _____

    H = _____

3. triangle *IJK*

    I = _____

    J = _____

    K = _____

4. parallelogram *LMNO*

    L = _____

    M = _____

    N = _____

    O = _____

5. right triangle *PQR*

    P = _____

    Q = _____

    R = _____

6. pentagon *STVXY*

    S = _____

    T = _____

    V = _____

    X = _____

    Y = _____

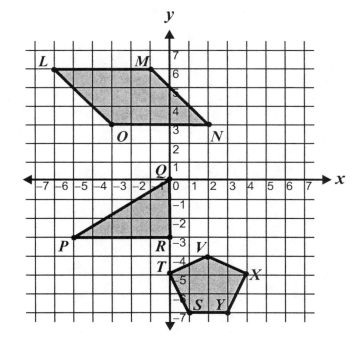

83

Plot and label the following points. Then construct and identify the geometric figures you plotted. Question 1 is done for you.

Figure

1. point $A = (-1, -1)$
    point $B = (-1, 2)$
    point $C = (2, 2)$
    point $D = (2, -1)$ ____square____

2. point $E = (3, -2)$
    point $F = (5, 1)$
    point $G = (7, -2)$ _____

3. point $H = (-4, 0)$
    point $I = (-6, 0)$
    point $J = (-4, 4)$
    point $K = (-2, 4)$ _____

4. point $L = (-1, -3)$
    point $M = (4, -6)$
    point $N = (-1, -6)$ _____

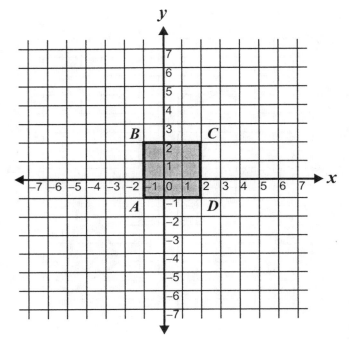

Figure

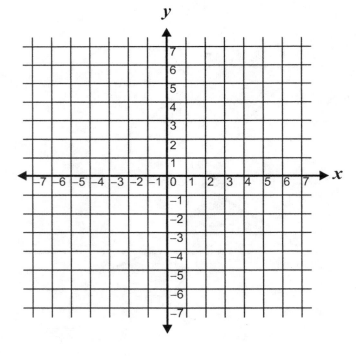

5. point $A = (-2, 3)$
    point $B = (-3, 5)$
    point $C = (-1, 6)$
    point $D = (1, 5)$
    point $E = (0, 3)$ _____

6. point $F = (-1, -3)$
    point $G = (-3, -5)$
    point $H = (-1, -7)$
    point $I = (1, -5)$ _____

7. point $J = (-1, 2)$
    point $K = (-1, -1)$
    point $L = (3, -2)$ _____

8. point $M = (6, 2)$
    point $N = (6, -4)$
    point $O = (4, -4)$
    point $P = (4, 2)$ _____

CHAPTER 8 REVIEW

1.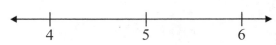

Plot and label $5\frac{3}{5}$ on the number line above.

2.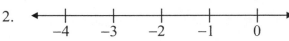

Plot and label $-3\frac{1}{2}$ on the number line above.

3.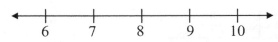

Plot and label $\sqrt{52}$ on the number line above.

4.

Plot and label -2.3 on the number line above.

Record the value represented by the point on the number line for questions 5–10.

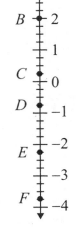

5. A _____

6. B _____

7. C _____

8. D _____

9. E _____

10. F _____

Record the coordinates and quadrants of the following points.

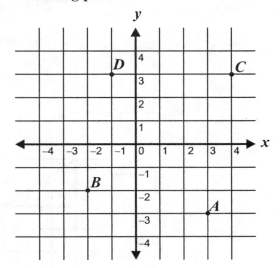

	Coordinates	Quadrant
11. $A =$	_____	_____
12. $B =$	_____	_____
13. $C =$	_____	_____
14. $D =$	_____	_____

On the same plane above, label these additional coordinates.

15. $E = (0, -3)$

16. $F = (-3, -1)$

17. $G = (4, 0)$

18. $H = (2, 2)$

Answer the following questions.

19. In which quadrant does the point $(2, 3)$ lie? _____

20. In which quadrant does the point $(-5, -2)$ lie? _____

Find the coordinates of the geometric figures graphed below.

21. point A _____

22. point B _____

23. point C _____

24. point D _____

25. point E _____

26. point F _____

27. point G _____

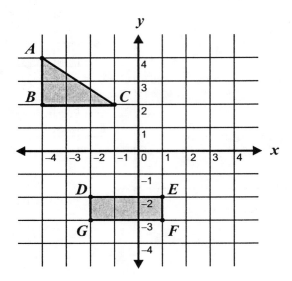

Plot and label the following points on the same graph.

28. point $H = (1, 1)$

29. point $I = (3, 1)$

30. point $J = (4, -2)$

31. point $K = (2, -2)$

32. What type figure did you plot?

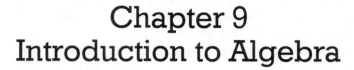

Chapter 9
Introduction to Algebra

ALGEBRA VOCABULARY

Vocabulary Word	Example	Definition
variable	$4x$ (x is the variable)	a letter that can be replaced by a number
coefficient	$4x$ (4 is the coefficient)	a number multiplied by a variable or variables
term	$5x^2 + x - 2$ terms	numbers or variables separated by $+$ or $-$ signs
constant	$5x + 2y + 4$ constant	a term that does not have a variable
numerical expression	$2^3 + 6 - 5$	two or more terms using only constants (numbers)
algebraic expression	$2x + 5^2 - 7$	two or more terms that include one or more variables
sentence	$2x = 7$ or $5 \leq x$	two algebraic expressions connected by $=, \neq, <, >, \leq, \geq,$ or $\approx$
equation	$4x = 8$	a sentence with an equal sign
inequality	$7x < 30$ or $x \neq 6$	a sentence with one of the following signs: $\neq, <, >, \leq,$ or $\geq$
base	$6^3 \longleftarrow$ base	the number used as a factor
exponent	$6^3 \longleftarrow$ exponent	the number of times the base is multiplied by itself

SUBSTITUTING NUMBERS FOR VARIABLES

These problems may look difficult at first glance, but they are very easy. Simply replace the variable with the number the variable is equal to, and solve the problems.

EXAMPLE 1: In the following problems, substitute 10 for a.

PROBLEM	CALCULATION	SOLUTION
1. $a + 1$	Simply replace the a with 10. $10 + 1$	11
2. $17 - a$	$17 - 10$	7
3. $9a$	This means multiply. 9×10	90
4. $\dfrac{30}{a}$	This means divide. $30 \div 10$.	3
5. a^3	$10 \times 10 \times 10$	1000
* 6. $5a + 6$	$(5 \times 10) + 6$	56

*   **Note: Be sure to do all multiplying and dividing before adding and subtracting.**

EXAMPLE 2: In the following problems, let $x = 2$, $y = 4$, and $z = 5$.

PROBLEM	CALCULATION	SOLUTION
1. $5xy + z$	$5 \times 2 \times 4 + 5$	45
2. $xz^2 + 5$	$2 \times 5^2 + 5 = 2 \times 25 + 5$	55
3. $\dfrac{yz}{x}$	$(4 \times 5) \div 2 = 20 \div 2$	10

In the following problems, $t = 7$. Solve the problems.

1. $t + 3 =$ _____   4. $3t - 5 =$ _____   7. $9t \div 3 =$ _____

2. $18 - t =$ _____   5. $t^2 + 1 =$ _____   8. $\dfrac{t^2}{7} =$ _____

3. $\dfrac{21}{t} =$ _____   6. $2t - 4 =$ _____   9. $5t + 6 =$ _____

In the following problems $a = 4$, $b = -2$, $c = 5$, and $d = 10$.   Solve the problems.

10. $4a + 2c =$ _____   14. $a^2 - b =$ _____   18. $\dfrac{6b}{a} =$ _____

11. $3bc - d =$ _____   15. $abd =$ _____   19. $9a + b =$ _____

12. $\dfrac{ac}{d} =$ _____   16. $5c - ad =$ _____   20. $5 + 3bc =$ _____

13. $d - 2a =$ _____   17. $cd + bc =$ _____   21. $d^2 + d + 1 =$ _____

UNDERSTANDING ALGEBRA WORD PROBLEMS

The biggest challenge to solving word problems is figuring out whether to add, subtract, multiply, or divide. Below is a list of key words and their meanings. This list does not include every situation you might see, but it includes the most common examples.

Words Indicating Addition	Example	Add
and	6 **and** 8	$6 + 8$
increased	The original price of $15 **increased** by $5.	$15 + 5$
more	3 coins and 8 **more**	$3 + 8$
more than	Josh has 10 points. Will has 5 **more than** Josh.	$10 + 5$
plus	8 baseballs **plus** 4 baseballs	$8 + 4$
sum	the **sum** of 3 and 5	$3 + 5$
total	the **total** of 10, 14, and 15	$10 + 14 + 15$

Words Indicating Subtraction	Example	Subtract
decreased	$16 **decreased** by $5	$16 - 5$
difference	the **difference** between 18 and 6	$18 - 6$
less	14 days **less** 5	$14 - 5$
fewer than	Joe completed 2 laps **fewer than** Mike's 9.	* $9 - 2$
left	Ray sold 15 out of 35 tickets. How many did he have **left**?	* $35 - 15$
lower than	This month's rain fall is 2 inches **lower than** last month's rain fall of 8 inches.	* $8 - 2$
minus	15 **minus** 6	$15 - 6$

* In subtraction word problems, you cannot always subtract the numbers in the order that they appear in the problem. Sometimes the first number should be subtracted from the last. You must read each problem carefully.

Words Indicating Multiplication	Example	Multiply
double	Her $1000 profit **doubled** in a month.	1000×2
half	**Half** of the $600 collected went to charity.	$\frac{1}{2} \times 600$
product	the **product** of 4 and 8	4×8
times	Todd scored 3 **times** as many points as Ted who only scored 4.	3×4
triple	The bacteria **tripled** its original colony of 10,000 in just one day.	$3 \times 10,000$
twice	Ron has 6 CDs. Tom has **twice** as many.	2×6

Words Indicating Division	Example	Divide
divide into, by, or among	The group of 70 **divided into** 10 teams.	$70 \div 10$ or $\frac{70}{10}$
quotient	the **quotient** of 30 and 6	$30 \div 6$ or $\frac{30}{6}$

Match the phrase on the left with the correct algebraic expression on the right. The answers on the right will be used more than once.

1. _____ 2 more than y
2. _____ 2 divided into y
3. _____ 2 less than y
4. _____ twice y
5. _____ the quotient of y and 2
6. _____ y increased by 2
7. _____ 2 less y
8. _____ the product of 2 and y
9. _____ y decreased by 2
10. _____ y doubled
11. _____ 2 minus y
12. _____ the total of 2 and y

A. $y - 2$

B. $2y$

C. $y + 2$

D. $\dfrac{y}{2}$

E. $2 - y$

Now practice writing parts of algebraic expressions from the following word problems.

EXAMPLE: the product of 3 and a number, t Answer: $3t$

13. 3 less than x _____
14. y divided among 10 _____
15. the sum of t and 5 _____
16. n minus 14 _____
17. 5 times k _____
18. the total of z and 12 _____
19. double the number b _____
20. x increased by 1 _____
21. the quotient of t and 4 _____
22. half of a number y _____

23. bacteria culture, b, doubled _____
24. triple John's age, y _____
25. a number, n, plus 4 _____
26. quantity, t, less 6 _____
27. 18 divided by a number, x _____
28. n feet lower than 10 _____
29. 3 more than p _____
30. the product of 4 and m _____
31. a number, y, decreased by 20 _____
32. 5 times as much as x _____

If a word problem contains the word "sum" or "difference," put the numbers that "sum" or "difference" refer to in parentheses to be added or subtracted first. Do not separate them. Look at the examples below.

EXAMPLES:

	RIGHT	**WRONG**
sum of 2 and 4, times 5	$5(2 + 4) = 30$	$2 + 4 \times 5 = 22$
the sum of 4 and 6, divided by 2	$\dfrac{(4 + 6)}{2} = 5$	$4 + \dfrac{6}{2} = 7$
4 times the difference between 10 and 5	$4(10 - 5) = 20$	$4 \times 10 - 5 = 35$
20 divided by the difference between 4 and 2	$\dfrac{20}{(4 - 2)} = 10$	$20 \div 4 - 2 = 3$
the sum of x and 4, multiplied by 2	$2(x + 4) = 2x + 8$	$x + 4 \times 2 = x + 8$

Change the following phrases into algebraic expressions.

1. 5 times the sum of x and 6

2. the difference between 5 and 3, divided by 4

3. 30 divided by the sum of 2 and 3

4. twice the sum of 10 and x

5. the difference between x and 9, divided by 10

6. 7 times the difference between x and 4

7. 9 multiplied by the sum of 3 and 4

8. the difference between x and 5, divided by 6

9. x divided by the sum of 4 and 9

10. x minus 5, times 10

11. 100 multiplied by the sum of x and 6

12. twice the difference between 3 and x

13. 4 times the sum of 5 and 1

14. 5 times the difference between 4 and 2

15. 12 divided by the sum of 2 and 4

16. four minus x, multiplied by 2

Look at the examples below for more phrases that may be used in algebra word problems.

EXAMPLES:

one-half of the sum of x and 4 $\qquad$ $\frac{1}{2}(x+4)$ or $\frac{x+4}{2}$

six more than four times a number, x $\qquad$ $6+4x$

100 decreased by the product of a number, x, and 5 $\qquad$ $100-5x$

ten less than the product of 3 and x $\qquad$ $3x-10$

Change the following phrases into algebraic expressions.

1. one-third of the sum of x and 5

2. three more than the product of a number, x, and 7

3. ten less than the sum of t and 4

4. the product of 4 and n, minus 3

5. 15 less than the sum of 3 and x

6. the difference of 10, and 3 times a number, n

7. one-fifth of t

8. the product of 3 and x, minus 14

9. x times the difference between 4 and x

10. five plus the quotient of x and 6

11. the sum of 5 and k, divided by 2

12. one less than the product of 3 and x

13. 5 increased by one-half of a number, n

14. 10 more than twice x

15. six subtracted from four times m

16. 8 times x, subtracted from 20

SETTING UP ALGEBRA WORD PROBLEMS

So far, you have seen only the first part of algebra word problems. To complete an algebra problem, an equal sign must be added. The words "**is**" and "**are**" as well as "**equal(s)**" signal that you should add an equal sign.

EXAMPLE: Double Jake's age, x, minus 4 is 22.

$$2x - 4 = 22$$

Translate the following word problems into algebra problems. DO NOT find the solutions to the problems yet.

1.   Triple the original number, n, is 2,700.

_____

2.   The product of a number, y, and 5 is equal to 15.

_____

3.   Four times the difference of a number, x, and 2 is 20.

_____

4.   The total, t, divided into 5 groups is 45.

_____

5.   The number of parts in inventory, p, minus 54 parts sold today is 320.

_____

6.   One-half an amount, x, added to $50 is $262.

_____

7.   One hundred seeds divided by 5 rows equals n number of seeds per row.

_____

8.   A number, y, less than 50 is 82.

_____

9.   His base pay of $200 increased by his commission, x, is $500.

_____

10.   Seventeen more than half a number, h, is 35.

_____

11.   This month's sales of $2,300 are double January's sales, x.

_____

12.   The quotient of a number, w, and 4 is 32.

_____

13.   Six less a number, d, is 12.

_____

14.   Four times the sum of a number, y, and 10 is 48.

_____

15.   We started with x number of students. When 5 moved away, we had 42 left.

_____

16.   A number, b, divided into 36 parts is 12.

_____

MATCHING ALGEBRAIC EXPRESSIONS

Match each set of algebraic expressions with the correct phrase underneath them.

1. _____ $2x + 5$

2. _____ $2(x + 5)$

3. _____ $2x - 5$

4. _____ $2(x - 5)$

A. twice the sum of x and 5

B. five less than the product of 2 and x

C. five more than the product of 2 and x

D. two times the difference of x and 5

---

5. _____ $4(y - 2)$

6. _____ $\dfrac{y - 2}{4}$

7. _____ $4y - 2$

8. _____ $\dfrac{y}{4} - 2$

A. two less than the product of y and 4

B. the difference of y and 2 divided by 4

C. two less than one-fourth of y

D. four times the difference of y and 2

---

9. _____ $5y + 8$

10. _____ $5(y + 8)$

11. _____ $8y + 5$

12. _____ $8(y + 5)$

A. eight times the sum of y and 5

B. eight more than the product of 5 and y

C. five more than eight times y

D. five multiplied by the sum of y and 8

---

13. _____ $9 - x = 7$

14. _____ $x - 9 = 7$

15. _____ $9 - 7 = x$

A. nine less than x is 7

B. nine less x is 7

C. the difference between 9 and 7 is x

---

16. _____ $\dfrac{n + 5}{2} = 10$

17. _____ $\dfrac{n}{2} + 5 = 10$

18. _____ $\frac{1}{2}n - 5 = 10$

A. one-half the sum of n and 5 is 10

B. five less than half of n is 10

C. five added to half of n is 10

---

19. _____ $x + \dfrac{4}{5} = 8$

20. _____ $\dfrac{x}{5} + 4 = 8$

21. _____ $\dfrac{x + 4}{5} = 8$

A. the sum of x and 4, divided by 5 is 8

B. x added to the quotient of 4 and 5 is 8

C. four more than x divided by 5 is 8

---

22. _____ $7t + 1 = 5$

23. _____ $7(t + 1) = 5$

24. _____ $7t = 5$

A. one more than seven times t is 5

B. seven times the sum of t and 1 is 5

C. the product of seven and t is 5

CHANGING ALGEBRA WORD
PROBLEMS TO ALGEBRAIC EQUATIONS

EXAMPLE: There are 3 people who have a total weight of 595 pounds. Sally weighs 20 pounds less than Jessie. Rafael weighs 15 pounds more than Jessie. How much does Jessie weigh?

Step 1: Notice everyone's weight is given in terms of Jessie. Sally weighs 20 pounds less than Jessie. Rafael weighs 15 pounds more than Jessie. First, we write everyone's weight in terms of Jessie, j.

$$Jessie = j$$
$$Sally = j - 20$$
$$Rafael = j + 15$$

Step 2: We know that all three together weigh 595 pounds. We write the sum of everyone's weight equal to 595.

$$j + j - 20 + j + 15 = 595$$

We will learn to solve these problems in the next chapter.

Change the following word problems to algebraic equations.

1. Fluffy, Spot, and Shampy have a combined age in dog years of 91. Spot is 14 years younger than Fluffy. Shampy is 6 years older than Fluffy. What is Fluffy's age, f, in dog years?

2. Jerry Marcosi puts 5% of the amount he makes per week into a retirement account, r. He is paid $11.00 per hour and works 40 hours per week for a certain number of weeks, w. Write an equation to help him find out how much he puts into his retirement account.

3. A furniture store advertises a 40% off liquidation sale on all items. What would the sale price (p) be on a $2530 dining room set?

4. Kyle Thornton buys an item which normally sells for a certain price, x. Today the item is selling for 25% off the regular price. A sales tax of 6% is added to the equation to find the final price, f.

5. Tamika Francois runs a floral shop. On Tuesday, Tamika sold a total of $600 worth of flowers. The flowers cost her $100, and she paid an employee to work 8 hours for a given wage, w. Write an equation to help Tamika find her profit, p, on Tuesday.

6. Sharice is a waitress at a local restaurant. She makes an hourly wage, $3.50, plus she receives tips. On Monday, she worked 6 hours and received tip money, t. Write an equation showing what Sharice made on Monday, y.

7. Jenelle buys x shares of stock in a company at $34.50 per share. She later sells the shares at $40.50 per share. Write an equation to show how much money, m, Jenelle has made.

CHAPTER 9 REVIEW

Solve the following problems, using $x = 2$.

1. $3x + 4 =$ _____

2. $\dfrac{6x}{4} =$ _____

3. $x^2 - 5 =$ _____

4. $\dfrac{x^3 + 8}{2} =$ _____

5. $12 - 3x =$ _____

6. $x - 5 =$ _____

7. $-5x + 4 =$ _____

8. $9 - x =$ _____

9. $2x + 2 =$ _____

Solve the following problems. Let $w = -1$, $y = 3$, $z = 5$.

10. $5w - y =$ _____

11. $wyz + 2 =$ _____

12. $z - 2w =$ _____

13. $\dfrac{3z + 5}{wz} =$ _____

14. $\dfrac{6w}{y} + \dfrac{z}{w} =$ _____

15. $25 - 2yz =$ _____

16. $-2y + 3 =$ _____

17. $4w - (yw) =$ _____

18. $7y - 5z =$ _____

Write out the algebraic expression given in each word problem.

19. three less the sum of x and 5 _____

20. double Amy's age, a _____

21. the number of bacteria, b, tripled _____

22. five less than the product of 5 and y _____

23. half of a number, n, less 15 _____

24. the quotient of a number, x, and 6 _____

For questions 25-27, write an equation to match each problem.

25. Calista earns $450 per week for a 40 hour work week plus $16.83 per hour for each hour of overtime after 40 hours. Write an equation that would be used to determine her weekly wages using w as her wages and v as the number of overtime hours worked.

_____

26. Daniel purchased a 1 year CD, c, from a bank. He bought it at an annual interest rate of 6%. After 1 year, Daniel cashes in the CD. What is the total amount it is worth?

_____

27. Jake is a salesman. He earns an hourly wage of $8.00 per hour plus he receives a commission of 7% on the sales he makes. Write an equation which would be used to determine his weekly salary, w, where x is the number of hours worked, and y is the amount of sales for the week.

_____

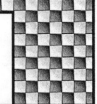

Chapter 10: Solving Equations and Inequalities

ONE-STEP ALGEBRA PROBLEMS
WITH ADDITION AND SUBTRACTION

You have been solving algebra problems since second grade by filling in blanks. For example, $5 + \underline{\quad} = 8$. The answer is 3. You can solve the same kind of problems using algebra. The problems only look a little different because the blank has been replaced with a letter. The letter is called a **variable**.

EXAMPLE: Arithmetic $\quad 5 + \underline{\quad} = 14$
Algebra $\qquad\quad 5 + x = 14$

The goal in any algebra problem is to move all the numbers to one side of the equal sign and have the letter (called a **variable**) on the other side. In this problem, the 5 and the "x" are on the same side. The 5 is added to x. To move it, do the **opposite** of **add**. The **opposite** of **add** is **subtract**, so subtract 5 from both sides of the equation. Now the problem looks like this:

$$\begin{array}{r} 5 + x = 14 \\ \underline{-5 \qquad -5} \\ x = \ \ 9 \end{array}$$

To check your answer, put 9 in the place of x in the original problem. Does $5 + 9 = 14$? Yes, it does.

EXAMPLE: $y - 16 = 27$ Again, the 16 has to move. To move it to the other side of the equation, we do the **opposite** of **subtract**. We **add** 16 to both sides.

$$\begin{array}{r} y - 16 = 27 \\ \underline{+16 \ +16} \\ y \qquad = 43 \end{array}$$

Check by putting 43 in place of the y in the original problem. Does $43 - 16 = 27$? Yes.

Solve the problems below.

1. $n + 9 = 27$
2. $12 + y = 55$
3. $51 + v = 67$
4. $f + 16 = 31$
5. $5 + x = 23$

6. $15 + x = 24$
7. $w - 14 = 89$
8. $t - 26 = 20$
9. $m - 12 = 17$
10. $c - 7 = 21$

11. $k - 5 = 29$
12. $a + 17 = 45$
13. $d + 26 = 56$
14. $15 + x = 56$
15. $y + 19 = 32$

16. $t - 16 = 28$
17. $m + 14 = 37$
18. $y - 21 = 29$
19. $f + 7 = 31$
20. $h - 12 = 18$

21. $r - 12 = 37$
22. $h - 17 = 22$
23. $x - 37 = 46$
24. $r - 11 = 28$
25. $t - 5 = 52$

ONE-STEP ALGEBRA PROBLEMS
WITH MULTIPLICATION AND DIVISION

Solving one-step algebra problems with multiplication and division is just as easy as solving addition and subtraction problems. Again, you perform the **opposite** operation. If the problem is a **multiplication** problem, you **divide** to find the answer. If it is a **division** problem, you **multiply** to find the answer. Carefully read the examples below, and you will see how easy they are.

EXAMPLE 1: $4x = 20$ (**4x** means **4 times x. 4** is the **coefficient** of x.)

The goal is to get the numbers on one side of the equal sign and the variable x on the other side. In this problem, the **4** and x are on the same side of the equal sign. The **4** has to be moved over. **4x** means **4** times x. The opposite of **multiply** is **divide**. If we divide both sides of the equation by **4**, we will find the answer.

$4x = 20$ **We need to divide both sides by 4.**

This means divide by 4. $\dfrac{\cancel{4}^1 x}{\cancel{4}_1} = \dfrac{\cancel{20}^5}{\cancel{4}_1}$ **We see that $1x = 5$ so $x = 5$**

When you put 5 in place of x in the original problem, it is correct. $4 \times 5 = 20$

EXAMPLE 2: $\dfrac{y}{4} = 2$ This problem means y divided by **4** is equal to **2**. In this case, the opposite of **divide** is **multiply**. We need to multiply both sides of the equation by **4**.

$\cancel{4} \times \dfrac{y}{\cancel{4}} = 2 \times 4$ so $y = 8$

When you put 8 in place of y in the original problem, it is correct. $\dfrac{8}{4} = 2$

Solve the problems below.

1. $2x = 14$ 5. $5a = 60$ 9. $7r = 98$ 13. $8t = 96$ 17. $6d = 84$

2. $\dfrac{w}{5} = 11$ 6. $\dfrac{x}{3} = 9$ 10. $\dfrac{y}{3} = 2$ 14. $\dfrac{z}{2} = 15$ 18. $\dfrac{t}{3} = 3$

3. $3h = 45$ 7. $6d = 66$ 11. $\dfrac{x}{4} = 36$ 15. $\dfrac{n}{9} = 5$ 19. $\dfrac{m}{6} = 9$

4. $10y = 30$ 8. $\dfrac{w}{9} = 3$ 12. $\dfrac{r}{4} = 7$ 16. $4z = 24$ 20. $9p = 72$

Sometimes the answer to the algebra problem is a **fraction**. Read the example below.

EXAMPLE

$4x = 5$ Problems like this are solved just like the problems on the previous page. The only difference is that the answer is a **fraction**.

In this problem, the 4 is **multiplied** by x. To solve, we need to divide both sides of the equation by 4.

$4x = 5$ Now **divide** by 4. $\dfrac{4x}{4} = \dfrac{5}{4}$ Now cancel. $\dfrac{\cancel{4}x}{\cancel{4}} = \dfrac{5}{4}$ so $x = \dfrac{5}{4}$

When you put $\dfrac{5}{4}$ in place of x in the original problem, it is correct.

$4 \times \dfrac{5}{4} = 5$ Now cancel. $\longrightarrow$ $\cancel{4} \times \dfrac{5}{\cancel{4}} = 5$ so $5 = 5$

Solve the problems below. Some of the answers will be fractions. Some answers will be integers.

1. $2x = 3$

2. $4y = 5$

3. $5t = 2$

4. $12b = 144$

5. $9a = 72$

6. $8y = 16$

7. $7x = 21$

8. $4z = 64$

9. $7x = 126$

10. $6p = 10$

11. $2n = 9$

12. $5x = 11$

13. $15m = 180$

14. $5h = 21$

15. $3y = 8$

16. $2t = 10$

17. $3b = 2$

18. $5c = 14$

19. $4d = 3$

20. $5z = 75$

21. $9y = 4$

22. $7d = 12$

23. $2w = 13$

24. $9g = 81$

25. $6a = 18$

26. $2p = 16$

27. $15w = 3$

28. $5x = 13$

MULTIPLYING AND DIVIDING WITH NEGATIVE NUMBERS

EXAMPLE 1: $-3x = 15$ In the problem, -3 is **multiplied** by x. To find the solution, we must do the opposite. The opposite of **multiply** is **divide**. We must **divide** both sides of the equation by -3.

$\dfrac{-3x}{-3} = \dfrac{15}{-3}$ Then cancel. $\dfrac{\cancel{-3}x}{\cancel{-3}} = \dfrac{\cancel{15}^{5}}{\cancel{-3}_{1}}$ $x = -5$

EXAMPLE 2: $\dfrac{y}{-4} = -20$ In this problem, y is **divided** by -4. To find the answer, do the opposite. **Multiply** both sides by -4.

$\cancel{-4} \times \dfrac{y}{\cancel{-4}} = (-20) \times (-4)$ so $y = 80$

EXAMPLE 3: $-6a = 2$ The answer to an algebra problem can also be a negative fraction.

$\dfrac{\cancel{-6}a}{\cancel{-6}} = \dfrac{2}{-6}$ $\longleftarrow$ reduce to get $a = \dfrac{1}{-3}$ or $-\dfrac{1}{3}$

> **Note:** A negative fraction can be written several different ways.
>
> $$\dfrac{1}{-3} \; = \; \dfrac{-1}{3} \; = \; -\dfrac{1}{3} \; = \; -\left(\dfrac{1}{3}\right)$$
>
> **All mean the same thing.**

Solve the problems below. Reduce any fractions to lowest terms.

1. $2z = -6$

2. $\dfrac{y}{-5} = 20$

3. $-6k = 54$

4. $4x = -24$

5. $\dfrac{t}{7} = -4$

6. $\dfrac{r}{-2} = -10$

7. $9x = -72$

8. $\dfrac{x}{-6} = 3$

9. $\dfrac{w}{-11} = 5$

10. $5y = -35$

11. $\dfrac{x}{-4} = -9$

12. $7t = -49$

13. $-14x = -28$

14. $\dfrac{m}{3} = -12$

15. $-8z = 32$

16. $-15w = -60$

17. $\dfrac{y}{-9} = -4$

18. $\dfrac{d}{8} = -7$

19. $-12v = 36$

20. $\dfrac{c}{-6} = -6$

21. $-4x = -3$ 26. $\dfrac{b}{-2} = -14$ 31. $-9y = -1$ 36. $-8d = -12$

22. $-12y = 7$ 27. $-24x = -6$ 32. $\dfrac{d}{5} = -10$ 37. $-24w = 9$

23. $\dfrac{a}{-2} = 22$ 28. $-6p = 42$ 33. $\dfrac{z}{-13} = -2$ 38. $\dfrac{y}{-9} = -6$

24. $-18b = 6$ 29. $\dfrac{x}{-23} = -1$ 34. $-5c = 45$ 39. $-9a = -18$

25. $13a = -36$ 30. $7x = -7$ 35. $2d = -3$ 40. $\dfrac{p}{-2} = 15$

VARIABLES WITH A COEFFICIENT OF NEGATIVE ONE

The answer to an algebra problem should not have a negative sign in front of the variable. For example, the problem $-x = 5$ is not completely simplified. Study the examples below to learn how to finish simplifying this problem.

EXAMPLE 1: $-x = 5$ $-x$ means the same thing as $-1x$ or -1 times x. To simplify this problem, **multiply** by -1 on both sides of the equation.

$$(-1)(-1x) = (-1)(5) \quad \text{so} \quad x = -5$$

EXAMPLE 2: $-y = -3$ Solve the same way.

$$(-1)(-y) = (-1)(-3) \quad \text{so} \quad y = 3$$

Simplify the following equations.

1. $-w = 14$ 4. $-x = -25$ 7. $-p = -34$ 10. $-v = -9$

2. $-a = 20$ 5. $-y = -16$ 8. $-m = 81$ 11. $-k = 13$

3. $-x = -15$ 6. $-t = 62$ 9. $-w = 17$ 12. $-q = 7$

SOLVING INEQUALITIES BY ADDITION AND SUBTRACTION

If you add or subtract the same number to or from both sides of an inequality, the inequality remains the same. It works just like an equation.

EXAMPLE: Solve and graph the solution set for $x - 2 \leq 5$.

Add 2 to both sides of the inequality.

$$
\begin{aligned}
x - 2 &\leq 5 \\
+2 \quad &+2 \\
\hline
x &\leq 7
\end{aligned}
$$

Solve and graph the solution set for the following inequalities.

1. $x + 5 > 3$
2. $x - 10 < 5$
3. $x - 2 \leq 1$
4. $9 + x \geq 7$

5. $x - 4 > -2$
6. $x + 11 \leq 20$
7. $x - 3 < -12$
8. $x + 6 \geq -3$

9. $x + 12 \leq 8$
10. $15 + x > 5$
11. $x - 6 < -2$
12. $x + 7 \geq 44$.

13. $14 + x \leq 8$
14. $x - 8 > 24$
15. $x + 1 \leq 12$
16. $11 + x \geq 11$

SOLVING INEQUALITIES BY MULTIPLICATION AND DIVISION

If you multiply or divide both sides of an inequality by a **positive** number, the inequality symbol stays the same. However, if you multiply or divide both sides of an inequality by a **negative** number, **you must reverse the direction of the inequality symbol**.

EXAMPLE 1: Solve and graph the solution set for $4x \leq 20$.

Divide both sides of the inequality by 4. $\quad \dfrac{\overset{1}{\cancel{4}}x}{\underset{1}{\cancel{4}}} \leq \dfrac{\overset{5}{\cancel{20}}}{\cancel{4}} \qquad x \leq 5$

EXAMPLE 2: Solve and graph the solution set for $6 > -\dfrac{x}{3}$.

Multiply both sides of the inequality by −3, and **reverse the direction of the symbol**.

$$(-3) \times 6 < \frac{x}{\cancel{-3}} \times (\cancel{-3})$$

$$-18 < x$$

1. $\dfrac{x}{5} > 4$
2. $2x \leq 24$
3. $-6x \geq 36$
4. $\dfrac{x}{10} > -2$
5. $-\dfrac{x}{4} > 8$

6. $-7x \leq -49$
7. $-3x > 18$
8. $\dfrac{x}{7} \geq 9$
9. $9x \leq 54$
10. $\dfrac{x}{5} > 1$

11. $\dfrac{x}{9} \leq 3$
12. $-4x < -12$
13. $-\dfrac{x}{2} \geq -20$
14. $10x \leq 30$
15. $\dfrac{x}{12} > -4$

16. $-8x \leq -64$
17. $-\dfrac{x}{3} > 1$
18. $-6x \geq -24$
19. $-3x > -12$
20. $-\dfrac{x}{6} \leq -3$

TWO-STEP ALGEBRA PROBLEMS

In the following two-step algebra problems, **additions** and **subtractions** are performed **first** and *then* **division**.

EXAMPLE 1: $-4x + 7 = 31$

Step 1:   Subtract 7 from both sides.

$$\begin{array}{r} -4x + 7 = 31 \\ \underline{-7 \quad -7} \\ -4x \quad\;\; = 24 \end{array}$$

Step 2:   Divide both sides by –4.

$$\frac{-4x}{-4} = \frac{24}{-4} \quad \text{so} \quad x = -6$$

EXAMPLE 2: $-8 - y = 12$

Step 1:   Add 8 to both sides.

$$\begin{array}{r} -8 - y = 12 \\ \underline{+8 \qquad +8} \\ -y = 20 \end{array}$$

Step 2:   **REMEMBER:** To finish solving an algebra problem with a negative sign in front of the variable, multiply both sides by –1.

$$(-1)(-y) = (-1)(20) \quad \text{so} \quad y = -20$$

Solve the two-step algebra problems below.

1. $6x - 4 = -34$

2. $5y - 3 = 32$

3. $8 - t = 1$

4. $10p - 6 = -36$

5. $11 - 9m = -70$

6. $4x - 12 = 24$

7. $3x - 17 = -41$

8. $9d - 5 = 49$

9. $10h + 8 = 78$

10. $-6b - 8 = 10$

11. $-g - 24 = -17$

12. $-7k - 12 = 30$

13. $9 - 5r = 64$

14. $6y - 14 = 34$

15. $12f + 15 = 51$

16. $21t + 17 = 80$

17. $20y + 9 = 149$

18. $15p - 27 = 33$

19. $22h + 9 = 97$

20. $-5 + 36w = 175$

TWO-STEP ALGEBRA PROBLEMS WITH FRACTIONS

An algebra problem may contain a fraction. Study the following example to understand how to solve algebra problems that contain a fraction.

EXAMPLE: $\frac{x}{2} + 4 = 3$

Step 1: $\quad \frac{x}{2} + 4 = 3 \quad$ Subtract 4 from both sides.
$$\underline{\quad -4 \quad -4 \quad}$$

Step 2: $\quad \frac{x}{2} \quad = -1 \quad$ Now this looks like the one-step algebra problems you solved on page 100. Multiply both sides by 2 to solve for x.

$$\frac{x}{2} \times 2 = -1 \times 2 \quad x = -2$$

Simplify the following algebra problems.

1. $4 + \frac{y}{3} = 7$

2. $\frac{a}{2} + 5 = 12$

3. $\frac{w}{5} - 3 = 6$

4. $\frac{x}{9} - 9 = -5$

5. $\frac{b}{6} + 2 = -4$

6. $7 + \frac{z}{2} = -13$

7. $\frac{x}{2} - 7 = 3$

8. $\frac{c}{5} + 6 = -2$

9. $3 + \frac{x}{11} = 7$

10. $16 + \frac{m}{6} = 14$

11. $\frac{p}{3} + 5 = -2$

12. $\frac{t}{8} + 9 = 3$

13. $\frac{v}{7} - 8 = -1$

14. $5 + \frac{h}{10} = 8$

15. $\frac{k}{7} - 9 = 1$

16. $\frac{y}{4} + 13 = 8$

17. $15 + \frac{z}{14} = 13$

18. $\frac{b}{6} - 9 = -14$

19. $\frac{d}{3} + 7 = 12$

20. $10 + \frac{v}{6} = 4$

21. $2 + \frac{p}{4} = -6$

22. $\frac{t}{7} - 9 = -5$

23. $\frac{a}{10} - 1 = 3$

24. $\frac{a}{8} + 16 = 9$

MORE TWO-STEP ALGEBRA PROBLEMS WITH FRACTIONS

Study the following example to understand how to solve algebra problems that contain a different type of fraction.

EXAMPLE: $\dfrac{x+2}{4} = 3$ In this example, "$x + 2$" is divided by 4, and not *just* the x or the 2.

Step 1: $\dfrac{x+2}{\cancel{4}} \times \cancel{4} = 3 \times 4$ First, multiply both sides by 4 to eliminate the fraction.

Step 2: $x + 2 = 12$ Next, subtract 2 from both sides.

$$\begin{array}{r} x + 2 = 12 \\ -2 \quad -2 \\ \hline x = 10 \end{array}$$

Solve the following problems.

1. $\dfrac{x+1}{5} = 4$

2. $\dfrac{z-9}{2} = 7$

3. $\dfrac{b-4}{4} = -5$

4. $\dfrac{y-9}{3} = 7$

5. $\dfrac{d-10}{-2} = 12$

6. $\dfrac{w-10}{-8} = -4$

7. $\dfrac{x-1}{-2} = -5$

8. $\dfrac{c+40}{-5} = -7$

9. $\dfrac{13+h}{2} = 12$

10. $\dfrac{k-10}{3} = 9$

11. $\dfrac{a+11}{-4} = 4$

12. $\dfrac{x-20}{7} = 6$

13. $\dfrac{t+2}{6} = -5$

14. $\dfrac{b+1}{-7} = 2$

15. $\dfrac{f-9}{3} = 8$

16. $\dfrac{4+w}{6} = -6$

17. $\dfrac{3+t}{3} = 10$

18. $\dfrac{x+5}{5} = -3$

19. $\dfrac{g+3}{2} = 11$

20. $\dfrac{k+1}{-6} = 5$

21. $\dfrac{y-14}{2} = -8$

22. $\dfrac{z-4}{-2} = 13$

23. $\dfrac{w+2}{15} = -1$

24. $\dfrac{3+h}{3} = 6$

COMBINING LIKE TERMS

In an algebra problem, **terms** are separated by $+$ and $-$ signs. The expression $5x - 4 - 3x + 7$ has 4 terms: $5x$, 4, $3x$, and 7. Terms having the same variable can be combined (added or subtracted) to simplify the expression. $5x - 4 - 3x + 7$ simplifies to $2x + 3$.

$$5x - 3x \qquad -4 + 7$$

Simplify the following expressions.

1. $7x + 12x \quad =$ _____
2. $8y - 5y + 8 \quad =$ _____
3. $4 - 2c + 9 \quad =$ _____
4. $11a - 16 - a \quad =$ _____
5. $9w + 3w + 3 =$ _____
6. $-5x + x + 2x =$ _____
7. $w - 15 + 9w =$ _____

8. $21 - 10t + 9 - 2t \quad =$ _____
9. $-3 + x - 4x + 9 \quad =$ _____
10. $7b + 12 + 4b \quad =$ _____
11. $4h - h + 2 - 5 \quad =$ _____
12. $-6k + 10 - 4k \quad =$ _____
13. $2a + 12a - 5 + a \quad =$ _____
14. $5 + 9c - 10 \quad =$ _____

15. $-d + 1 + 2d - 4 =$ _____
16. $-8 + 4h + 1 - h =$ _____
17. $12x - 4x + 7 \quad =$ _____
18. $10 + 3z + z - 5 =$ _____
19. $14 + 3y - y - 2 \quad =$ _____
20. $11p - 4p + p \quad =$ _____
21. $11m + 2 - m + 1 =$ _____

SOLVING EQUATIONS WITH LIKE TERMS

When an equation has two or more like terms on the same side of the equation, like terms should be combined as the **first** step in solving the equation.

EXAMPLE: $7x + 2x - 7 = 21 + 8$

Step 1: Combine like terms on both sides of the equation.

Step 2: Solve the two-step algebra problem as explained previously.

$$7x + 2x - 7 = 21 + 8$$
$$9x - 7 = 29$$
$$\underline{+7 \quad +7}$$
$$\frac{9x}{9} = \frac{36}{9}$$
$$x = 4$$

Solve the equations below combining like terms first.

1. $3w - 2w + 4 = 6$
2. $7x + 3 + x = 16 + 3$
3. $5 - 6y + 9y = -15 + 5$
4. $-14 + 7a + 2a = -5$

5. $-2t + 4t - 7 = 9$
6. $9d + d - 3d = 14$
7. $-6c - 4 - 5c = 10 + 8$
8. $15m - 9 - 6m = 9$

9. $-4 - 3x - x = -16$
10. $9 - 12p + 5p = 14 + 2$
11. $10y + 4 - 7y = -17$
12. $-8a - 15 - 4a = 9$

If the equation has like terms on both sides of the equation, you must get all of the terms with a **variable** on one side of the equation and all of the **integers** on the other side of the equation.

EXAMPLE: $3x + 2 = 6x - 1$

Step 1:	$3x + 2 = 6x - 1$ $\underline{-6x \qquad -6x}$	Subtract $6x$ from both sides to move all the **variables** to the left side.
Step 2:	$-3x + 2 = -1$ $\underline{\quad -2 \quad -2}$	Subtract 2 from both sides to move all the **integers** to the right side.
Step 3:	$\dfrac{-3x}{-3} = \dfrac{-3}{-3}$ $x = 1$	Divide by -3 to solve for x.

Solve the following problems.

1. $3a + 1 = a + 9$

2. $2d - 12 = d + 3$

3. $5x + 6 = 14 - 3x$

4. $15 - 4y = 2y - 3$

5. $9w - 7 = 12w - 13$

6. $10b + 19 = 4b - 5$

7. $-7m + 9 = 29 - 2m$

8. $5x - 26 = 13x - 2$

9. $19 - p = 3p - 9$

10. $-7p - 14 = -2p + 11$

11. $16y + 12 = 9y + 33$

12. $13 - 11w = 3 - w$

13. $-17b + 23 = -4 - 8b$

14. $k + 5 = 20 - 2k$

15. $12 + m = 4m + 21$

16. $7p - 30 = p + 6$

17. $19 - 13z = 9 - 12z$

18. $8y - 2 = 4y + 22$

19. $5 + 16w = 6w - 45$

20. $-27 - 7x = 2x + 18$

21. $-12x + 14 = 8x - 46$

22. $27 - 11h = 5 - 9h$

23. $5t + 36 = -6 - 2t$

24. $17y + 42 = 10y + 7$

25. $22x - 24 = 14x - 8$

26. $p - 1 = 4p + 17$

27. $4d + 14 = 3d - 1$

28. $7w - 5 = 8w + 12$

29. $-3y - 2 = 9y + 22$

30. $17 - 9m = m - 23$

REMOVING PARENTHESES

In this chapter, you will use the distributive principle to remove parentheses in problems with a variable (letter).

EXAMPLE 1: $2(a + 6)$ You multiply 2 by each term inside the parentheses. $2 \times a = 2a$ and $2 \times 6 = 12$. The 12 is a positive number, so use a plus sign between the terms in the answer.

$2(a + 6) = 2a + 12$

EXAMPLE 2: $7(2b - 5)$ $7 \times 2b = 14b$ and $7 \times -5 = -35$

$7(2b - 5) = 14b - 35$

EXAMPLE 3: $4(-5c + 2)$ The first term inside the parentheses could be negative. Multiply in exactly the same way as in the examples above. $4 \times (-5c) = -20c$ and $4 \times 2 = 8$

$4(-5c + 2) = -20c + 8$

Remove parentheses in the problems below.

1. $7(n + 6)$

2. $8(2g - 5)$

3. $11(5z - 2)$

4. $6(-y - 4)$

5. $3(-3k + 5)$

6. $4(d - 8)$

7. $2(-4x + 6)$

8. $7(4 + 6p)$

9. $5(-4w - 8)$

10. $6(11x + 2)$

11. $10 (9 - y)$

12. $9(c - 9)$

13. $12(-3t + 1)$

14. $3(4y + 9)$

15. $8(b + 3)$

16. $5(8a + 7)$

17. $3(2b - 4)$

18. $2(-9x - 7)$

19. $4(8 - 7v)$

20. $10(3c + 5)$

21. $5(2x - 9)$

22. $11(y + 3)$

23. $9(7t + 4)$

24. $6(8 - g)$

The number in front of the parentheses can also be negative. Remove these parentheses the same way.

EXAMPLE: $-2(b-4)$ First, multiply $-2 \times b$. $-2 \times b = -2b$
Second, multiply -2×-4 $-2 \times -4 = 8$

Copy the two products. The second product is a positive number, so put a plus sign between the terms in the answer.

$-2(b-4) = -2b + 8$

Remove the parentheses in the following problems.

1. $-7(x+2)$

2. $-5(4-y)$

3. $-4(2b-2)$

4. $-2(8c+6)$

5. $-5(-w-8)$

6. $-3(4x-2)$

7. $-2(-z+2)$

8. $-4(7p+7)$

9. $-9(t-6)$

10. $-10(2w+4)$

11. $-3(9-7p)$

12. $-9(-k-3)$

13. $-1(7b-9)$

14. $-6(-5t-2)$

15. $-7(-v+4)$

16. $-3(-x-5)$

17. $-11(4y+2)$

18. $-1(-c+100)$

19. $-5(-2t-4)$

20. $-2(7z-12)$

21. $-45(y-1)$

22. $-100(a+1)$

23. $-6(-x-11)$

24. $-12(-2b+1)$

MULTI-STEP ALGEBRA PROBLEMS

You can now use what you know about removing parentheses, combining like terms, and solving simple algebra problems to solve problems that involve three or more steps. Study the examples below to see how easy it is to solve multi-step problems.

EXAMPLE 1: $3(x + 6) = 5x - 2$

Step 1: $3x + 18 = 5x - 2$ Use the distributive property to remove parentheses.

Step 2:
$$\frac{-5x \qquad -5x}{-2x + 18 = -2}$$
Subtract $5x$ from each side to move the terms with variables to the left side of the equation.

Step 3:
$$\frac{-18 \quad -18}{-2x = -20}$$
Subtract 18 from each side to move the integers to the right side of the equation.

Step 4: $-2 \quad -2$ Divide both sides by -2 to solve for x.

$x = 10$

EXAMPLE 2: $\dfrac{3(x - 3)}{2} = 9$

Step 1: $\dfrac{3x - 9}{2} = 9$ Use the distributive property to remove parentheses.

Step 2: $\dfrac{\cancel{2}(3x - 9)}{\cancel{2}} = 2(9)$ Multiply both sides by 2 to eliminate the fraction.

Step 3:
$$\begin{array}{r} 3x - 9 = 18 \\ +9 \quad +9 \\ \hline 3x = 27 \end{array}$$
Add 9 to both sides, and combine like terms.

Step 4: $3 \qquad 3$ Divide both sides by 3 to solve for x.

$x = 9$

Solve the following multi-step algebra problems.

1. $2(y - 3) = 4y + 6$

2. $\dfrac{2(a + 4)}{2} = 12$

3. $\dfrac{10(x - 2)}{5} = 14$

4. $\dfrac{12y - 18}{6} = 4y + 3$

5. $2x + 3x = 30 - x$

6. $\dfrac{2a + 11}{3} = a + 5$

7. $5(b - 4) = 3b - 6$

8. $-8(y + 4) = 10y + 4$

9. $\dfrac{x + 4}{-3} = 6 - x$

110

10. $\dfrac{4(n+3)}{5} = n - 3$

11. $3(2x - 5) = 8x - 9$

12. $7 - 10a = 9 - 9a$

13. $7 - 5x = 10 - (6x + 7)$

14. $4(x - 3) - x = x - 6$

15. $4a + 4 = 3a - 4$

16. $-3(x - 4) + 5 = -2x - 2$

17. $5b - 11 = 13 - b$

18. $\dfrac{-4x + 3}{2x} = \dfrac{7}{2x}$

19. $-(x + 1) = -2(5 - x)$

20. $4(2c + 3) - 7 = 13$

21. $6 - 3a = 9 - 2(2a + 5)$

22. $-5x + 9 = -3x + 11$

23. $3y + 2 - 2y - 5 = 4y + 3$

24. $3y - 10 = 4 - 4y$

25. $-(a + 3) = -2(2a + 1) - 7$

26. $5m - 2(m + 1) = m - 10$

27. $\dfrac{1}{2}(b - 2) = 5$

28. $-3(b - 4) = -2b$

29. $4x + 12 = -2(x + 3)$

30. $\dfrac{7x + 4}{3} = 2x - 1$

31. $9x - 5 = 8x - 7$

32. $7x - 5 = 4x + 10$

33. $\dfrac{4x + 8}{2} = 6$

34. $2(c + 4) + 8 = 10$

35. $y - (y + 3) = y + 6$

36. $4 + x - 2(x - 6) = 8$

MULTI-STEP INEQUALITIES

Remember that adding and subtracting with inequalities follows the same rules as equations. When you multiply or divide both sides of an inequality by the same positive number, the rules are also the same as for equations. However, when you multiply or divide both sides of an inequality by a **negative** number, you must **reverse** the inequality symbol.

EXAMPLE 1: $-x > 4$
$(-1)(-x) < (-1)(4)$
$x < -4$

EXAMPLE 2: $-4x < 2$

$\dfrac{-4x}{-4} > \dfrac{2}{-4}$

$x > -\dfrac{1}{2}$

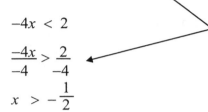

Reverse the symbol when you multiply or divide by a negative number.

When solving multi-step inequalities, first add and subtract to isolate the term with the variable. Then multiply and divide.

EXAMPLE 3: $2x - 8 > 4x + 1$

$\underline{+8+8}$ **Step 1:** Add 8 to both sides.
$2x > 4x + 9$

$\underline{-4x-4x}$ **Step 2:** Subtract $4x$ from both sides.
$-2x > 9$

$\dfrac{-2x}{-2} < \dfrac{9}{-2}$ **Step 3:** Divide by -2. Remember to change the direction of the inequality sign.

$x < -\dfrac{9}{2}$

Solve each of the following inequalities.

1. $8 - 3x \leq 7x - 2$ 4. $7 + 3y > 2y - 5$

2. $3(2x - 5) \geq 8x - 5$ 5. $3a + 5 < 2a - 6$

3. $4 + 2(3 - 2y) \leq 6y - 20$ 6. $3(a - 2) > -5a - 2(3 - a)$

Solve each of the following inequalities.

7. $2x - 7 \geq 4(x - 3) + 3x$

8. $6x - 2 \leq 5x + 5$

9. $-\dfrac{x}{4} > 12$

10. $-\dfrac{2x}{3} \leq 6$

11. $3b + 5 < 2b - 8$

12. $4x - 5 \leq 7x + 13$

13. $4x + 5 \leq -2$

14. $2y - 4 > 7$

15. $\dfrac{1}{3} b - 2 > 5$

16. $-4c + 6 \leq 8$

17. $-\dfrac{1}{2} x + 2 > 9$

18. $\dfrac{1}{4} y - 3 \leq 1$

19. $-3x + 4 > 5$

20. $\dfrac{y}{2} - 2 \geq 10$

21. $7 + 4c < -2$

22. $2 - \dfrac{a}{2} > 1$

23. $10 + 4b \leq -2$

24. $-\dfrac{1}{2} x + 3 > 4$

DIRECT AND INDIRECT VARIATION

The graphs shown below represent functions where x varies with y directly or indirectly. Graph A shows direct variation. Graph B shows an indirect variation. In direct variation, when y increases, the x increases, and when y decreases, x decreases. In indirect variation, also called inverse variation, when y increases, x decreases, and when y decreases, x increases.

Graph A
Direct Variation

Graph B
Indirect Variation

EXAMPLE 1: Direct and indirect variation can be determined by function tables.

Table 1

x	y
0	3
1	4
2	7
3	12
4	19

Table 2

x	y
0	20
1	18
2	16
3	14
4	12

Notice in table 1, as x increases, y increases also. This means that function table 1 represents a direct variation between x and y. On the other hand, table 2 shows a decrease in y when x increases. This means that function table 2 represents an indirect variation between x and y.

Direct variation occurs in a function when y varies directly, or in the same way, as x varies. The two values vary by a proportional factor, k. Direct variation is expressed in the equation $y = xk$.

EXAMPLE 2: If y varies directly as x varies and $y = 18$ when $x = 12$, what is the value of y when $x = 6$?

Step 1: Use the direct variation formula, $y = xk$, to solve for k:
$$y = xk \implies 18 = 12(k) \implies \frac{18}{12} = \frac{12(k)}{12} \implies k = 1.5$$

Step 2: Use the given value of x, 6, and k, 1.5, to calculate the new value of y.
$$y = xk \implies y = 6(1.5) \implies y = 9$$

For an **indirect variation**, y varies inversely with, or opposite of, x. With indirect variation, divide k, the proportional factor, by the value of x. Indirect variation is given by the equation $y = \frac{k}{x}$.

EXAMPLE 3: In a function, y varies inversely as x varies. If $y = 18$ when $x = 12$, what is the value of y when $x = 6$?

Step 1: Use the formula to solve for k:
$$y = \frac{k}{x} \implies 18 = \frac{k}{12} \implies (18)(12) = \frac{k(12)}{12} \implies k = 216$$

Step 2: Substitute 216 for k and the new value of x, 6, to find the new value of y.
$$y = \frac{k}{x} \implies y = \frac{216}{6} \implies y = 36$$

114

You have done direct and indirect variation **word problems** before. For example, direct variation word problems work out just like proportion word problems. To review direct variation word problems, refer back to page 68. Indirect word problems, on the other hand, do not work exactly like proportional word problems because when one value goes up, the other one goes down.

EXAMPLE 4: It takes 45 minutes for 2 copiers to finish a printing job. If 5 copiers worked together to print a job, how long would it take?

Step 1: It will take less time to finish a job if more copiers work together. As the number of copiers increase, the number of minutes needed to complete a job decreases. Therefore, this is an indirect variation problem, and we will need to use the formula, $y = \dfrac{k}{x}$.

Step 2: Find the value of x and y. Let y represent the number of minutes the copiers need to complete the job. Let x represent the number of copiers working to print the job. $y = 45$ minutes, and $x = 2$ copiers.

Step 3: Find k.
$$y = \frac{k}{x} \implies 45 = \frac{k}{2} \implies (45)(2) = \frac{k(2)}{2} \implies k = 90$$

Step 4: Substitute 90 for k and the new value of x, 5 copiers, to find the new value of y.
$$y = \frac{k}{x} \implies y = \frac{90}{5} \implies y = 18 \text{ minutes}$$

It will take 5 copiers only 18 minutes to complete the printing job.

Solve these <u>direct</u> variation problems.

1. If $y = 6$ and $x = 3$, what is the value of y when $x = 5$?

2. If $y = 10$ and $x = 5$, what is the value of y when $x = 4$?

3. If $y = 6$ and $x = 2$, what is the value of y when $x = 7$?

4. If $y = 8$ and $x = 4$, what is the value of y when $x = 6$?

5. If $y = 15$ and $x = 3$, what is the value of y when $x = 5$?

6. If $y = 6$ and $x = 1$, what is the value of y when $x = 3$?

Solve these <u>indirect</u> variation problems.

7. If $y = 6$ and $x = 4$, what is the value of y when $x = 8$?

8. If $y = 12$ and $x = 6$, what is the value of y when $x = 8$?

9. If $y = 9$ and $x = 6$, what is the value of y when $x = 3$?

10. If $y = 6$ and $x = 5$, what is the value of y when $x = 3$?

11. If $y = 3$ and $x = 12$, what is the value of y when $x = 9$?

12. If $y = 8$ and $x = 14$, what is the value of y when $x = 7$?

CHAPTER 10 REVIEW

Solve the following one-step algebra problems.

1. $5y = -25$

2. $x + 4 = 24$

3. $d - 11 = 14$

4. $\dfrac{a}{6} = -8$

5. $-t = 2$

6. $-12b = 10$

7. $\dfrac{c}{-10} = -3$

8. $z - 15 = -19$

9. $-16d = 4$

10. $\dfrac{x}{-14} = 2$

11. $-4k = -12$

12. $y + 13 = 27$

13. $15 + h = 4$

14. $14p = 2$

15. $\dfrac{b}{4} = 11$

16. $p - 26 = 12$

17. $x + (-2) = 5$

18. $m + 17 = 27$

19. $\dfrac{k}{-4} = 13$

20. $x + 10 \le 4$

21. $21t = -7$

22. $z - (-9) = 14$

23. $23 + w = 28$

24. $n - 35 = -16$

25. $-a = 26$

26. $-19 + f = -9$

27. $\dfrac{w}{11} = 3$

28. $-7y = 28$

29. $x - 2 > 8$

30. $z - 12 = -7$

31. $6x \ge 54$

32. $-2x \le 8$

33. $\dfrac{x}{2} > -1$

34. $-x < -9$

35. $-\dfrac{x}{3} \le 5$

36. $x + 10 \le 4$

37. $x - 6 \ge -2$

38. $7x < -14$

39. $-\dfrac{x}{4} \le 5$

40. $4 + x < -1$

Solve each of the following equations.

41. $4a - 8 = 28$

42. $-7 + 23w = 108$

43. $5 + \dfrac{x}{8} = -4$

44. $\dfrac{c}{3} - 13 = 5$

45. $\dfrac{y - 8}{6} = 7$

46. $\dfrac{b + 9}{12} = -3$

47. $\dfrac{x - 9}{4} = 7$

Simplify problems 8-10.

48. $-4a + 8 + 3a - 9$

49. $14 + 3z - 8 - 5z$

50. $-7 - 7x - 2 - 9x$

Solve.

51. $19 - 8d = d - 17$

52. $6 + 16x = -2x - 12$

53. $7w - 8 = -4w - 30$

Remove parentheses.

54. $3(-4x + 7)$

55. $11(2y + 5)$

56. $6(8 - 9b)$

57. $-8(-2 + 3a)$

58. $-2(5c - 3)$

59. $-5(7y - 1)$

Solve each of the following equations and inequalities.

60. $6(b - 4) = 8b - 18$

61. $\dfrac{4x - 16}{2} = 7x + 2$

62. $\dfrac{-11c - 35}{4} = 4c - 2$

63. $5 + x - 3(x + 4) = -17$

64. $-9b - 3 = -3(b + 2)$

65. $7a - 5 = 2(2a - 13)$

66. $4(2x + 3) \geq 2x$

67. $7 - 3x \leq 6x - 2$

68. $3(x + 2) < 7x - 10$

69. $7x < 4(3x + 1)$

70. $-\dfrac{y}{2} > 14$

71. $-\dfrac{3}{4}x \leq 6$

Solve the following direct variation problems.

72. If $y = 2$ and $x = 5$, what is the value of y when $x = 15$?

73. If $y = 5$ and $x = 4$, what is the value of y when $x = 10$?

Solve the following indirect variation problems.

74. If $y = 2$ and $x = 5$, what is the value of y when $x = 15$?

75. If $y = 12$ and $x = 7$, what is the value of y when $x = 4$?

117

Chapter 11: Graphing and Writing Equations and Inequalities

GRAPHING LINEAR EQUATIONS

In addition to graphing ordered pairs, the Cartesian plane can be used to graph the solution set for an equation. Any equation with two variables that are both to the first power is called a **linear equation**. The graph of a linear equation will always be a straight line.

EXAMPLE 1: Graph the solution set for $x + y = 7$.

Step 1: Make a list of some pairs of numbers that will work in the equation.

$$\begin{array}{ll} \underline{x + y = 7} & \\ 4 + 3 = 7 & (4, 3) \\ -1 + 8 = 7 & (-1, 8) \\ 5 + 2 = 7 & (5, 2) \\ 0 + 7 = 7 & (0, 7) \end{array} \left.\rule{0pt}{5em}\right\} \text{ordered pair solutions}$$

Step 2: Plot these points on a Cartesian plane.

Step 3: By passing a line through these points, we graph the solution set for $x + y = 7$.

This means that every point on this line is a solution to the equation $x + y = 7$. For example, $(1, 6)$ is a solution; therefore, the line passes through the point $(1, 6)$

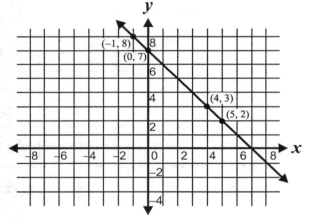

Make a table of solutions for each linear equation below. Then, plot the ordered pair solutions on graph paper. Draw a line through the points. (If one of the points does not line up, you have made a mistake.)

1. $x + y = 6$

2. $y = x + 1$

3. $y = x - 2$

4. $x + 2 = y$

5. $x - 5 = y$

6. $x - y = 0$

118

EXAMPLE 2: Graph the equation $y = 2x - 5$.

Step 1: This equation has 2 variables, both to the first power, so we know the graph will be a straight line.

Substitute some numbers for x or y to find pairs of numbers that satisfy the equation. For the above equation, it will be easier to substitute values of x in order to find the corresponding value for y. Record the values for x and y in a table.

x	y
0	-5
1	-3
2	-1
3	1

If x is 0, y would be -5
If x is 1, y would be -3
If x is 2, y would be -1
If x is 3, y would be 1

Step 2: Graph the ordered pairs, and draw a line through the points.

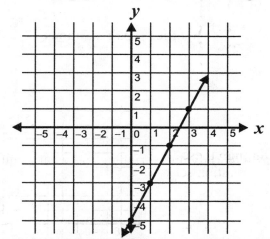

Find pairs of numbers that satisfy the equations below, and graph the line on graph paper.

1. $y = -2x + 2$

2. $2x - 2 = y$

3. $-x + 3 = y$

4. $y = x + 1$

5. $4x - 2 = y$

6. $y = 3x - 3$

7. $x = 4y - 3$

8. $2x = 3y + 1$

9. $x + 2y = 4$

GRAPHING HORIZONTAL AND VERTICAL LINES

The graph of some equations is a horizontal or a vertical line.

EXAMPLE 1: $y = 3$

Step 1: Make a list of ordered pairs that satisfy the equation $y = 3$.

x	y
0	3
1	3
2	3
3	3

$\Big\}$ No matter what value of x you choose, y is always 3.

Step 2: Plot these points on a Cartesian plane, and draw a line through the points.

The graph is a horizontal line.

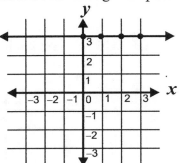

EXAMPLE 2: $2x + 3 = 0$

Step 1: For these equations with only one variable, find what x equals first.

$$2x + 3 = 0$$
$$2x = -3$$
$$x = \frac{-3}{2}$$

Step 2: Just like Example 1, find ordered pairs that satisfy the equation, plot the points, and graph the line.

x	y
$\frac{-3}{2}$	0
$\frac{-3}{2}$	1
$\frac{-3}{2}$	2
$\frac{-3}{2}$	3

$\Big\}$ No matter which value of y you choose, the value of x does not change.

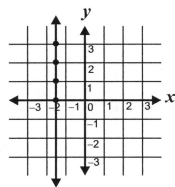

Find pairs of numbers that satisfy the equations below, and graph the lines on graph paper.

1. $2y + 2 = 0$

2. $x = -4$

3. $3x = 3$

4. $y = 5$

5. $4x - 2 = 0$

6. $2x - 6 = 0$

7. $4y = 1$

8. $5x + 10 = 0$

9. $3y + 12 = 0$

10. $x + 1 = 0$

11. $2y - 8 = 0$

12. $3x = -9$

13. $x = -2$

14. $6y - 2 = 0$

15. $5x - 5 = 0$

16. $2y - 4 = 0$

17. $2y - 2 = 0$

18. $3x + 1 = 0$

19. $4y = -2$

20. $-2y = 6$

21. $-4x = -8$

22. $3y = -6$

23. $x = 2$

24. $4y = 8$

FINDING THE INTERCEPTS OF A LINE

The *x*-intercept is the point where the graph of a line crosses the *x*-axis. The *y*-intercept is the point where the graph of a line crosses the *y*-axis.

> **To find the *x*-intercept, set $y = 0$**
> **To find the *y*-intercept, set $x = 0$**

EXAMPLE: Find the *x*- and *y*-intercepts of the line $6x + 2y = 18$.

Step 1:   To find the *x*-intercept, set $y = 0$.

$$6x + 2(0) = 18$$
$$\frac{6x}{6} = \frac{18}{6}$$
$$x = 3 \qquad \text{The } x\text{-intercept is at the point } (3, 0).$$

Step 2:   To find the *y*-intercept, set $x = 0$.

$$6(0) + 2y = 18$$
$$\frac{2y}{2} = \frac{18}{2}$$
$$y = 9 \qquad \text{The } y\text{-intercept is at the point } (0, 9).$$

Step 3:   You can now use the two intercepts to graph the line.

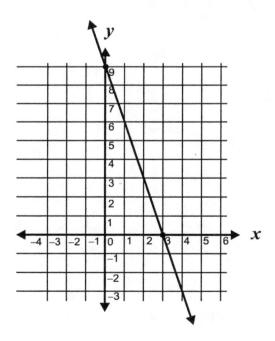

For each of the following equations, find both the *x*- and the *y*-intercepts of the line. For extra practice, draw each of the lines on graph paper.

1. $6x - 2y = 6$

2. $2x + 4y = 8$

3. $4x + 3y = 12$

4. $x - 3y = -4$

5. $8x + 3y = 8$

6. $5x - 4y = 10$

7. $-2x - 2y = 6$

8. $-6x + 4y = 12$

9. $6x - 2y = -6$

10. $-5x - 5y = 15$

11. $9x - 6y = -18$

12. $6x + 6y = 18$

13. $-3x - 6y = 21$

14. $8x + 3y = -8$

15. $-3x + 9y = 9$

16. $12x + 6y = 24$

17. $x - 2y = -4$

18. $-2x - 4y = 8$

19. $5x + 4y = 15$

20. $12x + 18y = 60$

21. $7x - 14y = 21$

22. $5x + 10y = 15$

23. $-12x + 16y = 48$

24. $33x - 11y = -33$

25. $-2x - 6y = -8$

26. $14x + 3y = 21$

27. $10x - 5y = 20$

28. $10x + 15y = 30$

29. $-18x + 27y = 54$

30. $21x + 42y = 63$

UNDERSTANDING SLOPE

The **slope** of a line refers to how steep a line is. Slope is also defined as the rate of change. When we graph a line using ordered pairs, we can easily determine the slope. Slope is often represented by the letter **m**.

> The formula for slope of a line is: $m = \dfrac{y_2 - y_1}{x_2 - x_1}$ or $\dfrac{\text{rise}}{\text{run}}$

EXAMPLE 1: What is the slope of the following line that passes through the ordered pairs $(-4, -3)$ and $(1, 3)$?

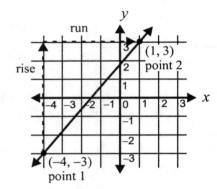

y_2 is 3, the y-coordinate of point 2.

y_1 is -3, the y-coordinate of point 1.

x_2 is 1, the x-coordinate of point 2.

x_1 is -4, the x-coordinate of point 1.

Use the formula for slope given above. $m = \dfrac{3 - (-3)}{1 - (-4)} = \dfrac{6}{5}$

The slope is $\dfrac{6}{5}$. This shows us that we can go up 6 (rise) and over 5 to the right (run) to find another point on the line.

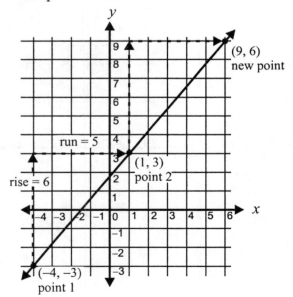

EXAMPLE 2: Find the slope of a line through the points $(-2, 3)$ and $(1, -2)$. It doesn't matter which pair we choose for point 1 and point 2. The answer is the same.

let point 1 be $(-2, 3)$
let point 2 be $(1, -2)$

$$\text{slope} = \frac{(y_2 - y_1)}{(x_2 - x_1)} = \frac{-2 - 3}{1 - (-2)} = \frac{-5}{3}$$

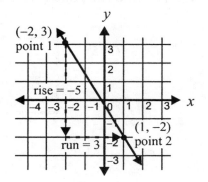

When the slope is negative, the line will slant left. For this example, the line will go **down** 5 units and then over 3 to the **right**.

EXAMPLE 3: What is the slope of a line that passes through $(1, 1)$ and $(3, 1)$?

$$\text{slope} = \frac{1 - 1}{3 - 1} = \frac{0}{2} = 0$$

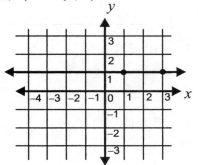

When $y_2 - y_1 = 0$, the slope will equal 0, and the line will be horizontal.

EXAMPLE 4: What is the slope of a line that passes through $(2, 1)$ and $(2, -3)$?

$$\text{slope} = \frac{-3 - 1}{2 - 2} = \frac{4}{0} = \text{undefined}$$

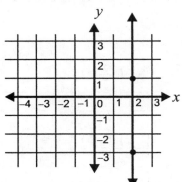

When $x_2 - x_1 = 0$, the slope is undefined, and the line will be vertical.

The following lines summarize what we know about slope.

slope > 0

slope < 0

slope = 0

slope is undefined

125

Find the slope of the line that goes through the following pairs of points. Use the formula slope $= \dfrac{y_2 - y_1}{x_2 - x_1}$. Then, using graph paper, graph the line through the two points, and label the rise and the run. (See Examples 1 through 4.)

1. (2, 3) (4, 5)

2. (1, 3) (2, 5)

3. (–1, 2) (4, 1)

4. (1, –2) (4, –2)

5. (3, 0) (3, 4)

6. (3, 2) (–1, 8)

7. (4, 3) (2, 4)

8. (2, 2) (1, 5)

9. (3, 4) (1, 2)

10. (3, 2) (3, 6)

11. (6, –2) (3, –2)

12. (1, 2) (3, 4)

13. (–2, 1) (–4, 3)

14. (5, 2) (4, –1)

15. (1, –3) (–2, 4)

16. (2, –1) (3, 5)

17. (2, 4) (5, 3)

18. (5, 2) (2, 5)

19. (4, 5) (6, 6)

20. (2, 1) (–1, –3)

SLOPE-INTERCEPT FORM OF A LINE

An equation that contains two variables, each to the first degree, is a **linear equation**. The graph for a linear equation is a straight line. To put a linear equation in slope-intercept form, solve the equation for y. This form of the equation shows the slope and the y-intercept. Slope-intercept form follows the pattern of $y = mx + b$. The "m" represents slope, and the "b" represents the y-intercept. The y-intercept is the point at which the line crosses the y-axis.

When the slope of a line is not 0, the graph of the equation shows a **direct variation** between y and x. When y increases, x increases in a certain proportion. The proportion stays constant. The constant is called the **slope** of the line.

EXAMPLE: Put the equation $2x + 3y = 15$ in slope-intercept form. What is the slope of the line? What is the y-intercept? Graph the line.

Step 1: Solve for y:

$$2x + 3y = 15$$
$$\underline{-2x \qquad\quad -2x}$$
$$\frac{3y}{3} = \frac{-2x}{3} + \frac{15}{3}$$

slope-intercept form: $\qquad y = \frac{-2}{3}x + 5$

The slope is $\frac{-2}{3}$ and the y-intercept is 5

Step 2: Knowing the slope and the y-intercept, we can graph the line.

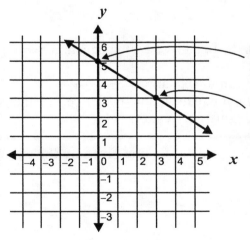

The y-intercept is 5, so the line passes through the point (0, 5) on the y-axis.

The slope is $\frac{-2}{3}$, so go down 2 and over 3 to get a second point.

Put each of the following equations in slope-intercept form by solving for *y*. On your graph paper, graph the line using the slope and *y*-intercept.

1. $4x - y = 5$
2. $2x + 4y = 16$
3. $3x - 2y = 10$
4. $x + 3y = -12$
5. $6x + 2y = 0$
6. $8x - 5y = 10$
7. $-2x + y = 4$

8. $-4x + 3y = 12$
9. $-6x + 2y = 12$
10. $x - 5y = 5$
11. $3x - 2y = -6$
12. $3x + 4y = 2$
13. $-x = 2 + 4y$
14. $2x = 4y - 2$

15. $6x - 3y = 9$
16. $4x + 2y = 8$
17. $6x - y = 4$
18. $-2x - 4y = 8$
19. $5x + 4y = 16$
20. $6 = 2y - 3x$

VERIFY THAT A POINT LIES ON A LINE

To know whether or not a point lies on a line, substitute the coordinates of the point into the formula for the line. If the point lies on the line, the equation will be true. If the point does not lie on the line, the equation will be false.

EXAMPLE 1: Does the point (5, 2) lie on the line given by the equation $x + y = 7$?

Solution: Substitute 5 for *x* and 2 for *y* in the equation. $5 + 2 = 7$. Since this is a true statement, the point (5, 2) does lie on the line $x + y = 7$.

EXAMPLE 2: Does the point (0, 1) lie on the line given by the equation $5x + 4y = 16$?

Solution: Substitute 0 for *x* and 1 for *y* in the equation. $5x + 4y = 16$.
Does $5(0) + 4(1) = 16$? No, it equals 4, not 16. Therefore, the point (0, 1) is not on the line given by the equation $5x + 4y = 16$.

For each point below, state whether or not it lies on the line given by the equation that follows the point coordinates.

1. (2, 4) $6x - y = 8$
2. (1, 1) $6x - y = 5$
3. (3, 8) $-2x + y = 2$
4. (9, 6) $-2x + y = 0$

5. (3, 7) $x - 5y = -32$
6. (0, 5) $-6x - 5y = 3$
7. (2, 4) $4x + 2y = 16$
8. (9, 1) $3x - 2y = 29$

9. (6, 8) $6x - y = 28$
10. (-2, 3) $x + 2y = 4$
11. (4, -1) $-x - 3y = -1$
12. (-1, -3) $2x + y = 1$

GRAPHING A LINE KNOWING A POINT AND SLOPE

If you are given a point of a line and the slope of a line, the line can be graphed.

EXAMPLE 1: Given that line *l* has a slope of $\frac{4}{3}$ and contains the point $(2, -1)$, graph the line.

Step 1: Plot and label the point $(2, -1)$ on a Cartesian plane.

Step 2: The slope, *m*, is $\frac{4}{3}$, so the rise is 4, and the run is 3. From the point $(2, -1)$, count 4 units up and 3 units to the right.

Step 3: Draw the line through the two points.

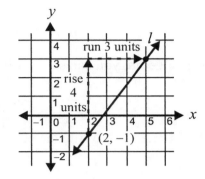

EXAMPLE 2: Given a line that has a slope of $\frac{-1}{4}$ and passes through the point $(-3, 2)$, graph the line.

Step 1: Plot the point $(-3, 2)$.

Step 2: Since the slope is negative, go **down** 1 unit and over 4 to get a second point.

Step 3: Graph the line through the two points.

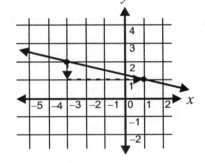

Graph a line on your own graph paper for each of the following problems. First, plot the point. Then, use the slope to find a second point. Draw the line formed from the point and the slope.

1. $(2, -2)$, $m = \frac{3}{4}$
2. $(3, -4)$, $m = \frac{1}{2}$
3. $(1, 3)$, $m = \frac{-1}{3}$
4. $(2, -4)$, $m = 1$
5. $(3, 0)$, $m = \frac{-1}{2}$

6. $(-2, 1)$, $m = \frac{4}{3}$
7. $(-4, -2)$, $m = \frac{1}{2}$
8. $(1, -4)$, $m = \frac{3}{4}$
9. $(2, -1)$, $m = \frac{-1}{2}$
10. $(5, -2)$, $m = \frac{1}{4}$

11. $(-2, -3)$, $m = \frac{2}{3}$
12. $(4, -1)$, $m = \frac{-1}{3}$
13. $(-1, 5)$, $m = \frac{2}{5}$
14. $(-2, 3)$, $m = \frac{3}{4}$
15. $(4, 4)$, $m = \frac{-1}{2}$

16. $(3, -3)$, $m = \frac{-3}{4}$
17. $(-2, 5)$, $m = \frac{1}{3}$
18. $(-2, -3)$, $m = \frac{-3}{4}$
19. $(4, -3)$, $m = \frac{2}{3}$
20. $(1, 4)$, $m = \frac{-1}{2}$

FINDING THE EQUATION OF A LINE USING
TWO POINTS OR A POINT AND SLOPE

If you can find the slope of a line and know the coordinates of one point, you can write the equation for the line. You know the formula for the slope of a line is:

$$m = \frac{y_2 - y_1}{x_2 - x_1} \text{ or } \frac{y_2 - y_1}{x_2 - x_1} = m$$

Using algebra, you can see that if you multiply both sides of the equation by $x_2 - x_1$, you get:

$$y - y_1 = m(x - x_1) \longleftarrow \text{point-slope form of an equation}$$

EXAMPLE: Write the equation of the line passing through the points $(-2, 3)$ and $(1, 5)$.

Step 1: First, find the slope of the line using the two points given.

$$m = \frac{y_2 - y_1}{x_2 - x_1} = \frac{5 - 3}{1 - (-2)} = \frac{2}{3}$$

Step 2: Pick one of the points to use in the point-slope equation. For point $(-2, 3)$, we know $x_1 = -2$ and $y_1 = 3$, and we know $m = \frac{2}{3}$. Substitute these values into the point-slope form of the equation.

$$y - y_1 = m(x - x_1)$$

$$y - 3 = \frac{2}{3}[x - (-2)]$$

$$y - 3 = \frac{2}{3}x + \frac{4}{3}$$

$$y = \frac{2}{3}x + \frac{13}{3}$$

Use the point-slope formula to write an equation for each of the following lines.

1. $(1, -2)$, $m = 2$

2. $(-3, 3)$, $m = \frac{1}{3}$

3. $(4, 2)$, $m = \frac{1}{4}$

4. $(5, 0)$, $m = 1$

5. $(3, -4)$, $m = \frac{1}{2}$

6. $(-1, 4)$ $(2, -1)$

7. $(2, 1)$ $(-1, -3)$

8. $(-2, 5)$ $(-4, 3)$

9. $(-4, 3)$ $(2, -1)$

10. $(3, 1)$ $(5, 5)$

11. $(-3, 1)$, $m = 2$

12. $(-1, -2)$, $m = \frac{4}{3}$

13. $(2, -5)$, $m = -2$

14. $(-1, 3)$, $m = \frac{1}{3}$

15. $(0, -2)$, $m = -\frac{3}{2}$

130

FINDING THE DISTANCE BETWEEN TWO POINTS

To find the distance between any two points on a Cartesian plane, use the following formula:

$$d = \sqrt{(y_2 - y_1)^2 + (x_2 - x_1)^2}$$

EXAMPLE: Find the distance between $(-2, 1)$ and $(3, -4)$.

Plugging the values from the ordered pairs into the formula, we find:

$$d = \sqrt{(-4 - 1)^2 + [3 - (-2)]^2}$$

$$d = \sqrt{(-5)^2 + (5)^2}$$

$$d = \sqrt{25 + 25} = \sqrt{50}$$

To simplify, we look for perfect squares that are factors of 50.
$50 = 25 \times 2$. Therefore,

$$d = \sqrt{25} \times \sqrt{2}$$

$$d = 5\sqrt{2}$$

Find the distance between the following pairs of points using the distance formula above.

1. $(6, -1)\ (5, 2)$

2. $(-4, 3)\ (2, -1)$

3. $(10, 2)\ (6, -1)$

4. $(-2, 5)\ (-4, 3)$

5. $(8, -2)\ (3, -9)$

6. $(2, -2)\ (8, 1)$

7. $(3, 1)\ (5, 5)$

8. $(-2, -1)\ (3, 4)$

9. $(5, -3)\ (-1, -5)$

10. $(6, 5)\ (3, -4)$

11. $(-1, 0)\ (-9, -8)$

12. $(-2, 0)\ (-6, 6)$

13. $(2, 4)\ (8, 10)$

14. $(-10, -5)\ (2, -7)$

15. $(-3, 6)\ (1, -1)$

GRAPHING INEQUALITIES

EXAMPLE 1: In the previous sections, you would graph the equation $x = 3$ as:

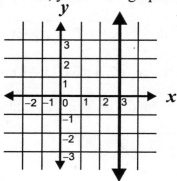

In this section, we graph inequalities such as $x > 3$ (read x is greater than 3). To show this, we use a broken line since the points on the line $x = 3$ are not included in the solution. We shade all points greater than 3.

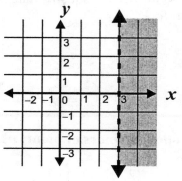

When we graph $x \geq 3$ (read x is greater than or equal to 3), we use a solid line because the points on the line $x = 3$ are included in the graph.

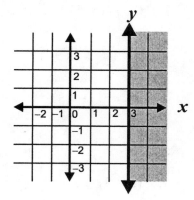

Graph the following inequalities on your own graph paper.

1. $y < 2$
2. $x \geq 4$
3. $y \geq 1$
4. $x < -1$
5. $y \geq -2$
6. $x \leq -4$
7. $x > -3$
8. $y \leq 3$

9. $x \leq 5$
10. $y > -5$
11. $x \geq 3$
12. $y < -1$
13. $x \leq 0$
14. $y > -1$
15. $y \leq 4$
16. $x \geq 0$

17. $y \geq 3$
18. $x < 4$
19. $x \leq -2$
20. $y < -2$
21. $y \geq -4$
22. $x \geq -1$
23. $y \leq 5$
24. $x < -3$

EXAMPLE 2: Graph $x + y \geq 3$

Step 1:   First, we graph $x + y \geq 3$ by changing the inequality to an equality. Think of ordered pairs that will satisfy the equation $x + y = 3$. Then, plot the points, and draw the line.

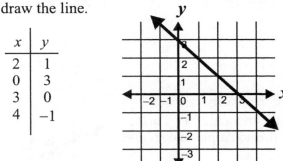

x	y
2	1
0	3
3	0
4	-1

This divides the Cartesian plane into 2 half-planes, $x + y \geq 3$ and $x + y \leq 3$. One half-plane is above the line, and the other is below the line.

Step 2:   To determine which side of the line to shade, first choose a test point. If the point you choose makes the inequality true, then the point is on the side you shade. If the point you choose does not make the inequality true, then shade the side that does not contain the test point.

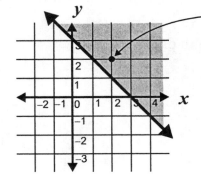

For our test point, let's choose (2, 2). Substitute (2, 2) into the inequality.

$x + y \geq 3$
$2 + 2 \geq 3$

$4 \geq 3$ is true, so shade the side that includes this point.

Use a solid line because of the $\geq$ sign.

Graph the following inequalities on your own graph paper.

1. $x + y \le 4$

2. $x + y \ge 3$

3. $x \ge 5 - y$

4. $x \le 1 + y$

5. $x - y \ge -2$

6. $x < y + 4$

7. $x + y < -1$

8. $x - y \le 0$

9. $x \ge y + 2$

10. $x < -y + 1$

11. $-x + y > 1$

12. $-x - y < -2$

For more complex inequalities, it is easier to graph by first changing the inequality to an equality and then putting the equation in slope-intercept form.

EXAMPLE: $2x + 4y \le 8$

Step 1:   Change the inequality to an equality.
$2x + 4y = 8$

Step 2:   Put the equation in slope-intercept form by solving the equation for y.

$$2x + 4y = 8$$
$$\underline{-2x \qquad\qquad -2x}$$
$$\frac{4y}{4} = \frac{-2x}{4} + \frac{8}{4}$$
$$y = -\tfrac{1}{2}x + 2$$

Step 3:   Graph the line. If the inequality is $<$ or $>$, use a dotted line. If the inequality is $\le$ or $\ge$, use a solid line. For this example, we should use a solid line.

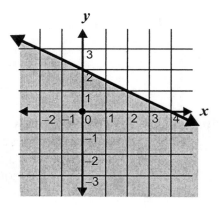

Step 4:   Determine which side of the line to shade. Pick a point such as $(0, 0)$ to see if it is true in the inequality.

$2x + 4y \le 8$, so substitute $(0, 0)$.
Is $0 + 0 \le 8$? Yes, $0 \le 8$, so shade the side of the line that includes the point $(0, 0)$.

Graph the following inequalities on your own graph paper.

1. $2x + y \ge 1$

2. $3x - y \le 3$

3. $x + 3y > 12$

4. $4x - 3y < 12$

5. $y \ge 3x + 1$

6. $x - 2y > -2$

7. $x \le y + 4$

8. $x + y < -1$

9. $-4y \ge 2x + 1$

10. $x \le 4y - 2$

11. $3x - y \ge 4$

12. $y \ge 2x - 5$

13. $x + 7y < 1$

14. $-2y < 4x - 1$

15. $y > 4x + 1$

1. Graph the solution set for the linear equation: $x - 3 = y$.

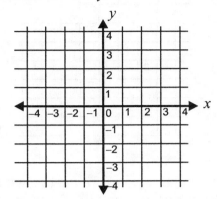

2. Which of the following is not a solution of $3x = 5y - 1$?

   A. $(3, 2)$
   B. $(7, 4)$
   C. $(-\frac{1}{3}, 0)$
   D. $(-2, -1)$

3. $(-2, 1)$ is a solution for which of the following equations?

   A. $y + 2x = 4$
   B. $-2x - y = 5$
   C. $x + 2y = -4$
   D. $2x - y = -5$

4. Graph the equation $2x - 4 = 0$.

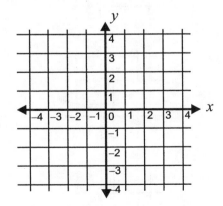

5. What is the slope of the line that passes through the points $(5, 3)$ and $(6, 1)$?

6. What is the slope of the line that passes through the points $(-1, 4)$ and $(-6, -2)$?

7. What is the x-intercept for the following equation?
$$6x - y = 30$$

8. What is the y-intercept for the following equation?
$$4x + 2y = 28$$

9. Graph the equation $3y = 9$.

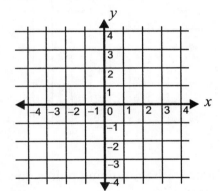

10. Write the following equation in slope-intercept form:

$$3x = -2y + 4$$

11. What is the slope of the line $y = -\frac{1}{2}x + 3$?

12. What is the x-intercept of the line $y = 5x + 6$?

13. What is the y-intercept of the line $y - \frac{2}{3}x + 2 = 0$?

14. Graph the line which has a slope of 2 and a y-intercept of -3.

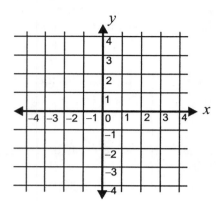

15. Graph the line which has a slope of -2 and a y-intercept of -3.

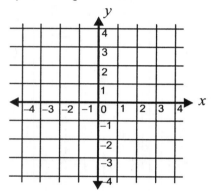

16. Which of the following points does **not** lie on the line $y = 3x - 2$?

   A. $(0, -2)$
   B. $(1, 1)$
   C. $(-1, 5)$
   D. $(2, 4)$

17. Which of the following points lies on the line $2y = -x + 1$?

   A. $(\frac{1}{2}, 0)$
   B. $(2, -\frac{1}{2})$
   C. $(0, 1)$
   D. $(-1, -1)$

18. Graph the equation $-x = 6 + 2y$.

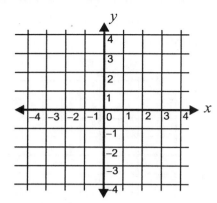

19. Find the equation of the line which contains the point $(0, 2)$ and has a slope of $\frac{3}{4}$.

20. Which is the graph of $x - 3y = 6$?

   A.

   B.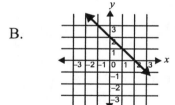

   C.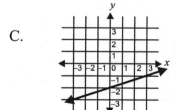

   D.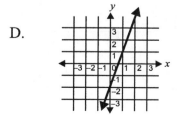

136

21. Which of the following is the graph of the line which has a slope of −2 and a y-intercept of $(0, 3)$?

A.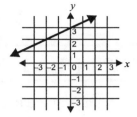

B.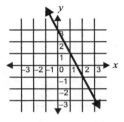

C.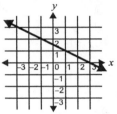

D.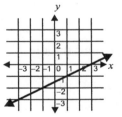

22. Given that a line contains the point $(2, 3)$ and has a slope of $-\frac{1}{2}$, graph the line.

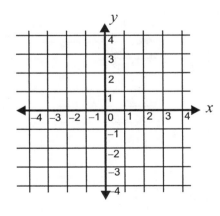

Graph the following inequalities on a Cartesian plane using your own graph paper.

23. $x \geq 4$

24. $x \leq -2$

25. $5y > -10x + 5$

26. $y \leq 2$

27. $2x + y < 5$

28. $-2x + y < 1$

29. $2y \geq 8$

30. $y - 2x \leq 3$

31. $y + 5 \leq x$

32. $-4y \geq 12$

33. $2x - y \geq 4$

34. $-2x - 3y > 9$

35. $x < -3$

36. $y \geq x + 2$

37. $y \leq 2x - 6$

38. $y \geq -1$

39. $3 + y > x$

40. $3x - 4y > 8$

41. $3x < 6$

42. $2y + 6 < x$

43. $2x - y \geq -1$

44. $-2x \leq 4$

Chapter 12: Applications of Graphs

CHANGING THE SLOPE OR *Y*-INTERCEPT OF A LINE

When the slope and/or the *y*-intercept of a linear equation changes, the graph of the line will also change.

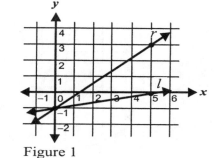

EXAMPLE 1:   Consider line *l* shown in figure 1 at right. What happens to the graph of the line if the slope is changed to $\frac{4}{5}$?

Step 1:   Determine the *y*-intercept of the line. For line *l*, it can easily be seen from the graph that the *y*-intercept is at the point $(0, -1)$.

Figure 1

Step 2:   Find the slope of the line using two points that the line goes through: $(0, -1)$ and $(5, 0)$.
$$m = \frac{y_2 - y_1}{x_2 - x_1} = \frac{0 - (-1)}{5 - 0} = \frac{1}{5}$$

Step 3:   Write the equation of line *l* in slope-intercept form: $y = mx + b$.
$y = \frac{1}{5}x - 1$

Step 4:   Rewrite the equation of the line using a slope of $\frac{4}{5}$, and then graph the line.
Equation of new line: $y = \frac{4}{5}x - 1$
The graph of the new line is labeled line *r* and is shown in Figure 1.
A line with slope $\frac{4}{5}$ is steeper than a line with slope $\frac{1}{5}$.

Note: The greater the numerator, or "rise," of the slope, the steeper the line will be. The greater the denominator, or "run," of the slope, the flatter the line will be.

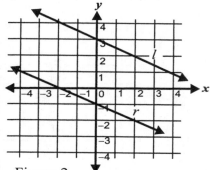

EXAMPLE 2:   Consider line *l* shown in figure 2 at right. The equation of the line is $y = -\frac{1}{2}x + 3$. What happens to the graph of the line if the *y*-intercept is changed to -1?

Step 1:   Rewrite the equation of the line replacing the *y*-intercept with -1.
Equation of new line: $y = -\frac{1}{2}x - 1$.

Step 2:   Graph the new line. Line *r* in figure 2 is the graph of the equation $y = -\frac{1}{2}x - 1$.
Since both lines *l* and *r* have the same slope, they are parallel. Line *r*, with a *y*-intercept of -1, sits below line *l*, with a *y*-intercept of 3.

Figure 2

Put each pair of the following equations in slope-intercept form. Write P if the lines are parallel and NP if the lines are not parallel.

1. $y = x + 1$ _____
    $2y - 2x = 6$

2. $2x + y = 6$ _____
    $2x = 8 - y$

3. $x + 5y = 0$ _____
    $5y + 5 = x$

4. $y = 3 - \frac{1}{3}x$ _____
    $3y + x = -6$

5. $x = 2y$ _____
    $-x = -2y + 14$

6. $y = x + 2$ _____
    $-y = x + 4$

7. $y = 4 - \frac{1}{4}x$ _____
    $3x + 4y = 4$

8. $x + y = 5$ _____
    $5 - y = 2x$

9. $x - 4y = 0$ _____
    $4y = x - 8$

Consider the line (*l*) shown on each of the following graphs, and write the equation of the line in the space provided. Then, on the same graph, graph the line (*r*) for which the equation is given. Write how the slope and *y*-intercept of line *l* compare to the slope and *y*-intercept of line *r* for each graph.

10.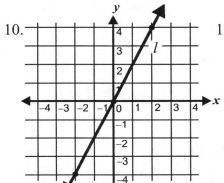

line *l*: _____
line *r*: _____ $y = -2x$ _____
slopes: _____
y-intercepts: _____

12.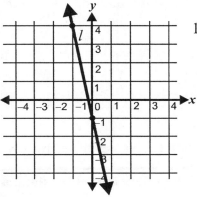

line *l*: _____
line *r*: _____ $y = -3x - 1$ _____
slopes: _____
y-intercepts: _____

14.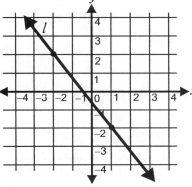

line *l*: _____
line *r*: _____ $y = \frac{1}{4}x - 2$ _____
slopes: _____
y-intercepts: _____

11.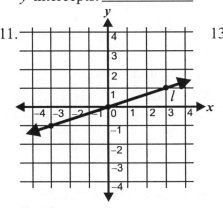

line *l*: _____
line *r*: _____ $y = \frac{1}{3}x + 2$ _____
slopes: _____
y-intercepts: _____

13.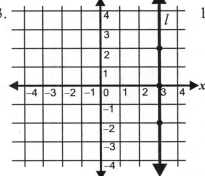

line *l*: _____
line *r*: _____ $y = -3$ _____
slopes: _____
y-intercepts: _____

15.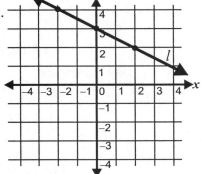

line *l*: _____
line *r*: _____ $y = -\frac{1}{2}x - 3$ _____
slopes: _____
y-intercepts: _____

139

WRITING AN EQUATION FROM DATA

Data is often written in a two column format. If the increases or decreases in the ordered pairs are at a constant rate, then a linear equation for the data can be found.

EXAMPLE: **Write an equation for the following set of data.**

Dan set his car on cruise control and noted the distance he went every 5 minutes.

Minutes in operation (x)	Odometer Reading (y)
5	28,490 miles
10	28,494 miles

Step 1: Write two ordered pairs in the form (minutes, distance) for Dan's driving, (5, 28,490) and (10, 28,494), and find slope.

Step 2: Use the ordered pairs to write the equation in the form $y = mx + b$.
Place the slope, m, that you found and one of the pairs of points as x_1 and y_1 in the following formula:

$y - y_1 = m(x - x_1)$
$y - 28,490 = \frac{4}{5}(x - 5)$
$y - 28,490 + 28,490 = \frac{4}{5}x - 4 + 28,490$
$y = \frac{4}{5}x + 28,486$

It doesn't matter which pair of points you use, the answer will be the same.

Write an equation for each of the following sets of data, assuming the relationship is linear.

1. **Doug's Doughnut Shop**

Year in Business	Total Sales
1	$55,000
4	$85,000

4. **Jim's Depreciation on His Jet Ski**

Years	Value
1	$4,500
6	$2,500

2. **Gwen's Green Beans**

Days Growing	Height in Inches
2	5
6	12

5. **Stepping on the Brakes**

Seconds	MPH
2	51
5	18

3. **At the Gas Pump**

Gallons Purchased	Total Cost
5	$6.00
7	$8.40

6. **Stepping on the Accelerator**

Seconds	MPH
4	35
7	62

GRAPHING LINEAR DATA

Many types of data are related by a constant ratio. As you learned on the previous page, this type of data is linear. The slope of the line described by linear data is the ratio between the data. Plotting linear data with a constant ratio can be helpful in finding additional values.

EXAMPLE 1: A department store prices socks per pair. Each pair of socks costs $0.75. Plot pairs of socks versus price on a Cartesian plane.

Step 1: Since the price of the socks is constant, you know that one pair of socks costs $0.75, 2 pairs of socks cost $1.50, 3 pairs of socks cost $2.25, and so on. Make a list of a few points.

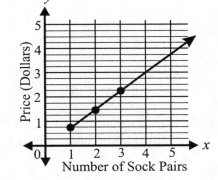

Pair(s) x	Price y
1	.75
2	1.50
3	2.25

Step 2: Plot these points on a Cartesian plane, and draw a straight line through the points.

EXAMPLE 2: What is the slope of the data? What does the slope describe?

Solution: You can determine the slope either by the graph or by the data points. For this data, the slope is .75. Remember, slope is rise/run. For every $0.75 going up the y-axis, you go across one pair of socks on the x-axis. The slope describes the price per pair of socks.

EXAMPLE 3: Use the graph created in Example 1 to answer the following questions. How much would 5 pairs of socks cost? How many pairs of socks could you purchase for $3.00? Extending the line gives useful information about the price of additional pairs of socks.

Solution 1: The line that represents 5 pairs of socks intersects the data line at $3.75 on the y-axis. Therefore, 5 pairs of socks would cost $3.75.

Solution 2: The line representing the value of $3.00 on the y-axis intersects the data line at 4 on the x-axis. Therefore, $3.00 will buy exactly 4 pairs of socks.

Use the information given to make a line graph for each set of data, and answer the questions related to each graph.

1. The diameter of a circle versus the circumference of a circle is a constant ratio. Use the data given below to graph a line to fit the data. Extend the line, and use the graph to answer the next question.

Circle

Diameter	Circumference
4	12.56
5	15.70

2. Using the graph of the data in question 1, estimate the circumference of a circle that has a diameter of 3 inches.

3. If the circumference of a circle is 3 inches, about how long is the diameter?

4. What is the slope of the line you graphed in question 1?

5. What does the slope of the line in question 4 describe?

6. The length of a side on a square and the perimeter of a square are a constant ratio. Use the data below to graph this relationship.

Square

Length of side	Perimeter
2	8
3	12

7. Using the graph from question 6, what is the perimeter of a square with a side that measures 4 inches?

8. What is the slope of the line graphed in question 6?

9. Conversions are often constant ratios. For example, converting from pounds to ounces follows a constant ratio. Use the data below to graph a line that can be used to convert pounds to ounces.

Measurement Conversion

Pounds	Ounces
2	32
4	64

10. Use the graph from question 9 to convert 40 ounces to pounds.

11. What does the slope of the line graphed for question 9 represent?

12. Graph the data below, and create a line that shows converting weeks to days.

Time

Weeks	Days
1	7
2	14

13. About how many days are in $2\frac{1}{2}$ weeks?

14. Graph a data line that converts feet to inches.

15. Using the graph in question 14, how many inches are in 4.5 feet?

16. What is the slope of the line converting feet to inches?

17. An electronics store sells DVDs for $25 each. Graph a data line showing total cost versus the number of DVDs purchased.

18. Using the graph in question 17, how many DVDs could be purchased for $150?

IDENTIFYING GRAPHS OF LINEAR EQUATIONS

Match each equation below with the graph of the equation.

A: $y = 4x$

B: $y = -4x$

C: $4x + y = 4$

D: $x - 2y = 6$

E: $y = 3x - 1$

F: $2x + 3y = 6$

G: $y = 3x + 2$

H: $x + 2y = 6$

I: $y = x - 3$

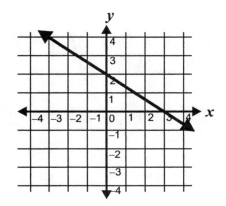

1. _____

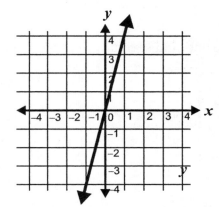

2. _____

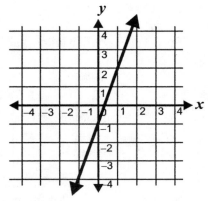

3. _____

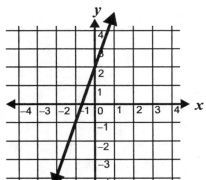

4. _____

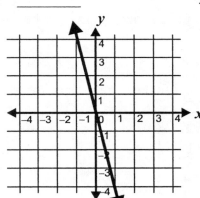

5. _____

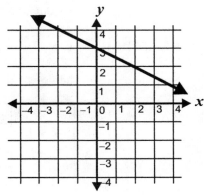

6. _____

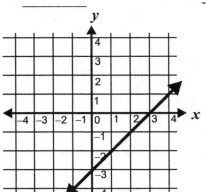

7. _____

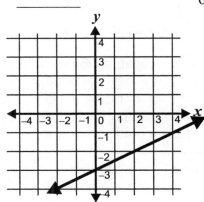

8. _____

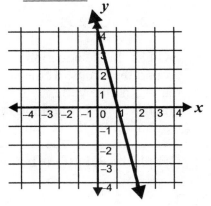

9. _____

GRAPHING NON-LINEAR EQUATIONS

Equations that you may encounter on the Ohio Graduation Test in Mathematics may involve variables which are squared (raised to the second power). The best way to find values for the x and y variables in an equation is to plug one number into x, and then find the corresponding value for y just as you did at the beginning of this chapter. Then, plot the points and draw a line through the points.

EXAMPLE 1: $y = x^2$

Step 1:   Make a table and find several values for x and y.

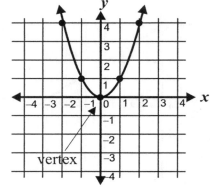

x	y
-2	4
-1	1
0	0
1	1
2	4

Step 2:   Plot the points, and draw a curve through the points. Notice the shape of the curve. This type of curve is called a **parabola**. Equations with one squared term will be parabolas.

EXAMPLE 2: $y = -2x^2 + 4$

Step 1:   Make a table and find several values for x and y.

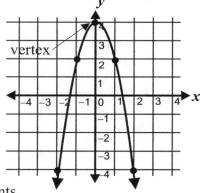

x	y
-2	-4
-1	2
0	4
1	2
2	-4

Step 2:   Plot the points, and draw a curve through the points.

NOTE: In the equation $y = ax^2 + c$, changing the value of a will widen or narrow the parabola around the y-axis. If the value of a is a negative number, the parabola will be reflected across the x-axis (the vertex will be at the top of the parabola instead of at the bottom). If $a = 0$, the graph will be a straight line, not a parabola. Changing the value of c will move the vertex of the parabola from the origin to a different point on the y-axis.

Graph the equations below on a Cartesian plane.

1. $y = 2x^2$
2. $y = 3 - x^2$
3. $y = x^2 - 2$

4. $y = -2x^2$
5. $y = x^2 + 3$
6. $y = -3x^2 + 2$

7. $y = 3x^2 - 5$
8. $y = x^2 + 1$
9. $y = -x^2 - 6$

10. $y = -x^2$
11. $y = 2x^2 - 1$
12. $y = 2 - 2x^2$

IDENTIFYING GRAPHS OF REAL-WORLD SITUATIONS

Real-world situations are sometimes modeled by graphs. Although an equation cannot be written for most of these graphs, interpreting these graphs provides valuable information. Situations may be represented on a graph as a function of time, length, temperature, etc.

The graph below depicts the temperature of a pond at different times of the day. Refer to the graph as you read through examples 1 and 2.

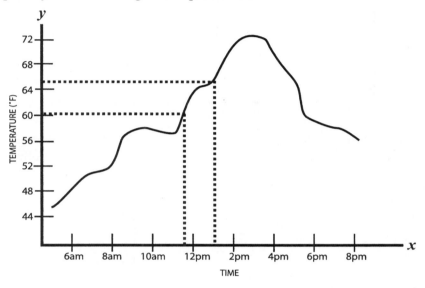

EXAMPLE 1: If it is known that a specific breed of fish is most active in waters between 60°F and 65°F, what time of the day would this fish be the most active in this particular pond?

To find the answer, draw lines from the 60°F and 65°F points on the y-axis to the graph. Then, draw vertical lines from the graph to the x-axis. The time range between the two vertical lines on the x-axis indicates the time that the fish are most active. It can be determined from the graph that the fish are most active between 11:30 a.m. and 1:00 p.m.

EXAMPLE 2: Describe the way the temperature of the pond acts as a function of time.

At 6 a.m., the temperature of the pond is about 47°F. The temperature increases relatively steadily throughout the morning and early afternoon. The temperature peaks at 72°F, which is around 2:30 p.m. during the day. Afterwards, the temperature of the pond starts to decrease. The later it gets in the evening, the more the temperature of the water decreases. The graph shows that at 8 p.m. the temperature of the pond is about 57°F.

Use the graphs to answer the questions. Circle your answers.

The following graph depicts the number of articles of clothing worn as a function of time throughout the year. Use this graph for questions 1 and 2.

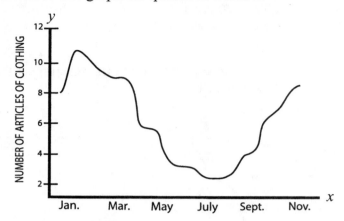

1. According to the graph, in what month are the most articles of clothing worn?

    A. February
    B. April
    C. July
    D. November

2. What is the average number of articles of clothing a person wears in June?

    A. 6
    B. 3
    C. 2
    D. 5

The graph below depicts the efficiency of energy transfer as a function of distance in a certain element. Use the graph to answer questions 3 and 4.

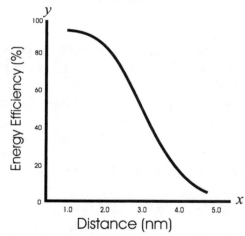

3. At what distance is the energy efficiency at 50%?

    A. 1.0 nm
    B. 2.0 nm
    C. 3.5 nm
    D. 3.0 nm

4. What is the energy efficiency at distance 2.5 nm?

    A. 100%
    B. 90%
    C. 80%
    D. 70%

Find the best non-linear graph to match each scenario.

1. ___Cathy begins her two hour drive to her mother's house in her new sedan. She drives slowly through her city for thirty minutes to reach Interstate 75. After she enters the highway, she travels a constant 60–70 miles per hour for the next hour until she reaches her mother's exit. She then drives slowly down back roads to arrive at her mother's house.

A.

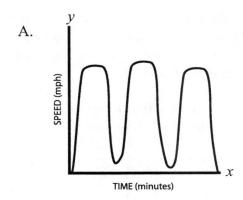

2. ___Phillip is going to fly to Texas for a business meeting. When his flight leaves, the airplane increases its speed a great deal until it reaches about 550 miles per hour. After 20 minutes, the plane levels off for the last 45 minutes at 500 miles per hour. As the airplane nears the airport in Fort Worth, TX, it decreases its speed until it lands and reaches zero miles per hour.

B.

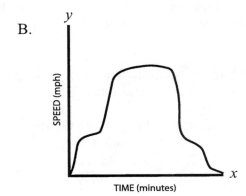

3. ___Erica and her father like to build rockets for fun, and every Saturday they go to the park by their house to launch the rockets. Almost immediately after takeoff, the rocket reaches its greatest speed. Affected by gravity, it slows down until it reaches its peak height. It again speeds up as it descends to the ground.

C.

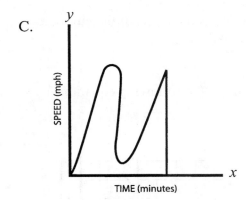

4. ___Molly and her mother ride the train each time they go to the zoo. Molly knows that the train slows down twice so that the passengers can view the animals. Her favorite part of the ride, though, is when the train moves very quickly before it slows down to approach the station and come to a stop.

D.

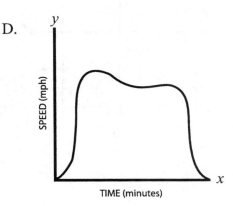

CHAPTER 12 REVIEW

1. Paulo turned on the oven to preheat it. After one minute, the oven temperature was 200°. After 2 minutes, the oven temperature was 325°.

   Oven Temperature

Minutes	Temperature
1	200°
2	325°

   Assuming the oven temperature rose at a constant rate, write an equation that fits the data.

2. Write an equation that fits the data given below. Assume the data is linear.

   Plumber Charges per Hour

Hour	Total Charge
2	$170
3	$220

3. What is the name of the curve described by the equation $y = 2x^2 - 1$?

4. Graph the following equation:
   $$y = -\frac{1}{2}x^2 + 1$$

   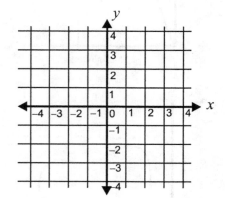

5. What happens to a graph if the slope changes from 2 to −2?

   A. The graph will move down 4 spaces.
   B. The graph will slant downward towards the left instead of the right.
   C. The graph will flatten out to be more vertical.
   D. The graph will slant downward towards the right instead of the left.

6. What happens to a graph if the y-intercept changes from 4 to −2?

   A. The graph will move down 2 spaces.
   B. The graph will slant towards the left instead of the right.
   C. The graph will move down 6 spaces.
   D. The graph will move up 6 spaces.

7. The graph of the line $y = 3x - 1$ is shown below. On the same graph, draw the line $y = -\frac{1}{3}x - 1$.

   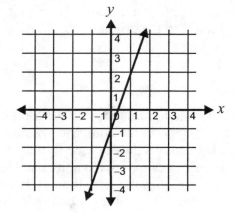

8. Which of the following statements is an accurate comparison of the lines $y = 3x - 1$ and $y = -\frac{1}{3}x - 1$?

   A. Only their y-intercepts are different.
   B. Only their slopes are different.
   C. Both their y-intercepts and their slopes are different.
   D. There is no difference between these two lines.

9. The data given below show conversions between miles per hour and kilometers per hour. Based on this data, graph a conversion line on the Cartesian plane below.

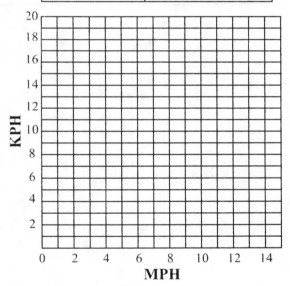

Speed

MPH	KPH
5	8
10	16

10. What would be the approximate conversion of 9 mph to kph?

11. What would be the approximate conversion of 13 kph to mph?

12. A bicyclist travels 12 mph downhill. Approximately how many kph is the bicyclist traveling?

13. Use the data given below to graph the interest rate versus the interest earned on $80.00 in one year.

$80.00 Principal

Interest Rate	Interest–1 year
5%	$4.00
10%	$8.00

14. About how much interest would accrue in one year at an 8% interest rate?

15. What is the slope of the line describing interest versus interest rate?

16. What information does the slope give in problem 15?

17. Draw the graph of the following situation on the Cartesian plane provided. A girl rode her bicycle up a hill, then coasted down the other side of the hill on her bike. At the bottom she stopped.

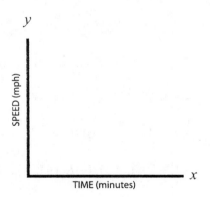

Chapter 13: Relations and Functions

RELATIONS

A **relation** is a set of ordered pairs. The set of the first members of each ordered pair is called the **domain** of the relation. The set of the second members of each ordered pair is called the **range**.

EXAMPLE: State the domain and range of the following relation.

$$\{(2, 4), (3, 7), (4, 9), (6, 11)\}$$

Solution: **Domain:** $\{2, 3, 4, 6\}$ the first member of each ordered pair
                Range: $\{4, 7, 9, 11\}$ the second member of each ordered pair

State the domain and range for each relation.

1. $\{(2, 5), (9, 12), (3, 8), (6, 7)\}$

2. $\{(12, 4), (3, 4), (7, 12), (26, 19)\}$

3. $\{(4, 3), (7, 14), (16, 34), (5, 11)\}$

4. $\{(2, 45), (33, 43), (98, 9), (43, 61), (67, 54)\}$

5. $\{(78, 14), (29, 67), (84, 49), (16, 18), (98, 46)\}$

6. $\{(-8, 16), (23, -7), (-4, -9), (16, -8), (-3, 6)\}$

7. $\{(-7, -4), (-3, 16), (-4, 17), (-6, -8), (-8, 12)\}$

8. $\{(-1, -2), (3, 6), (-7, 14), (-2, 8), (-6, 2)\}$

9. $\{(0, 9), (-8, 5), (3, 12), (-8, -3), (7, 18)\}$

10. $\{(58, 14), (44, 97), (74, 32), (6, 18), (63, 44)\}$

11. $\{(-7, 0), (-8, 10), (-3, 11), (-7, -32), (-2, 57)\}$

12. $\{(18, 34), (22, 64), (94, 36), (11, 18), (91, 45)\}$

When given an equation in two variables, the **domain** is the set of x values that satisfies the equation. The **range** is the set of y values that satisfies the equation.

EXAMPLE: Find the range of the relation $3x = y + 2$ for the domain $\{-1, 0, 1, 2, 3\}$.

Solution: Solve the equation for each value of x given. The result, the y values, will be the range.

Given:

x	y
-1	
0	
1	
2	
3	

Solution:

x	y
-1	-5
0	-2
1	1
2	4
3	7

The range is $\{-5, -2, 1, 4, 7\}$.

Find the range of each relation for the given domain.

Relation	Domain	Range
1. $y = 5x$	$\{1, 2, 3, 4\}$	
2. $y = \lvert x \rvert$	$\{-3, -2, -1, 0, 1\}$	
3. $y = 3x + 2$	$\{0, 1, 3, 4\}$	
4. $y = -\lvert x \rvert$	$\{-2, -1, 0, 1, 2\}$	
5. $y = -2x + 1$	$\{0, 1, 3, 4\}$	
6. $y = 10x - 2$	$\{-2, -1, 0, 1, 2\}$	
7. $y = 3\lvert x \rvert + 1$	$\{-2, -1, 0, 1, 2\}$	
8. $y - x = 0$	$\{1, 2, 3, 4\}$	
9. $y - 2x = 0$	$\{1, 2, 3, 4\}$	
10. $y = 3x - 1$	$\{0, 1, 3, 4\}$	
11. $y = 4x + 2$	$\{0, 1, 3, 4\}$	
12. $y = 2\lvert x \rvert - 1$	$\{-2, -1, 0, 1, 2\}$	

DETERMINING DOMAIN AND RANGE FROM GRAPHS

The domain is all of the x values that lie on the function in the graph from the lowest x value to the highest x value. The range is all of the y values that lie on the function in the graph from the lowest y to the highest y.

EXAMPLE: Find the domain and range of the graph.

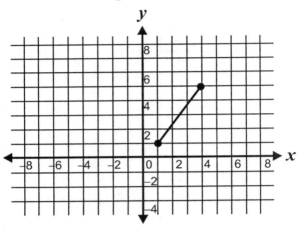

Step 1: First find the lowest x value depicted on the graph. In this case it is 1. Then find the highest x value depicted on the graph. The highest value of x on the graph is 4. The domain must contain all of the values between the lowest x value and the highest x value. The easiest way to write this is $1 \leq$ Domain ≤ 4 or $1 \leq x \leq 4$.

Step 2: Do the same process for the range, but this time look at the lowest and highest y values. The answer is $1 \leq$ Range ≤ 5 or $1 \leq y \leq 5$.

Find the domain and range of each graph below. Write your answers in the line provided.

1.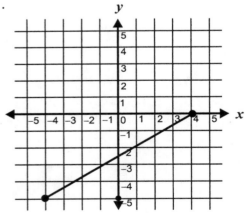

2.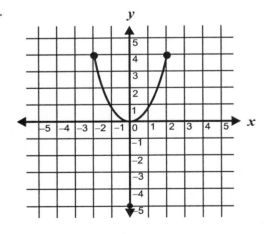

_____   _____

3.

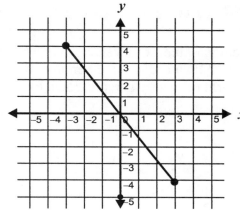

_____

4.

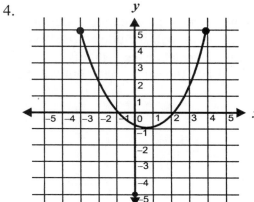

_____

5.

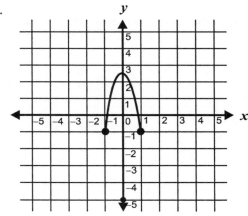

_____

6.

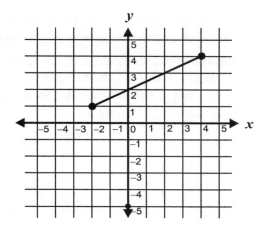

_____

7.

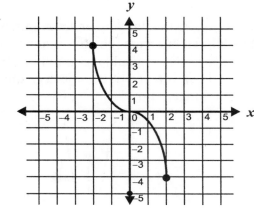

_____

8.

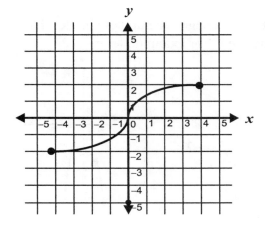

_____

DOMAIN AND RANGE OF QUADRATIC EQUATIONS

The **domain** of a quadratic equation is the set of independent variables, or x values, over which the equation is defined. The **range** is the set of y values for which an equation given in two variables, x and y, is satisfied. A quadratic equation in the form of $y = x^2$ is represented by the following graph:

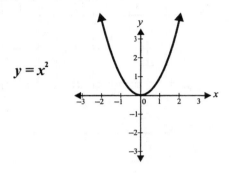

$y = x^2$

x	$y = x^2$
2	−8
1	−2
0	0
1	2
2	8
3	18

In this example the domain, or set of independent variables over which the equation is defined, will be all real numbers (positive and negative). The range, however, will include all **positive** real numbers. How would the graph be affected by multiplying x^2 by a constant, that is $y = ax^2$? If 'a' is a positive number greater than 1, the graph will be the same shape but will be taller and thinner. For example, let $a = 2$:

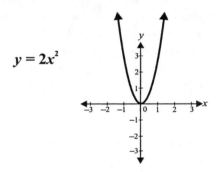

$y = 2x^2$

x	$y = 2x^2$
−2	4
−1	1
0	0
1	1
2	4
3	9

If 'a' is a negative number smaller than -1, the graph is the same shape (tall and thin), but is inverted. For example, let $a = -2$.

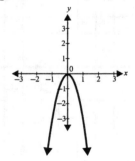

$y = -2x^2$

x	$y = -2x^2$
−2	−8
−1	−2
0	−2
1	−2
2	−8
3	− 18

Using the same logic, you can see that when $0 < a < 1$ or $-1 < a < 0$, the graph will widen and flatten as shown in the figures below:

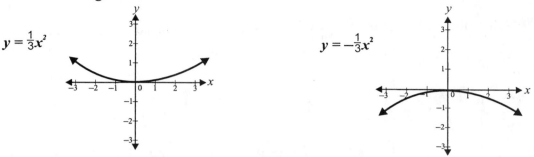

$y = \frac{1}{3}x^2$

$y = -\frac{1}{3}x^2$

When a constant 'c' is added to the equation, then the graph is shifted up (or down) the y-axis by the constant amount 'c':

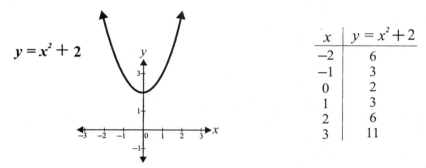

$y = x^2 + 2$

x	$y = x^2 + 2$
-2	6
-1	3
0	2
1	3
2	6
3	11

The magnitude of the constant 'a' determines the width of the curve, the sign of 'a' determines the orientation of the curve, and the constant 'c' determines the y-intercept.

Roots of the Quadratic Equation

When factoring quadratic equations, the answer is often left in the form of two factors in parentheses multiplied together. These factors are called the **roots** of the quadratic equation. For example, the quadratic equation $2x^2 - 11x + 12 = 0$ can be factored as $(2x - 3)(x - 4) = 0$. In this example, $(2x - 3)$ and $(x - 3)$ are the **roots** of the equation. To find the **solution** or **solution set** to the equation, each of these roots must be set equal to zero, and then solved for x. In this case, the solutions are:

$$2x - 3 = 0$$
$$\underline{+3 \quad +3}$$
$$\frac{2x}{2} = \frac{3}{2}$$
$$x = \frac{3}{2}$$

and

$$x - 4 = 0$$
$$\underline{+4 \quad +4}$$
$$x = 4$$

$x = 4$ are the solutions of the equation.

The solution set $\{\frac{3}{2}, 4\}$ of the equation is derived from the roots of the equation. The solution(s) will satisfy the original equation when substituted and simplified.

Answer the following questions about the quadratic equation graphs.

1. Which of the following graphs has the largest value of a in $y = ax^2$?

A.
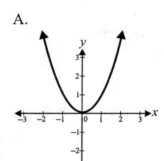

B.
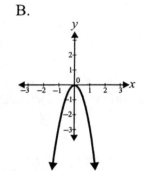

C.
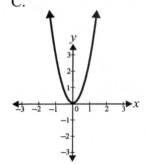

D.
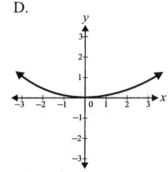

2. Fill in the tables and draw the graphs for the following equations:

A.

x	$y = -2x^2 + 2$
-3	
-2	
-1	
0	
1	
2	
3	

B.

x	$y = -\frac{1}{3}x^2 - 2$
-3	
-2	
-1	
0	
1	
2	
3	

What is the domain and range of each of these graphs? What is the y-intercept represented by the constant c in the equations?

3. Identify the domain, range, and y-intercept for the following equations. Constructing a table and graph on another sheet of paper would be helpful.

A. $y = x^2 - 4$

B. $y = 4x^2 - 3$

C. $y = -\frac{1}{5}x^2 - 5$

D. $y = -2x^2 - 2$

E. $y = \frac{1}{2}x^2 + 3$

F. $y = \frac{1}{2}x$

G. $\frac{y}{2} - 2 = 2x^2$

H. $7 + y = x^2$

I. $4 = x^2 + y$

4. Factor the quadratic equation $6x^2 + x - 2 = 0$. Show the roots of the equation, and solve for the solution set. Substitute one of the roots into the original equation, and verify that it does solve the equation.

156

FUNCTIONS

Some relations are also **functions**. A relation is a function if **for every element in the domain, there is exactly one element in the range.** In other words, for each value for *x* there is only one unique value for *y*.

EXAMPLE 1: {(2, 4), (2, 5), (3, 4)} is **NOT** a function because in the first pair, 2 is paired with 4, and in the second pair, 2 is paired with 5. The 2 can be paired with only one number to be a function. In this example, the *x* value of 2 has more than one value for *y*: 4 and 5.

EXAMPLE 2: {(1, 2), (3, 2), (5, 6)} **IS** a function. Each first number is paired with only one second number. The 2 is repeated as a second number, but the relation remains a function.

Determine whether the ordered pairs of numbers below represent a function. Write "F" if it is a function. Write "NF" if it is not a function.

1. {(−1, 1), (−3, 3), (0, 0), (2, 2)} _____

2. {(−4, −3), (−2, −3), (−1, −3), (2, −3)} _____

3. {(5, −1), (2, 0), (2, 2), (5, 3)} _____

4. {(−3, 3), (0, 2), (1, 1), (2, 0)} _____

5. {(−2, −5), (−2, −1), (−2, 1), (−2, 3)} _____

6. {(0, 2), (1, 1), (2, 2), (4, 3)} _____

7. {(4, 2), (3, 3), (2, 2), (0, 3)} _____

8. {(−1, −1), (−2, −2), (3, −1), (3, 2)} _____

9. {(2, −2), (0, −2), (−2, 0), (1, −3)} _____

10. {(2, 1), (3, 2), (4, 3), (5, −1)} _____

11. {(−1, 0), (2, 1), (2, 4), (−2, 2)} _____

12. {(1, 4), (2, 3), (0, 2), (0, 4)} _____

13. {(0, 0), (1, 0), (2, 0), (3, 0)} _____

14. {(−5, −1), (−3, −2), (−4, −9), (−7, −3)} _____

15. {(8, −3), (−4, 4), (8, 0), (6, 2)} _____

16. {(7, −1), (4, 3), (8, 2), (2, 8)} _____

17. {(4, −3), (2, 0), (5, 3), (4, 1)} _____

18. {(2, −6), (7, 3), (−3, 4), (2, −3)} _____

19. {(1, 1), (3, −2), (4, 16), (1, −5)} _____

20. {(5, 7), (3, 8), (5, 3), (6, 9)} _____

FUNCTION NOTATION

Function notation is used to represent relations which are functions. Some commonly used letters to represent functions include f, g, h, F, G, and H.

EXAMPLE 1: $f(x) = 2x - 1$; find $f(-3)$

Find $f(-3)$ means replace x with -3 in the relation $2x - 1$.

$$f(-3) = 2(-3) - 1$$
$$f(-3) = -6 - 1 = -7$$

Solution: $f(-3) = -7$

EXAMPLE 2: $g(x) = 4 - 2x^2$: find $g(2)$

$$g(2) = 4 - 2(2)^2 = 4 - 2(4) = 4 - 8 = -4$$

Solution: $g(2) = -4$

Find solutions for each of the following.

1. $F(x) = 2 + 3x^2$; find $F(3)$

2. $f(x) = 4x + 6$; find $f(-4)$

3. $H(x) = 6 - 2x^2$; find $H(-1)$

4. $g(x) = -3x + 7$; find $g(-3)$

5. $f(x) = -5 + 4x$; find $f(7)$

6. $G(x) = 4x^2 + 4$; find $G(0)$

7. $f(x) = 7 - 6x$; find $f(-4)$

8. $h(x) = 2x^2 + 10$; find $h(5)$

9. $F(x) = 7 - 5x$; find $F(2)$

10. $f(x) = -4x^2 + 5$; find $f(-2)$

RECOGNIZING FUNCTIONS

Recall that a relation is a function with only one y value for every x value. Functions can be depicted in many ways including through graphs.

EXAMPLE 1:

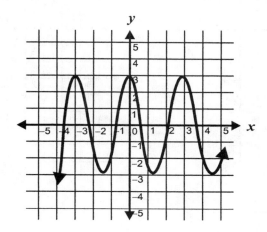

This graph **IS** a function because it has only one y value for each value of x.

EXAMPLE 2:

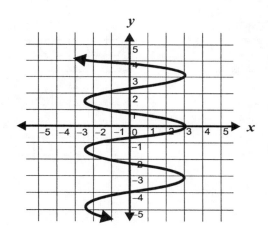

This graph is **NOT** a function because there are more than one y values for each value of x.

HINT: An easy way to determine a function from a graph is to do a vertical line test. First, draw a vertical line that crosses over the whole graph. If the line crosses the graph more than one time, then it is not a function. If it only crosses it once, it is a function. Take the example above.

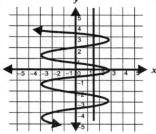

Since the vertical line passes over the graph six times, it is not a function.

Determine whether or not each of the following graphs is a function. If it is, write function on the line provided. If it is not a function, write NOT a function on the line provided.

1.
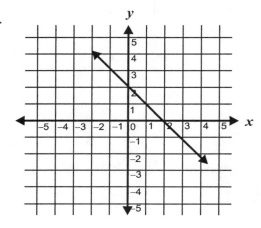

_____

4.
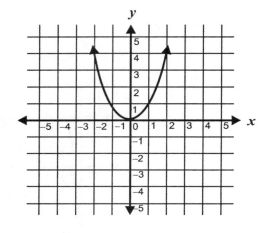

_____

2.
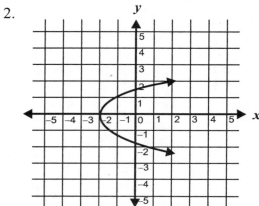

_____

5.
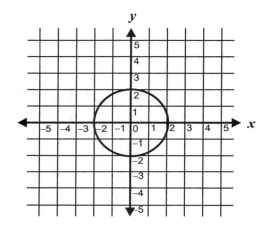

_____

3.
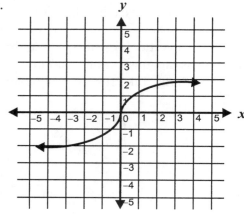

_____

6.
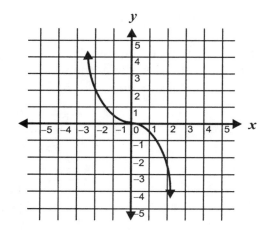

_____

160

7.

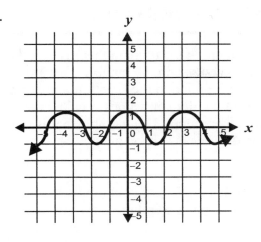

_____

10.

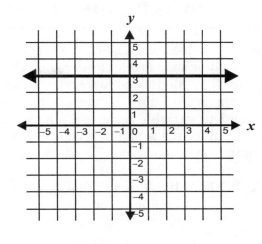

_____

8.

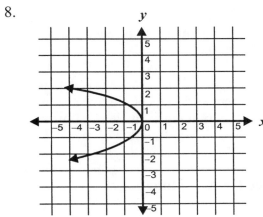

_____

11.

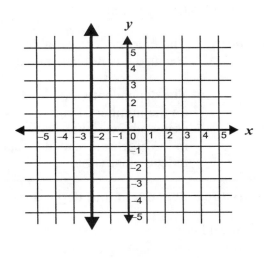

_____

9.

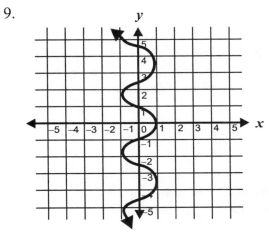

_____

12.

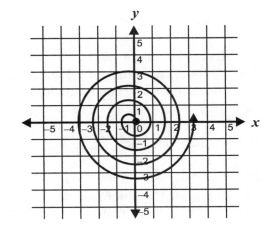

_____

INDEPENDENT AND DEPENDENT VARIABLES

As stated previously, a relation is a function if for every element in the domain there is exactly one element in the range. The domain values are generally known, and the range values are determined by solving the function. As each domain value is applied to the function, only one range value will result. The variable that is used to represent the domain values is called the **independent variable** because it is not dependent on any other value. The variable that is used to represent the range values is called the **dependent variable** because its value will be determined by its corresponding domain value.

EXAMPLE: Mrs. Alexander assigned to her students an open book quiz containing 35 questions to be completed at home. Those students who returned the completed quiz by the due date would receive 30 points for turning the assignment in on time and 2 points for each correct answer. A student's grade on the open book quiz can be expressed as the function $f(a) = 30 + 2a$, where a represents the number of correct answers. Identify the independent and dependent variables in this function.

Solution: The independent variable in this problem is a, the number of correct answers, because it is not dependent on any other value in the function.

The dependent variable in this problem is the grade, $f(a)$, because it is dependent on the number of correct answers. The dependent variable could have also been assigned a variable such as G, T, or y. Using function notation clearly illustrates in the algebraic sentence that the dependent variable is a function of the independent variable.

Identify the independent and dependent variables in the following functions.

1. A local bookstore is encouraging its customers to drop off used books to be given to schools, libraries, and other community organizations. They are offering to anyone who drops off books a special hard cover edition of *Oliver Twist* for $25.95 minus $.10 for each used book. The cost for the special edition of *Oliver Twist* can be expressed as $G(u) = \$25.95 - \$.10u$.

   Independent variable _____ Dependent variable _____

2. Claudia is planning a surprise birthday party for her best friend. To make sure that she has enough food, she is ordering 1 sub sandwich for every person who is coming to the party plus an additional 10 sub sandwiches. The number of sandwiches Claudia is ordering can be written algebraically as follows: $s = 10 + p$.

   Independent variable _____ Dependent variable _____

3. John and Mike are brothers who are training for their school swim team. John has been swimming longer than Mike and is able to swim more laps. For every lap that Mike swims, John swims 3, and the number of laps that John swims can be expressed as $j = 3m$.

   Independent variable _____ Dependent variable _____

Write a function for each of the following word problems. Identify the independent and dependent variables.

1. All delivery drivers at Victor's Pizza Pub are hired to work 5 hour shifts. For each shift worked, a delivery driver gets paid $40 plus $2 for every pizza delivered. Write a function that expresses a delivery driver's earnings for one shift.

2. At 8:00 a.m., the temperature outside was 50°. As the morning progressed, the temperature rose by 3° every hour. Write a function that describes the temperature at any given hour after 8:00 a.m.

3. Austin wanted to borrow $325 from his father to buy a new mountain bike. His father agreed if Austin would pay off the debt by doing odd jobs around the house and in the yard earning a wage of $6.50/hour. Write a function that will help Austin calculate how much debt he has left to pay his father.

4. A new shopping center is leasing store space at a monthly rate of $3.00/ft². Each individual store will be 20 ft wide, but the length will vary. Write a function that expresses the monthly lease rate of any individual store.
Remember that *Area = Length × Width.*

5. Every year a professional baseball player gives $10,000 to a national research fund. He also gives $1,500 for every home run he hits. Express the baseball player's contributions as an algebraic sentence.

6. The local natural gas company charges a monthly usage fee of $25.00. In addition, each household is charged $.67 per therm of natural gas used during the month. Write a function that a homeowner could use to calculate his/her monthly gas bill.

7. Boy Scout Troop 575 is planning an exciting summer mountain adventure. To raise money for the trip, the boys are selling popcorn. Each member of the troop must pay $400 for the trip. For each case of popcorn a Boy Scout sells, $10 will be applied toward his trip fees. Write a formula that describes the amount of money a Boy Scout must pay out of pocket.

8. Oak Hills High School is putting on a spring musical. Tickets are being sold for $6.50 per person. The drama club at Oak Hills gets $\frac{1}{3}$ of the total ticket sales to use for future programs. Write a function that expresses how much money the drama club will receive from the spring musical.

9. Josie rented a car for one day from a company that charges $30 per day plus $.20 per mile. What function would Josie use to calculate her total bill before taxes?

10. Hannah wanted to participate in a yard sale being sponsored by her school. She would have to pay $5.00 to rent the space for her items and would receive 65% of the money her items generated. The remaining 35% would be given to a local charity. Write a function that expresses Hannah's net profit.

RELATIONS THAT CAN BE REPRESENTED BY FUNCTIONS

Real-life examples can be represented by functions. The most common functions are exponential growth and decay and half-life.

EXAMPLE: Atlanta, GA has a population of about 410,000 people. The U.S. Census Bureau estimates that the population will double in 26 years. If the population continues at the same rate, what will the population be in
a) 10 years?   b) 50 years?

Step 1: Use the double growth equation $P = P_0(2^{t/d})$, where P = population at time t, P_0 = population at time $t = 0$, and d = double time.

Step 2: Determine the variable of each of the facts given in the problem. In this case, P_0 = 410,000 people, d = 26 years, and t = 10 years for part a and t = 50 years for part b.

Step 3: Plug all of the information into the given equation. Round to the nearest whole number.
a) $P = 410{,}000 \, (2^{10/26}) = 535{,}260$ people
b) $P = 410{,}000 \, (2^{50/26}) = 1{,}554{,}847$ people

Find the answers to the real-life problems by using the equations and variables given. Round your answer to the nearest whole numbers.

For questions 1 and 2 use the half-life formula.

$A = A_0(\tfrac{1}{2})^{t/h}$
A = amount at time t
A_0 = amount at time $t = 0$
h is the half-life

1. If you have 6000 atoms of hydrogen (H), and hydrogen's half-life is 12.3 years, how many atoms will you have left after 7 years?

2. Chlorine (Cl) has a half-life of 55.5 minutes. If you start with 200 milligrams of Chlorine, how many will be left after 5 hours?

For questions 3 and 4 use the double growth formula.

$P = P_0(2)^{t/d}$
P = amount at time t
P_0 = amount at time $t = 0$
d is the half-life

3. There are about 3,390,000 Girl Scouts in the United States. The Girl Scout council says that there is a growth rate of 5–10 % per year, so they expect the Girl Scout population in the United States to double in 12 years. If the Girl Scout's organization expands continuously like it has been, what will the population be   a) in 8 years? and   b) next year?

4. Dr. Kellie noticed the bacteria growth in her laboratory. After observing the bacteria, she concluded that the double time of the bacteria is 40 minutes, and she started off with just 2500 bacteria. Assuming this information is accurate and constant, how many bacteria will be in Dr. Kellie's lab   a) in 5 minutes?   and   b) after 3 hours?

For questions 5 and 6 use the compound interest formula.

$A = P(1 + \frac{r}{k})^{kt}$
A = amount at time, t
P = principle amount invested
k = how many times per year interest is compounded
n = rate

5. Lisa invested $1,000 into an account that pays 6% interest compounded monthly. If this account is for her newborn, how much will the account be worth on his 21st birthday, which is exactly 21 years from now?

6. Mr. Dumple wants to open up a savings account. He has looked at two different banks. Bank 1 is offering a rate of 5% compounded daily. Bank 2 is offering an account that has a rate of 8%, but is only compounded semi-yearly. Mr. Dumple puts $5000 and wants to take it out for his retirement in 10 years. Which bank will give him the most money back?

1. What is the domain of the following relation?
   {(−1, 2), (2, 5), (4, 9), (6, 11)}

2. What is the range of the following relation?
   {(0, −2), (−1, −4), (−2, 6), (−3, −8)}

3. Find the range of the relation $y = 5x$ for the domain {0, 1, 2, 3, 4}.

4. Find the values of $M(y)$ of the relation $M(y) = 2(1.1)^y$ for the domain {2, 3, 4, 5, 6}.

5. Find the range of the following relation for the domain {0, 2, 6, 8, 10}.
   $B(t) = 600(.75)^t$

6. Find the range of the following relation for the domain {−8, −3, 7, 12, 17}.
   $$y = \frac{3(x-2)}{5}$$

7. Find the range of the following relation for the domain {−8, −4, 0, 4, 8}.
   $$y = 10 - 2x$$

8. Find the range of the following relation for the domain {−7, −1, 2, 5, 8}.
   $$y = \frac{4+x}{3}$$

9. Trent sells computers and other electronic devices for Computer Town. He receives $300 per week and 60% of his total sales. Write a function that expresses Trent's weekly earnings. Identify the independent and dependent variables.
   Function _____
   Independent variable _____
   Dependent variable _____

For each of the following relations given in questions 10–14, write F if it is a function and NF if it is not a function.

10. {(1, 2), (2, 2), (3, 2)} _____

11. {(−1, 0), (0, 1), (1, 2), (2, 3)} _____

12. {(2, 1), (2, 2), (2, 3)} _____

13. {(1, 7), (2, 5), (3, 6), (2, 4)} _____

14. {(0, −1), (−1, −2), (−2, −3), (−3, −4)} _____

For questions 15-20, find the range of the following functions for the given value of the domain.

15. For $g(x) = 2x^2 - 4x$; find $g(-1)$

16. For $h(x) = 3x(x - 4)$; find $h(3)$

17. For $f(n) = \frac{1}{n+3}$; find $f(4)$

18. For $G(n) = \frac{2-n}{2}$; find $G(8)$

19. For $H(x) = 2x(x - 1)$; find $H(4)$

20. For $f(x) = 7x^2 + 3x - 2$, find $f(2)$

Chapter 14: Factoring and Solving Quadratic Equations

In a multiplication problem, the numbers multiplied together are called **factors**. The answer to a multiplication problem is called the **product**.

$$5 \times 4 = 20$$

factors   product

If we reverse the problem, $20 = 5 \times 4$, we say we have **factored** 20 into 5×4.

In this chapter, we will factor **polynomials**.

EXAMPLE: Find the greatest common factor of $2y^3 + 6y^2$.

Step 1: Look at the whole numbers. The greatest common factor of 2 and 6 is 2. Factor the 2 out of each term.

$$2(y^3 + 3y^2)$$

Step 2: Look at the remaining terms, $y^3 + 3y^2$. What are the common factors of each term?

$$\begin{aligned} y^3 &= y \times \boxed{y \times y} \\ 3y^2 &= 3 \times \boxed{y \times y} \end{aligned} \longleftarrow \text{common factors} = y^2$$

Step 3: Factor 2 and y^2 out of each term: $2y^2(y + 3)$

Check: $2y^2(y + 3) = 2y^3 + 6y^2$

Find the greatest common factor of each of the following.

1. $6x^4 + 18x^2$

2. $14y^3 + 7y$

3. $4b^5 + 12b^3$

4. $10a^3 + 5$

5. $2y^3 + 8y^2$

6. $6x^4 - 12x^2$

7. $18y^2 - 12y$

8. $15a^3 - 25a^2$

9. $4x^3 + 16x^2$

10. $6b^2 + 21b^5$

11. $27m^3 + 18m^4$

12. $100x^4 - 25x^3$

13. $4b^4 - 12b^3$

14. $18c^2 + 24c$

15. $20y^3 + 30y^5$

16. $16x^2 - 24x^5$

17. $15a^4 - 25a^2$

18. $24b^3 + 16b^6$

19. $36y^4 + 9y^2$

20. $42x^3 + 49x$

Factoring larger polynomials with 3 or 4 terms works the same way.

EXAMPLE: $4x^5 + 16x^4 + 12x^3 + 8x^2$

Step 1:   Find the greatest common factor of the whole numbers. 4 can be divided evenly into 4, 16, 12, and 8; therefore, 4 is the greatest common factor.

$$4x^5 + 16x^4 + 12x^3 + 8x^2 = 4(x^5 + 4x^4 + 3x^3 + 2x^2)$$

Step 2:   Find the greatest common factor of the variables. x^5, x^4, x^3, and x^2 can each be divided by x^2, the lowest power of x in each term.

$$4x^5 + 16x^4 + 12x^3 + 8x^2 = 4x^2(x^3 + 4x^2 + 3x + 2)$$

Factor each of the following polynomials.

1. $5a^3 + 15a^2 + 20a$

2. $18y^4 + 6y^3 + 24y^2$

3. $12x^5 + 21x^3 + x^2$

4. $6b^4 + 3b^3 + 15b^2$

5. $14c^3 + 28c^2 + 7c$

6. $15b^4 - 5b^2 + 20b$

7. $t^3 + 3t^2 - 5t$

8. $8a^3 - 4a^2 + 12a$

9. $16b^5 - 12b^4 - 20b^2$

10. $20x^4 + 16x^3 - 24x^2 + 28x$

11. $40b^7 + 30b^5 - 50b^3$

12. $20y^4 - 15y^3 + 30y^2$

13. $4m^5 + 8m^4 + 12m^3 + 6m^2$

14. $16x^5 + 20x^4 - 12x^3 + 24x^2$

15. $18y^4 + 21y^3 - 9y^2$

16. $3n^5 + 9n^3 + 12n^2 + 15n$

17. $4d^6 - 8d^2 + 2d$

18. $10w^2 + 4w + 2$

19. $6t^3 - 3t^2 + 9t$

20. $25p^5 - 10p^3 - 5p^2$

21. $18x^4 + 9x^2 - 36x$

22. $6b^4 - 12b^2 - 6b$

23. $y^3 + 3y^2 - 9y$

24. $10x^5 - 2x^4 + 4x^2$

FACTORING BY GROUPING

Polynomials can sometimes be factored by grouping. First, however, they must be arranged in descending order. In the example below, you could try to factor it by grouping without rearranging it in descending order, but you will see it does not work.

EXAMPLE: $2n^3 - 8 + 8n^2 - 2n$

Step 1: Arrange in descending order (exponents go from highest to lowest).

$$2n^3 - 8 + 8n^2 - 2n = 2n^3 + 8n^2 - 2n - 8$$

Step 2: Factor by grouping the first two terms and the last two terms.

$$2n^3 + 8n^2 - 2n - 8 = 2n^2(n + 4) - 2(n + 4) = (2n^2 - 2)(n + 4)$$

Check: Check using the FOIL method.

$$(2n^2 - 2)(n + 4) = 2n^3 + 8n^2 - 2n - 8$$

It is correct. The terms are the same as the terms in the original problem above. Only the order of the terms is different.

Factor the following polynomials by grouping. Be sure to arrange terms in descending order first.

1. $a^3 - 3 - 3a^2 + a$

2. $3c^2 - 4c + c^3 - 12$

3. $x^3 - 28 \ddot{A} 4x^2 + 7x$

4. $-8 + y^3 - y + 8y^2$

5. $b^3 - 15 - 5b^2 + 3b$

6. $d^3 + 20 - 4d - 5d^2$

7. $-3y^2 - 18 + y^3 + 6y$

8. $x^3 - 2x + 5x^2 - 10$

9. $-2y^2 - 3y + 6 + y^3$

10. $6a^2 - 3a - 18 + a^3$

11. $b^3 - 5 + b - 5b^2$

12. $c^3 - 14 - 7c + 2c^2$

13. $3d^2 - 4d - 12 + d^3$

14. $12 + a^3 + 6a + 2a^2$

15. $x^3 - 20 + 4x^2 - 5x$

16. $y^3 - 8y - 8 + y^2$

17. $b^3 - 6 - 3b^2 + 2b$

18. $-7 - c + c^3 + 7c^2$

FINDING THE NUMBERS

The next kind of factoring we will do requires thinking of two numbers with a certain sum and a certain product.

EXAMPLE: Which two numbers have a sum of 8 and a product of 12? In other words, what pair of numbers would answer both equations?

$$\underline{\quad} + \underline{\quad} = 8 \text{ and } \underline{\quad} \times \underline{\quad} = 12$$

You may think $4 + 4 = 8$, but 4×4 does not equal 12.
Or you may think $7 + 1 = 8$, but 7×1 does not equal 12.

$6 + 2 = 8$ and $6 \times 2 = 12$, so 6 and 2 are the pair of numbers that will work in both equations.

For each problem below, find one pair of numbers that will solve both equations.

1. $\underline{\quad} + \underline{\quad} = 14$ and $\underline{\quad} \times \underline{\quad} = 40$

2. $\underline{\quad} + \underline{\quad} = 10$ and $\underline{\quad} \times \underline{\quad} = 21$

3. $\underline{\quad} + \underline{\quad} = 18$ and $\underline{\quad} \times \underline{\quad} = 81$

4. $\underline{\quad} + \underline{\quad} = 12$ and $\underline{\quad} \times \underline{\quad} = 20$

5. $\underline{\quad} + \underline{\quad} = 7$ and $\underline{\quad} \times \underline{\quad} = 12$

6. $\underline{\quad} + \underline{\quad} = 8$ and $\underline{\quad} \times \underline{\quad} = 15$

7. $\underline{\quad} + \underline{\quad} = 10$ and $\underline{\quad} \times \underline{\quad} = 25$

8. $\underline{\quad} + \underline{\quad} = 14$ and $\underline{\quad} \times \underline{\quad} = 48$

9. $\underline{\quad} + \underline{\quad} = 12$ and $\underline{\quad} \times \underline{\quad} = 36$

10. $\underline{\quad} + \underline{\quad} = 17$ and $\underline{\quad} \times \underline{\quad} = 72$

11. $\underline{\quad} + \underline{\quad} = 15$ and $\underline{\quad} \times \underline{\quad} = 56$

12. $\underline{\quad} + \underline{\quad} = 9$ and $\underline{\quad} \times \underline{\quad} = 18$

13. $\underline{\quad} + \underline{\quad} = 13$ and $\underline{\quad} \times \underline{\quad} = 40$

14. $\underline{\quad} + \underline{\quad} = 16$ and $\underline{\quad} \times \underline{\quad} = 63$

15. $\underline{\quad} + \underline{\quad} = 10$ and $\underline{\quad} \times \underline{\quad} = 16$

16. $\underline{\quad} + \underline{\quad} = 8$ and $\underline{\quad} \times \underline{\quad} = 16$

17. $\underline{\quad} + \underline{\quad} = 9$ and $\underline{\quad} \times \underline{\quad} = 20$

18. $\underline{\quad} + \underline{\quad} = 13$ and $\underline{\quad} \times \underline{\quad} = 36$

19. $\underline{\quad} + \underline{\quad} = 15$ and $\underline{\quad} \times \underline{\quad} = 50$

20. $\underline{\quad} + \underline{\quad} = 11$ and $\underline{\quad} \times \underline{\quad} = 30$

MORE FINDING THE NUMBERS

Now that you have mastered positive numbers, take up the challenge of finding pairs of negative numbers or pairs where one number is negative and one is positive.

EXAMPLE: Which two numbers have a sum of −3 and a product of −40? In other words, what pair of numbers would answer both equations?

$$\underline{\hspace{1cm}} + \underline{\hspace{1cm}} = -3 \text{ and } \underline{\hspace{1cm}} \times \underline{\hspace{1cm}} = -40$$

It is faster to look at the factors of 40 first. 8 and 5 and 10 and 4 are possibilities. 8 and 5 have a difference of 3, and in fact, $5 + (-8) = -3$ and $5 \times (-8) = -40$. This pair of numbers, 5 and −8, will satisfy both equations.

For each problem below, find one pair of numbers that will solve both equations.

1. $\underline{\hspace{1cm}} + \underline{\hspace{1cm}} = -2$ and $\underline{\hspace{1cm}} \times \underline{\hspace{1cm}} = -35$

2. $\underline{\hspace{1cm}} + \underline{\hspace{1cm}} = 4$ and $\underline{\hspace{1cm}} \times \underline{\hspace{1cm}} = -5$

3. $\underline{\hspace{1cm}} + \underline{\hspace{1cm}} = 4$ and $\underline{\hspace{1cm}} \times \underline{\hspace{1cm}} = -12$

4. $\underline{\hspace{1cm}} + \underline{\hspace{1cm}} = -6$ and $\underline{\hspace{1cm}} \times \underline{\hspace{1cm}} = 8$

5. $\underline{\hspace{1cm}} + \underline{\hspace{1cm}} = 3$ and $\underline{\hspace{1cm}} \times \underline{\hspace{1cm}} = -40$

6. $\underline{\hspace{1cm}} + \underline{\hspace{1cm}} = 10$ and $\underline{\hspace{1cm}} \times \underline{\hspace{1cm}} = -11$

7. $\underline{\hspace{1cm}} + \underline{\hspace{1cm}} = 6$ and $\underline{\hspace{1cm}} \times \underline{\hspace{1cm}} = -27$

8. $\underline{\hspace{1cm}} + \underline{\hspace{1cm}} = 8$ and $\underline{\hspace{1cm}} \times \underline{\hspace{1cm}} = -20$

9. $\underline{\hspace{1cm}} + \underline{\hspace{1cm}} = -5$ and $\underline{\hspace{1cm}} \times \underline{\hspace{1cm}} = -24$

10. $\underline{\hspace{1cm}} + \underline{\hspace{1cm}} = -3$ and $\underline{\hspace{1cm}} \times \underline{\hspace{1cm}} = -28$

11. $\underline{\hspace{1cm}} + \underline{\hspace{1cm}} = -2$ and $\underline{\hspace{1cm}} \times \underline{\hspace{1cm}} = -48$

12. $\underline{\hspace{1cm}} + \underline{\hspace{1cm}} = -1$ and $\underline{\hspace{1cm}} \times \underline{\hspace{1cm}} = -20$

13. $\underline{\hspace{1cm}} + \underline{\hspace{1cm}} = -3$ and $\underline{\hspace{1cm}} \times \underline{\hspace{1cm}} = 2$

14. $\underline{\hspace{1cm}} + \underline{\hspace{1cm}} = 1$ and $\underline{\hspace{1cm}} \times \underline{\hspace{1cm}} = -30$

15. $\underline{\hspace{1cm}} + \underline{\hspace{1cm}} = -7$ and $\underline{\hspace{1cm}} \times \underline{\hspace{1cm}} = 12$

16. $\underline{\hspace{1cm}} + \underline{\hspace{1cm}} = 6$ and $\underline{\hspace{1cm}} \times \underline{\hspace{1cm}} = -16$

17. $\underline{\hspace{1cm}} + \underline{\hspace{1cm}} = 5$ and $\underline{\hspace{1cm}} \times \underline{\hspace{1cm}} = -24$

18. $\underline{\hspace{1cm}} + \underline{\hspace{1cm}} = -4$ and $\underline{\hspace{1cm}} \times \underline{\hspace{1cm}} = 4$

19. $\underline{\hspace{1cm}} + \underline{\hspace{1cm}} = -1$ and $\underline{\hspace{1cm}} \times \underline{\hspace{1cm}} = -42$

20. $\underline{\hspace{1cm}} + \underline{\hspace{1cm}} = -6$ and $\underline{\hspace{1cm}} \times \underline{\hspace{1cm}} = 8$

FACTORING TRINOMIALS

A trinomial is a quadratic expression with three terms.

For example, $x^2 + x - 30$

A trinomial can be factored into two binomials (expressions with two terms).

EXAMPLE 1: Factor $x^2 + 6x + 8$

Step 1: When the trinomial is in descending order, as in the example above, you need to find a pair of numbers in which the sum of the two numbers equals the number in the second term, while the product of the two numbers equals the third term. In the above example, find the pair of numbers that has a sum of 6 and a product of 8.

$$\underline{\quad} + \underline{\quad} = 6 \quad \text{and} \quad \underline{\quad} \times \underline{\quad} = 8$$

The pair of numbers that satisfy both equations is 4 and 2.

Step 2: Use the pair of numbers in the binomials.

The factors of $x^2 + 6x + 8$ are $(x + 4)\,(x + 2)$

Check: To check, use the FOIL method.

$$(x + 4)\,(x + 2) = x^2 + 4x + 2x + 8 = x^2 + 6x + 8$$

Notice, when the second term and the third term of the trinomial are both positive, both numbers in the solution pair are positive.

EXAMPLE 2: Factor $x^2 - x - 6$ Find the pair of numbers where ...

the sum is -1 and the product is -6

$$\underline{\quad} + \underline{\quad} = -1 \quad \text{and} \quad \underline{\quad} \times \underline{\quad} = -6$$

The pair of numbers that satisfies both equations is 2 and -3.

The factors of $x^2 - x - 6$ are $(x + 2)\,(x - 3)$

Notice, if the third term is negative, one number in the solution pair is positive, and the other number is negative.

EXAMPLE 3: Factor $x^2 - 7x + 12$ Find the pair of numbers where ...

the sum is -7 and the product is 12

$$\underline{\quad} + \underline{\quad} = -7 \quad \text{and} \quad \underline{\quad} \times \underline{\quad} = 12$$

The pair of numbers that satisfies both equations is -3 and -4.

The factors of $x^2 - 7x + 12$ are $(x - 3)\,(x - 4)$.

Notice, if the second term of a trinomial is negative and the third term is positive, both numbers in the solution pair are negative.

Find the factors of the following trinomials.

1. $x^2 - x - 2$

2. $y^2 + y - 6$

3. $w^2 + 3w - 4$

4. $t^2 + 5t + 6$

5. $x^2 + 2x - 8$

6. $k^2 - 4k + 3$

7. $t^2 + 3t - 10$

8. $x^2 - 3x - 4$

9. $y^2 - 5y + 6$

10. $y^2 + y - 20$

11. $a^2 - a - 6$

12. $b^2 - 4b - 5$

13. $c^2 - 5c - 14$

14. $c^2 - c - 12$

15. $d^2 + d - 6$

16. $x^2 - 3x - 28$

17. $y^2 + 3y - 18$

18. $a^2 - 9a + 20$

19. $b^2 - 2b - 15$

20. $c^2 + 7c - 8$

21. $t^2 - 11t + 30$

22. $w^2 + 13w + 36$

23. $m^2 - 2m - 48$

24. $y^2 + 14y + 49$

25. $x^2 + 7x + 10$

26. $a^2 - 7a + 6$

27. $d^2 - 6d - 27$

MORE FACTORING TRINOMIALS

Sometimes a trinomial has a greatest common factor which must be factored out first.

EXAMPLE : Factor $4x^2 + 8x - 32$

Step 1:   Begin by factoring out the greatest common factor, 4.

$$4(x^2 + 2x - 8)$$

Step 2:   Factor by finding a pair of numbers whose sum is 2 and product is –8.
4 and –2 will work, so

$$4(x^2 + 2x - 8) = 4\,(x + 4)\,(x - 2)$$

Check: Multiply to check. $4\,(x + 4)\,(x - 2) = 4x^2 + 8x - 32$

Factor the following trinomials. Be sure to factor out the greatest common factor first.

1. $2x^2 + 6x + 4$

2. $3y^2 - 9y + 6$

3. $2a^2 + 2a - 12$

4. $4b^2 + 28b + 40$

5. $3y^2 - 6y - 9$

6. $10x^2 + 10x - 200$

7. $5c^2 - 10c - 40$

8. $6d^2 + 30d - 36$

9. $4x^2 + 8x - 60$

10. $6a^2 - 18a - 24$

11. $5b^2 + 40b + 75$

12. $3c^2 - 6c - 24$

13. $2x^2 - 18x + 28$

14. $4y^2 - 20y + 16$

15. $7a^2 - 7a - 42$

16. $6b^2 - 18b - 60$

17. $11d^2 + 66d + 88$

18. $3x^2 - 24x + 45$

In the following problems, instead of factoring out just a whole number first, you need to factor out a whole number with a variable or a whole number with a variable and an exponent. Study the following two examples.

EXAMPLE 1: $4a^3 - 4a^2 - 24a = 4a(a^2 - a - 6) = 4a(a - 3)(a + 2)$

EXAMPLE 2: $y^4 + 3y^3 - 4y^2 = y^2(y^2 + 3y - 4) = y^2(y - 1)(y + 4)$

Factor the following polynomials.

1. $x^4 - x^3 - 12x^2$

2. $3c^3 - 6c^2 - 24c$

3. $5b^3 + 10b^2 - 40b$

4. $3y^4 - 9y^3 - 12y^2$

5. $2x^5 + 8x^4 - 10x^3$

6. $6d^3 + 24d^2 + 24d$

7. $2y^3 - 16y^2 + 32y$

8. $6b^4 - 18b^3 - 60b^2$

9. $a^3 - 3a^2 - 4a$

10. $4x^4 + 4x^3 - 24x^2$

11. $y^5 - y^4 - 42y^3$

12. $b^4 + 11b^3 + 24b^2$

13. $4c^3 - 4c^2 - 48c$

14. $11a^4 + 33a^3 + 22a^2$

15. $2x^5 + 2x^4 - 112x^3$

16. $10d^3 - 70d^2 - 180d$

17. $4y^6 + 4y^5 - 24y^4$

18. $2a^3 - 14a^2 + 20a$

19. $6b^5 - 24b^4 + 18b^3$

20. $x^6 + 2x^5 + x^4$

21. $5d^4 - 35d^3 + 50d^2$

22. $a^3 + 3a^2 - 54a$

23. $3y^3 - 42y^2 + 147y$

24. $8x^3 + 24x^2 + 16x$

175

FACTORING MORE TRINOMIALS

Some trinomials have a whole number in front of the first term that cannot be factored out of the trinomial. The trinomial can still be factored.

EXAMPLE : Factor $2x^2 + 5x - 3$

Step 1: To get a product of $2x^2$, one factor must begin with $2x$ and the other with x.

$$(2x \quad)(x \quad)$$

Step 2: Now think: What two numbers give a product of -3? The two possibilities are 3 and -1 or -3 and 1. We know they could be in any order, so there are 4 possible arrangements.

$$(2x + 3)(x - 1)$$
$$(2x - 3)(x + 1)$$
$$(2x + 1)(x - 3)$$
$$(2x - 1)(x + 3)$$

Step 3: Multiply each possible answer until you find the arrangement of the numbers that works. Multiply the outside terms and the inside terms and add them together to see which one will equal $5x$.

$$(2x + 3)(x - 1) = 2x^2 + x - 3$$
$$(2x - 3)(x + 1) = 2x^2 - x - 3$$
$$(2x + 1)(x - 3) = 2x^2 - 5x - 3$$
$$\boxed{(2x - 1)(x + 3) = 2x^2 + 5x - 3} \longleftarrow \quad \text{This arrangement works so:}$$

The factors of $2x^2 + 5x - 3$ are $(2x - 1)(x + 3)$

Alternative: You can do some of the multiplying in your head. For the above example, ask yourself the following question: What two numbers give a product of -3 and give a sum of 5 (the whole number in the second term) when one of the numbers is first multiplied by 2 (the whole number in front of the first term)? The pair of numbers, -1 and 3, have a product of -3 and a sum of 5 when the 3 is first multiplied by 2. Therefore, the 3 will go opposite the factor with the $2x$ so that when the terms are multiplied, you get -5.

You can use this method to narrow down the possible pairs of numbers when you have several to choose from.

Factor the following trinomials.

1. $3y^2 + 14y + 8$

2. $5a^2 + 24a - 5$

3. $7b^2 + 30b + 8$

4. $2c^2 - 9c + 9$

5. $2y^2 - 7y - 15$

6. $3x^2 + 4x + 1$

7. $7y^2 + 13y - 2$

8. $11a^2 + 35a + 6$

9. $5y^2 + 17y - 12$

10. $3a^2 + 4a - 7$

11. $2a^2 + 3a - 20$

12. $5b^2 - 13b - 6$

13. $3y^2 - 4y - 32$

14. $2x^2 - 17x + 36$

15. $11x^2 - 29x - 12$

16. $5c^2 + 2c - 16$

17. $7y^2 - 30y + 27$

18. $2x^2 - 3x - 20$

19. $5b^2 + 24b - 5$

20. $7d^2 + 18d + 8$

21. $3x^2 - 20x + 25$

22. $2a^2 - 7a - 4$

23. $5m^2 + 12m + 4$

24. $9y^2 - 5y - 4$

25. $2b^2 - 13b + 18$

26. $7x^2 + 31x - 20$

27. $3c^2 - 2c - 21$

FACTORING THE DIFFERENCE OF TWO SQUARES

The product of a term and itself is called a **perfect square**.

> 25 is a perfect square because $5 \times 5 = 25$
> 49 is a perfect square because $7 \times 7 = 49$

Any variable with an even exponent is a perfect square.

> y^2 is a perfect square because $y \times y = y^2$
> y^4 is a perfect square because $y^2 \times y^2 = y^4$

When two terms that are both perfect squares are subtracted, factoring those terms is very easy. To factor the difference of perfect squares, you use the square root of each term, a plus sign in the first factor, and a minus sign in the second factor.

EXAMPLE 1 : Factor $4x^2 - 9$

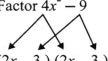

The example has two terms which are both perfect squares, and the terms are subtracted.

Step 1: $(2x \quad 3)(2x \quad 3)$

Find the square root of each term.
Use the square roots in each of the factors.

Step 2: $(2x + 3)(2x - 3)$

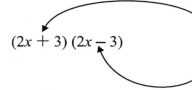

Use a plus sign in one factor and a minus sign in the other factor.

Check: Multiply to check. $(2x + 3)(2x - 3) = 4x^2 - 6x + 6x - 9 = 4x^2 - 9$

The inner and outer terms add to zero.

EXAMPLE 2: Factor $81y^4 - 1$.

Step 1: $(9y^2 + 1)(9y^2 - 1)$

Factor like the example above. Notice the second factor is also the difference of two perfect squares.

Step 2: $(9y^2 + 1)(3y + 1)(3y - 1)$

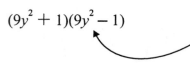

Factor the second term further.
Note: You cannot factor the *sum* of two perfect squares.

Check: Multiply in reverse to check your answer.
$(9y^2 + 1)(3y + 1)(3y - 1) = (9y^2 + 1)(9y^2 - 3y + 3y - 1) = (9y^2 + 1)(9y^2 - 1)$
$(9y^2 + 1)(9y^2 - 1) = 81y^4 - 9y^2 + 9y^2 - 1 = 81y^4 - 1$

Factor the following differences of perfect squares.

1. $64x^2 - 49$

2. $4y^4 - 25$

3. $9a^4 - 4$

4. $25c^4 - 9$

5. $64y^2 - 9$

6. $x^4 - 16$

7. $49x^2 - 4$

8. $4d^2 - 25$

9. $9a^2 - 16$

10. $100y^4 - 49$

11. $c^4 - 36$

12. $36x^2 - 25$

13. $25x^2 - 4$

14. $9x^4 - 64$

15. $49x^2 - 100$

16. $16x^2 - 81$

17. $9y^4 - 1$

18. $64c^2 - 25$

19. $25d^2 - 64$

20. $36a^4 - 49$

21. $16x^4 - 16$

22. $b^2 - 25$

23. $c^4 - 144$

24. $9y^2 - 4$

25. $81x^4 - 16$

26. $4b^2 - 36$

27. $9w^2 - 9$

28. $64a^2 - 25$

29. $49y^2 - 121$

30. $x^6 - 9$

SOLVING QUADRATIC EQUATIONS

In this section, we learn that any equation that can be put in the form $ax^2 + bx + c = 0$ is a quadratic equation if a, b, and c are real numbers and $a \neq 0$. $ax^2 + bx + c = 0$ is the standard form of a quadratic equation. To solve these equations, follow the steps below.

EXAMPLE: Solve $y^2 - 4y - 5 = 0$

Step 1: Factor the left side of the equation.

$$y^2 - 4y - 5 = 0$$
$$(y + 1)(y - 5) = 0$$

Step 2: If the product of these two factors equals zero, then the two factors individually must be equal to zero. Therefore, to solve, we set each factor equal to zero.

$$\frac{(y + 1) = 0}{-1 \quad -1}$$
$$y = -1$$

$$\frac{(y - 5) = 0}{+5 \quad +5}$$
$$y = 5$$

The equation has two solutions: $y = -1$ and $y = 5$

Check: To check, substitute each solution into the original equation.

When $y = -1$, the equation becomes:

$$(-1)^2 - (4)(-1) - 5 = 0$$
$$1 + 4 - 5 = 0$$
$$0 = 0$$

When $y = 5$, the equation becomes:

$$5^2 - (4)(5) - 5 = 0$$
$$25 - 20 - 5 = 0$$
$$0 = 0$$

Both solutions produce true statements.
The solution set for the equation is $\{-1, 5\}$.

Solve each of the following quadratic equations by factoring and setting each factor equal to zero. Check by substituting answers back in the original equation.

1. $x^2 + x - 6 = 0$

2. $y^2 - 2y - 8 = 0$

3. $a^2 + 2a - 15 = 0$

4. $y^2 - 5y + 4 = 0$

5. $b^2 - 9b + 14 = 0$

6. $x^2 - 3x - 4 = 0$

7. $y^2 + y - 20 = 0$

8. $d^2 + 6d + 8 = 0$

9. $y^2 - 7y + 12 = 0$

10. $x^2 - 3x - 28 = 0$

11. $a^2 - 5a + 6 = 0$

12. $b^2 + 3b - 10 = 0$

13. $a^2 + 7a - 8 = 0$

14. $c^2 + 3c + 2 = 0$

15. $x^2 - x - 42 = 0$

16. $a^2 + a - 6 = 0$

17. $b^2 + 7b + 12 = 0$

18. $y^2 + 2y - 15 = 0$

19. $a^2 - 3a - 10 = 0$

20. $d^2 + 10d + 16 = 0$

21. $x^2 - 4x - 12 = 0$

Quadratic equations that have a whole number and a variable in the first term are solved the same way as the problems on the previous page. Factor the trinomial, and set each factor equal to zero to find the solution set.

EXAMPLE: Solve $2x^2 + 3x - 2 = 0$

$(2x - 1)(x + 2) = 0$

Set each factor equal to zero and solve:

$$2x - 1 = 0$$
$$\underline{+1 \quad +1}$$
$$\frac{2x}{2} = \frac{1}{2}$$
$$x = \frac{1}{2}$$

$$x + 2 = 0$$
$$\underline{-2 \quad -2}$$
$$x = -2$$

The solution set is $\{\frac{1}{2}, -2\}$

Solve the following quadratic equations.

1. $3y^2 + 12y + 32 = 0$

2. $5c^2 - 2c - 16 = 0$

3. $7d^2 + 18d + 8 = 0$

4. $3a^2 - 10a - 8 = 0$

5. $11x^2 - 31x - 6 = 0$

6. $5b^2 + 17b + 6 = 0$

7. $3x^2 - 11x - 20 = 0$

8. $5a^2 + 47a - 30 = 0$

9. $2c^2 - 5c - 25 = 0$

10. $2y^2 + 11y - 21 = 0$

11. $5a^2 + 23a - 42 = 0$

12. $3d^2 + 11d - 20 = 0$

13. $3x^2 - 10x + 8 = 0$

14. $7b^2 + 23b - 20 = 0$

15. $9a^2 - 58a + 24 = 0$

16. $4c^2 - 25c - 21 = 0$

17. $8d^2 + 53d + 30 = 0$

18. $4y^2 - 29y + 30 = 0$

19. $8a^2 + 37a - 15 = 0$

20. $3x^2 - 41x + 26 = 0$

21. $8b^2 + 2b - 3 = 0$

MORE SOLVING QUADRATIC EQUATIONS

Sometimes quadratic equations are not in standard form. They are not already set equal to zero. These equations must first be put in standard form in order to solve.

EXAMPLE 1: $y^2 - 11y + 10 = -14$

Step 1: Add 14 to both sides so the equation will be set equal to 0.

$$\begin{array}{r} y^2 - 11y + 10 = -14 \\ +14 \quad +14 \\ \hline y^2 - 11y + 24 = 0 \end{array}$$

Step 2: Factor: $(y - 8)(y - 3) = 0$

Step 3: Set each factor equal to 0 and solve for y.

$\quad y - 8 = 0 \qquad\qquad\qquad y - 3 = 0$
$\quad y = 8 \qquad\qquad\qquad\qquad y = 3$

The solution set is $\{8, 3\}$

EXAMPLE 2: $8x^2 = -42x - 10$

Step 1: Add $42x + 10$ to both sides so the equation will equal to zero.

$$\begin{array}{r} 8x^2 \qquad\quad = -42x - 10 \\ +42x + 10 \quad +42x + 10 \\ \hline 8x^2 + 42x + 10 = 0 \end{array}$$

Step 2: Factor the left side of the equation.

$\quad 8x^2 + 42x + 10 = 0$
$\quad (8x + 2)(x + 5) = 0$

Step 3: Set each factor equal to 0 and solve.

$$\begin{array}{r} 8x + 2 = 0 \\ -2 \;\; -2 \\ \hline 8x = -2 \\ \overline{8} \quad\;\; \overline{8} \end{array} \qquad\qquad \begin{array}{r} x + 5 = 0 \\ -5 \;\; -5 \\ \hline x = -5 \end{array}$$

$\quad x = -\dfrac{1}{4}$

The solution set is $\{-\dfrac{1}{4}, -5\}$

Solve each of the quadratic equations below. Put each in standard form first by setting the equation equal to zero.

1. $x^2 - x = 12$

2. $y^2 + 2y = 15$

3. $b^2 - 4b - 2 = 10$

4. $c^2 - 11c = -28$

5. $4x^2 = 4x + 15$

6. $10b^2 = 37b + 12$

7. $2y^2 = -9y - 18$

8. $c^2 = -4c + 21$

9. $a^2 - 5a + 8 = 14$

10. $b^2 - b = 20$

11. $c^2 + 9c = -14$

12. $y^2 - 6y - 3 = 13$

13. $5a^2 = 13a - 6$

14. $c^2 = 5c + 36$

15. $t^2 = 11t - 24$

16. $6x^2 = -11x - 3$

17. $x^2 - 4x - 10 = 35$

18. $a^2 + 2a = 8$

19. $b^2 - 7b + 2 = 10$

20. $y^2 + y + 7 = 13$

21. $5x^2 = -27x - 10$

22. $6y^2 = -11y + 7$

23. $a^2 = 8a - 12$

24. $b^2 = -13b - 42$

184

SOLVING THE DIFFERENCE OF TWO SQUARES

To solve the difference of two squares, first factor. Then set each factor equal to zero.

EXAMPLE: $25x^2 - 36 = 0$

Step 1:   Factor the left hand side of the equation.

$$25x^2 - 36 = 0$$
$$(5x + 6)(5x - 6) = 0$$

Step 2:   Set each factor equal to zero and solve.

$$
\begin{array}{ll}
5x + 6 = 0 & \qquad 5x - 6 = 0 \\
\quad\; -6 \;\; -6 & \qquad\quad\; +6 \;\; +6 \\
\hline
\dfrac{5x}{5} \;\;\; = \dfrac{-6}{5} & \qquad \dfrac{5x}{5} \;\;\; = \dfrac{6}{5} \\[2mm]
x = \dfrac{-6}{5} & \qquad x = \dfrac{6}{5}
\end{array}
$$

Check: Substitute each solution in the equation to check.

for $x = -\frac{6}{5}$:

$$25x^2 - 36 = 0$$

$25\left(-\frac{6}{5}\right)\left(-\frac{6}{5}\right) - 36 = 0$ ⟵ Substitute $\frac{-6}{5}$ for x.

$\cancel{25}\left(\frac{36}{\cancel{25}}\right) - 36 = 0$ ⟵ Cancel the 25's.

$36 - 36 = 0$ ⟵ A true statement. $x = \frac{-6}{5}$ is a solution.

for $x = \frac{6}{5}$:

$$25x^2 - 36 = 0$$

$25\left(\frac{6}{5}\right)\left(\frac{6}{5}\right) - 36 = 0$ ⟵ Substitute $\frac{6}{5}$ for x.

$\cancel{25}\left(\frac{36}{\cancel{25}}\right) - 36 = 0$ ⟵ Cancel the 25's.

$36 - 36 = 0$ ⟵ A true statement. $x = \frac{6}{5}$ is a solution.

The solution set is $\{-\frac{6}{5}, \frac{6}{5}\}$.

Find the solution sets for the following.

1. $25a^2 - 16 = 0$

2. $c^2 - 36 = 0$

3. $9x^2 - 64 = 0$

4. $100y^2 - 49 = 0$

5. $4b^2 - 81 = 0$

6. $d^2 - 25 = 0$

7. $9x^2 - 1 = 0$

8. $16a^2 - 9 = 0$

9. $36y^2 - 1 = 0$

10. $36y^2 - 25 = 0$

11. $d^2 - 16 = 0$

12. $64b^2 - 9 = 0$

13. $81a^2 - 4 = 0$

14. $64y^2 - 25 = 0$

15. $4c^2 - 49 = 0$

16. $x^2 - 81 = 0$

17. $49b^2 - 9 = 0$

18. $a^2 - 64 = 0$

19. $9x^2 - 1 = 0$

20. $4y^2 - 9 = 0$

21. $t^2 - 100 = 0$

22. $16k^2 - 81 = 0$

23. $81a^2 - 4 = 0$

24. $36b^2 - 16 = 0$

SOLVING PERFECT SQUARES

When the square root of a constant, variable, or polynomial results in a constant, variable, or polynomial without irrational numbers, the expression is a **perfect square**. Some examples are 49, x^2, and $(x-2)^2$.

EXAMPLE 1:   Solve the perfect square for x. $(x-5)^2 = 0$

Step 1:   Take the square root of both sides.
$\sqrt{(x-5)^2} = \sqrt{0}$
$(x-5) = 0$

Step 2:   Solve the equation.
$(x-5) = 0$
$x-5+5 = 0+5$
$x = 5$

EXAMPLE 2:   Solve the perfect square for x. $(x-5)^2 = 64$

Step 1:   Take the square root of both sides.
$\sqrt{(x-5)^2} = \sqrt{64}$
$(x-5) = \pm 8$
$(x-5) = 8$ and $(x-5) = -8$

Step 2:   Solve the two equations.
$(x-5) = 8$ and $(x-5) = -8$
$x-5+5 = 8+5$ and $x-5+5 = -8+5$
$x = 13$ **and** $x = -3$

Solve the perfect square for x.

1. $(x-5)^2 = 0$

2. $(x+1)^2 = 0$

3. $(x+11)^2 = 0$

4. $(x-4)^2 = 0$

5. $(x-1)^2 = 0$

6. $(x+8)^2 = 0$

7. $(x+3)^2 = 4$

8. $(x-5)^2 = 16$

9. $(x-10)^2 = 100$

10. $(x+9)^2 = 9$

11. $(x-4.5)^2 = 25$

12. $(x+7)^2 = 36$

13. $(x+2)^2 = 49$

14. $(x-1)^2 = 4$

15. $(x+8.9)^2 = 49$

16. $(x-6)^2 = 81$

17. $(x-12)^2 = 121$

18. $(x+2.5)^2 = 64$

COMPLETING THE SQUARE

"Completing the square" is another way of factoring a quadratic equation. To complete the square, the equation must be converted into a perfect square.

EXAMPLE 1: Solve $x^2 - 10x + 9 = 0$ by completing the square.

Completing the square:

Step 1: The first step is to get the constant on the other side of the equation. Subtract 9 from both sides:

$$x^2 - 10x + 9 - 9 = 0 - 9$$
$$x^2 - 10x = -9$$

Step 2: Determine the coefficient of the x. The coefficient in this example is 10. Divide the coefficient by 2 and square the result.

$$(10 \div 2)^2 = 5^2 = 25$$

Step 3: Add the resulting value, 25, to both sides:

$$x^2 - 10x + 25 = -9 + 25$$
$$x^2 - 10x + 25 = 16$$

Step 4: Now factor the $x^2 - 10x + 25$ into a perfect square:

$$(x - 5)^2 = 16$$

Solving the perfect square:

Step 5: Take the square root of both sides.

$$\sqrt{(x-5)^2} = \sqrt{16}$$
$$(x - 5) = \pm 4$$
$$(x - 5) = 4 \quad \text{and} \quad (x - 5) = -4$$

Step 6: Solve the two equations.

$$(x - 5) = 4 \qquad \text{and} \qquad (x - 5) = -4$$
$$x - 5 + 5 = 4 + 5 \quad \text{and} \quad x - 5 + 5 = -4 + 5$$
$$\mathbf{x = 9} \qquad\qquad \text{and} \qquad \mathbf{x = 1}$$

Solve for x by completing the square.

1. $x^2 + 2x - 3 = 0$

2. $x^2 - 8x + 7 = 0$

3. $x^2 + 6x - 7 = 0$

4. $x^2 - 16x - 36 = 0$

5. $x^2 - 14x + 49 = 0$

6. $x^2 - 4x = 0$

7. $x^2 + 12x + 27 = 0$

8. $x^2 + 2x - 24 = 0$

9. $x^2 + 12x - 85 = 0$

10. $x^2 - 8x + 15 = 0$

11. $x^2 - 16x + 60 = 0$

12. $x^2 - 8x - 48 = 0$

13. $x^2 + 24x + 44 = 0$

14. $x^2 + 6x + 5 = 0$

15. $x^2 - 11x + 5.25 = 0$

USING THE QUADRATIC FORMULA

On the Ohio Graduation Test in Mathematics, you may be asked to use the quadratic formula to solve a **quadratic equations**. The equation should be in the form $ax^2 + bx + c = 0$.

EXAMPLE: Using the quadratic formula, find x in the following equation: $x^2 - 8x = -7$.

Step 1: Make sure the equation is set equal to 0.

$$\begin{array}{r} x^2 - 8x = -7 \\ +7 = +7 \\ \hline x^2 - 8x + 7 = 0 \end{array}$$

The quadratic formula is given by: $\quad \dfrac{-b \pm \sqrt{b^2 - 4ac}}{2a}$

Step 2: In the formula, a is the number x^2 is multiplied by, b is the number x is multiplied by, and c is the last term of the equation. For the equation in the example, $x^2 - 8x + 7$, $a = 1$, $b = -8$, and $c = 7$. When we look at the formula, we notice a $\pm$ sign. This means there will be two solutions to the equation, one when we use the plus sign and one when we use the minus sign. Substituting the numbers from the problem into the formula, we have:

$$\frac{8 + \sqrt{8^2 - (4)(1)(7)}}{2(1)} = 7 \text{ and } \frac{8 - \sqrt{8^2 - (4)(1)(7)}}{2(1)} = 1 \quad \text{The solutions are } (7,1).$$

For each of the following equations, use the quadratic formula to find two solutions.

1. $x^2 + x - 6 = 0$

2. $y^2 - 2y - 8 = 0$

3. $a^2 + 2a - 15 = 0$

4. $y^2 - 5y + 4 = 0$

5. $b^2 - 9b + 14 = 0$

6. $x^2 - 3x - 4 = 0$

7. $y^2 + y - 20 = 0$

8. $d^2 + 6d + 8 = 0$

9. $y^2 - 7y + 12 = 0$

10. $x^2 - 3x - 28 = 0$

11. $a^2 - 5a + 6 = 0$

12. $b^2 + 3b - 10 = 0$

13. $a^2 + 7a - 8 = 0$

14. $c^2 + 3c + 2 = 0$

15. $x^2 - x - 42 = 0$

16. $a^2 + a - 6 = 0$

17. $b^2 + 7b + 12 = 0$

18. $y^2 + 2y - 15 = 0$

19. $a^2 - 3a - 10 = 0$

20. $d^2 + 10d + 16 = 0$

21. $x^2 - 4x - 12 = 0$

CHAPTER 14 REVIEW

Factor the following polynomials completely.

1. $8x - 18$

2. $16b^3 + 8b$

3. $15a^3 + 40$

4. $20y^6 - 12y^4$

5. $5a - 15a^2$

6. $4y^2 - 36$

7. $2b^2 - 2b - 12$

8. $3a^3 + 4a^2 + 9a + 12$

9. $27y^2 + 42y - 5$

10. $12b^2 + 25b - 7$

11. $6y^2 + 30y + 36$

12. $2b^2 + 6b - 20$

13. $9w^2 - 54w - 63$

14. $12x^2 + 27x$

15. $2a^4 - 32$

16. $21c^2 + 41c + 10$

17. $2b^3 - 24 + 16b - 3b^2$

18. $-2a - 25a^2 + 10a^3 + 5$

Factor and solve each of the following quadratic equations.

1. $16b^2 - 25 = 0$

2. $a^2 - a - 30 = 0$

3. $x^2 - x = 6$

4. $100x^2 - 49 = 0$

5. $81y^2 = 9$

6. $y^2 = 21 - 4y$

7. $y^2 - 7y + 8 = 16$

8. $6x^2 + x - 2 = 0$

9. $3y^2 + y - 2 = 0$

10. $b^2 + 2b - 8 = 0$

11. $4x^2 + 19x - 5 = 0$

12. $8x^2 = 6x + 2$

13. $2y^2 - 6y - 20 = 0$

14. $-6x^2 + 7x - 2 = 0$

15. $y^2 + 3y - 18 = 0$

Using the quadratic formula, find both solutions for the variable.

16. $x^2 + 10x - 11 = 0$

17. $y^2 - 14y + 40 = 0$

18. $b^2 + 9b + 18 = 0$

19. $y^2 - 12y - 13 = 0$

20. $a^2 - 8a - 48 = 0$

21. $x^2 + 2x - 63 = 0$

Chapter 15: Systems of Equations and Systems of Inequalities

SYSTEMS OF EQUATIONS

Two linear equations considered at the same time are called a **system** of linear equations. The graph of a linear equation is a straight line. The graphs of two linear equations can show that the lines are **parallel**, **intersecting**, or **collinear**. Two lines that are **parallel** will never intersect and have no ordered pairs in common. If two lines are **intersecting**, they have one point in common, and in this chapter, you will learn to find the ordered pair for that one point. If the graph of two linear equations is the same line, the lines are said to be **collinear**.

If you are given a system of two linear equations, and you put both equations in slope-intercept form, you can immediately tell if the graph of the lines will be **parallel**, **intersecting**, or **collinear**.

If two linear equations have the same slope and the same y-intercept, then they are both equations for the same line. They are called **collinear** or **coinciding** lines. A line is made up of an infinite number of points extending infinitely far in two directions. Therefore, collinear lines have an infinite number of points in common.

EXAMPLE: $2x + 3y = -3$ Or in slope intercept form $y = -\frac{2}{3}x - 1$
the equations become :

$4x + 6y = -6$ $y = -\frac{2}{3}x - 1$

We notice that both slopes are equal to $-\frac{2}{3}$
If two linear equations have the same slope but different y-intercepts, they are **parallel** lines. Parallel lines never touch each other, so they have no points in common.

If two linear equations have different slopes, then they are intersecting lines and share exactly one point in common.

The chart below summarizes what we know about the graphs of two equations in slope-intercept form.

y-Intercepts	Slopes	Graphs	Number of Solutions
same	same	collinear	infinite
different	same	distinct parallel lines	none (they never touch)
same or different	different	intersecting lines	exactly one

For the pairs of equations below, put each equation in slope-intercept form, and tell whether the graphs of the lines will be collinear, parallel, or intersecting.

1. $x - y = -1$ _____
   $-x + y = 1$

2. $x - 2y = 4$ _____
   $-x + 2y = 6$

3. $y - 2 = x$ _____
   $x + 2 = y$

4. $x = y - 1$ _____
   $-x = y - 1$

5. $2x + 5y = 10$ _____
   $4x + 10y = 20$

6. $x + y = 3$ _____
   $x - y = 1$

7. $2y = 4x - 6$ _____
   $-6x + y = 3$

8. $x + y = 5$ _____
   $2x + 2y = 10$

9. $2x = 3y - 6$ _____
   $4x = 6y - 6$

10. $2x - 2y = 2$ _____
    $3y = -x + 5$

11. $x = -y$ _____
    $x = 4 - y$

12. $2x = y$ _____
    $x + y = 3$

13. $x = y + 1$ _____
    $y = x + 1$

14. $x - 2y = 4$ _____
    $-2x + 4y = -8$

15. $2x + 3y = 4$ _____
    $-2x + 3y = 4$

16. $2x - 4y = 1$ _____
    $-6x + 12y = 3$

17. $-3x + 4y = 1$ _____
    $6x + 8y = 2$

18. $x + y = 2$ _____
    $5x + 5y = 10$

19. $x + y = 4$ _____
    $x - y = 4$

20. $y = -x + 3$ _____
    $x - y = 1$

192

FINDING COMMON SOLUTIONS FOR INTERSECTING LINES

When two lines intersect, they share exactly one point in common.

EXAMPLE: $3x + 4y = 20$ and $4x + 2y = 12$

Put each equation in slope-intercept form.

$$
\begin{array}{ll}
3x + 4y = 20 & 2y - 4x = 12 \\
4y = -3x + 20 & 2y = 4x + 12 \\
y = -\frac{3}{4}x + 5 & y = 2x + 6
\end{array}
$$

slope-intercept form

Straight lines with different slopes are **intersecting lines**. Look at the graph of the lines on the same Cartesian plane.

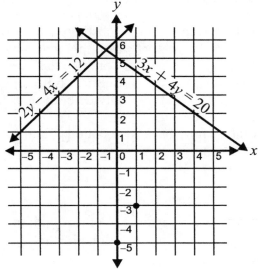

You can see from looking at the graph that the intersecting lines share one point in common. However, it is hard to tell from looking at the graph what the coordinates are for the point of intersection. To find the exact point of intersection, you can use the **substitution method** to solve the system of equations algebraically.

SOLVING SYSTEMS OF EQUATIONS BY SUBSTITUTION

You can solve systems of equations algebraically by using the substitution method.

EXAMPLE: Find the point of intersection of the following two equations:

Equation 1: $x - y = 3$
Equation 2: $2x + y = 9$

Step 1: Solve one of the equations for x or y. Let's choose to solve equation 1 for x.

Equation 1: $x - y = 3$

$$\underline{+ y \quad + y}$$ Add y to both sides of the equation.

$x + 0 = y + 3$
$x = y + 3$

Step 2: Substitute the value of x from equation 1 in place of x in equation 2.

Equation 2: $2x + y = 9$ and $x = y + 3$
$2(y + 3) + y = 9$ Substitute $y + 3$ in for x.
$2y + 6 + y = 9$ Multiply $y + 3$ by 2.
$3y + 6 = 9$ Combine the y's.
$3y = 3$ Subtract 6 from both sides of the equation.
$y = 1$ Divide both sides by 3.

Step 3: Substitute the solution for y back in equation 1, and solve for x.

Equation 1: $x - y = 3$
$x - 1 = 3$
$x = 4$

Step 4: The solution set is (4, 1). Substitute in one or both of the equations to check.

Equation 1: $x - y = 3$ Equation 2: $2x + y = 9$
$\quad\quad\quad\quad\quad 4 - 1 = 3$ $2(4) + 1 = 9$
$\quad\quad\quad\quad\quad\quad\ 3 = 3$ $8 + 1 = 9$
$\quad\quad\quad\quad\quad\quad\quad\quad\quad\quad\quad\quad\quad\quad\quad\quad\quad\quad\quad\quad\quad\quad\quad\ 9 = 9$

The point (4, 1) is common to both equations. This is the **point of intersection**.

For each of the following pairs of equations, find the point of intersection, the common solution, using the substitution method.

1. $x + 2y = 8$
   $2x - 3y = 2$

2. $x - y = -5$
   $x + y = 1$

3. $x - y = 4$
   $x + y = 2$

4. $x - y = -1$
   $x + y = 9$

5. $-x + y = 2$
   $x + y = 8$

6. $x + 4y = 10$
   $x + 5y = 12$

7. $2x + 3y = 2$
   $4x - 9y = -1$

8. $x + 3y = 5$
   $x - y = 1$

9. $-x = y - 1$
   $x = y - 1$

10. $x - 2y = 2$
    $2y + x = -2$

11. $5x + 2y = 1$
    $2x + 4y = 10$

12. $3x - y = 2$
    $5x + y = 6$

13. $2x + 3y = 3$
    $4x + 5y = 5$

14. $x - y = 1$
    $-x - y = 1$

15. $x = y + 3$
    $y = 3 - x$

SOLVING SYSTEMS OF EQUATIONS BY ADDING OR SUBTRACTING WITH MULTIPLICATION

You can solve systems of equations algebraically by adding or subtracting an equation from another equation or system of equations.

EXAMPLE 1: Find the point of intersection of the following two equations:
Equation 1: $x + y = 10$
Equation 2: $-x + 4y = 5$

Step 1: Eliminate one of the variables by adding the two equations together. Since the x has the same coefficient in each equation, but opposite signs, it will cancel nicely by adding.

$$\begin{array}{rl} x + y = 10 & \\ + (-x + 4y = 5) & \text{Add each like term together.} \\ \hline 0 + 5y = 15 & \text{Simplify.} \\ 5y = 15 & \text{Divide both sides by 5.} \\ y = 3 & \end{array}$$

Step 2: Substitute the solution for y back into an equation, and solve for x.
Equation 1: $x + y = 10$ Substitute 3 for y.
$x + 3 = 10$ Subtract 3 from both sides.
$x = 7$

Step 3: The solution set is (7, 3). Substitute in both of the equations to check.

Equation 1: $x + y = 10$ Equation 2: $-x + 4y = 5$
$7 + 3 = 10$ $-(7) + 4(3) = 5$
$10 = 10$ $-7 + 12 = 5$
$5 = 5$

The point (7, 3) is the point of intersection.

EXAMPLE 2: Find the point of intersection of the following two equations:
Equation 1: $3x - 2y = -1$
Equation 2: $-4y = -x - 7$

Step 1: Put the variables on the same side of each equation. Take equation 2 out of y-intercept form.

$$\begin{array}{rl} -4y = -x - 7 & \text{Add } x \text{ to both sides.} \\ x - 4y = -x + x - 7 & \text{Simplify.} \\ x - 4y = -7 & \end{array}$$

Step 2: Add the two equations together to cancel one variable. Since each variable has the same sign and different coefficients, we have to multiply one equation by a negative number so one of the variables will cancel. Equation 1's y variable has a coefficient of 2, and if multiplied by -2, the y will have the same variable as the y in equation 2, but a different sign. This will cancel nicely when added.

$$\begin{array}{rl} -2(3x - 2y = -1) & \text{Multiply by } -2. \\ -6x + 4y = 2 & \end{array}$$

Step 3:   Add the two equations.
$$-6x + 4y = 2$$
$$\underline{+\quad (x - 4y = -7)}\qquad \text{Add equation 2 to equation 1.}$$
$$-5x + 0 = -5 \qquad\qquad \text{Simplify.}$$
$$-5x = -5 \qquad\qquad\quad \text{Divide both sides by } -5.$$
$$x = 1$$

Step 4:   Substitute the solution for x back into an equation and solve for y.
Equation 1:	$3x - 2y = -1$	Substitute 1 for x.
	$3(1) - 2y = -1$	Simplify.
	$3 - 2y = -1$	Subtract 3 from both sides.
	$3 - 3 - 2y = -1 - 3$	Simplify.
	$-2y = -4$	Divide both sides by -2.
	$y = 2$	

Step 5:   The solution set is (1, 2). Substitute in both equations to check.

Equation 1:	$3x - 2y = -1$	Equation 2:	$-4y = -x - 7$
	$3(1) - 2(2) = -1$		$-4(2) = -1 - 7$
	$3 - 4 = -1$		$-8 = -8$
	$-1 = -1$		

The point (1, 2) is the point of intersection.

For each of the following pairs of equations, find the point of intersection by adding the 2 equations together. Remember you might need to change the coefficients and/or signs of the variables before adding.

1. $x + 2y = 8$
    $-x - 3y = 2$

2. $x - y = 5$
    $2x + y = 1$

3. $x - y = -1$
    $x + y = 9$

4. $3x - y = -1$
    $x + y = 13$

5. $-x + 4y = 2$
    $x + y = 8$

6. $x + 4y = 10$
    $x + 7y = 16$

7. $2x - y = 2$
    $4x - 9y = -3$

8. $x + 3y = 13$
    $5x - y = 1$

9. $-x = y - 1$
    $x = y - 1$

10. $x - y = 2$
     $2y + x = 5$

11. $5x + 2y = 1$
     $4x + 8y = 20$

12. $3x - 2y = 14$
     $x - y = 6$

13. $2x + 3y = 3$
     $3x + 5y = 5$

14. $x - 4y = 6$
     $-x - y = -1$

15. $x = 2y + 3$
     $y = 3 - x$

GRAPHING SYSTEMS OF INEQUALITIES

Systems of inequalities are best solved graphically. Look at the following example.

EXAMPLE: Sketch the solution set of the following system of inequalities:
$$y > -2x - 1 \text{ and } y \leq 3x$$

Step 1: Graph both inequalities on a Cartesian plane.

Step 2: Shade the portion of the graph that represents the solution set to each inequality.

Step 3: Any shaded region that overlaps is the solution set of both inequalities.

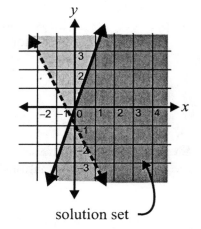

solution set

Graph the following systems of inequalities on your own graph paper. Shade and identify the solution set for both inequalities.

1. $2x + 2y \geq -4$
   $3y < 2x + 6$

2. $7x + 7y \leq 21$
   $8x < 6y - 24$

3. $9x + 12y < 36$
   $34x - 17y > 34$

4. $-11x - 22y \geq 44$
   $-4x + 2y \leq 8$

5. $24x < 72 + 36y$
   $11x + 22y \leq -33$

6. $15x - 60 < 30y$
   $20x + 10y < 40$

7. $-12x + 24y > -24$
   $10x < -5y + 15$

8. $y \geq 2x + 2$
   $y < -x - 3$

9. $3x + 4y \geq 12$
   $y > -3x + 2$

10. $-3x \leq 6 + 2y$
    $y \geq -x - 2$

11. $2x - 2y \leq 4$
    $3x + 3y \leq -9$

12. $-x \geq -2y - 2$
    $-2x - 2y > 4$

198

CHAPTER 15 REVIEW

For each pair of equations below, tell whether the graphs of the lines will be collinear, parallel, or intersecting.

1. $y = 4x + 1$
   $y = 4x - 3$

2. $y - 4 = x$
   $2x + 8 = 2y$

3. $x + y = 5$
   $x - y = -1$

4. $2y - 3x = 6$
   $4y = 6x + 8$

5. $5y = 3x - 7$
   $4x - 3y = -7$

6. $2x - 2y = 2$
   $y - x = -1$

Find the common solution for each of the following pairs of equations, using the substitution method.

7. $x - y = 2$
   $x + 4y = -3$

8. $x + y = 1$
   $x + 3y = 1$

9. $-4y = -2x + 4$
   $-x = -2y - 2$

10. $2x + 8y = 20$
    $5y = 12 - x$

11. $x = y - 3$
    $-x = y + 3$

12. $-2x + y = -3$
    $x - y = 9$

Graph the following systems of inequalities on your own graph paper. Identify the solution set to both inequalities.

13. $x + 2y \geq 2$
    $2x - y \leq 4$

14. $20x + 10y \leq 40$
    $3x + 2y \geq 6$

15. $6x + 8y \leq -24$
    $-4x + 8y \geq 16$

16. $14x - 7y \geq -28$
    $3x + 4y \leq -12$

17. $2y \geq 6x + 6$
    $2x - 4y \geq -4$

18. $9x - 6y \geq 18$
    $3y \geq 6x - 12$

Find the point of intersection for each pair of equations by adding and/or subtracting the two equations.

19. $2x + y = 4$
    $3x - y = 6$

20. $x + 2y = 3$
    $x + 5y = 0$

21. $x + y = 1$
    $y = x + 7$

22. $2x + 4y = 5$
    $3x + 8y = 9$

23. $2x - 2y = 7$
    $3x - 5y = \frac{5}{2}$

24. $x - 3y = -2$
    $y = -\frac{1}{3}x + 4$

Chapter 16
Statistics

Statistics is a branch of mathematics. Using statistics, mathematicians organize data (numbers) into forms that are easily understood.

RANGE

In **statistics,** the difference between the largest number and the smallest number in a list is called the **range.**

EXAMPLE: Find the range of the following list of numbers: 16, 73, 26, 15, and 35.

The largest number is 73, and the smallest number is 15.   73 − 15 = 58
The range is 58.

Find the range for each list of numbers below.

1.	2.	3.	4.	5.	6.	7.
21	6	89	41	23	2	77
51	7	22	3	20	38	94
48	31	65	56	64	29	27
42	55	36	41	38	33	46
12	8	20	19	21	59	63
___	___	___	___	___	___	___

8.	9.	10.	11.	12.	13.	14.
51	65	84	84	21	45	62
62	54	59	65	78	57	39
32	56	48	32	6	57	96
16	5	21	50	97	14	45
59	63	80	71	45	61	14
___	___	___	___	___	___	___

15.   2, 15, 3, 25, and 17   range _____

16.   15, 48, 52, 41, and 8   range _____

17.   54, 74, 2, 86, and 75   range _____

18.   15, 61, 11, 22, and 65   range _____

19.   33, 18, 65, 12, and 74   range _____

20.   47, 12, 33, 25, and 19   range _____

21.   56, 10, 33, 7, 16, and 5   range _____

22.   46, 25, 78, 49, and 6   range _____

23.   45, 75, 63, and 21   range _____

24.   97, 23, 56, 12, and 66   range _____

25.   87, 44, 63, and 12   range _____

26.   84, 55, 66, 38, and 31   range _____

27.   35, 44, 81, 99, and 78   range _____

28.   95, 54, 62, 14, 8, and 3   range _____

MEAN

In statistics, the **mean** is the same as the **average**. To find the **mean** of a list of numbers, first, add together all the numbers in the list, and then divide by the number of items in the list.

EXAMPLE: Find the mean of 38, 72, 110, 548.

Step 1: First add $38 + 72 + 110 + 548 = \mathbf{768}$

Step 2: There are 4 numbers in the list, so divide the total by 4.
The mean is 192.

$$\begin{array}{r} 192 \\ 4\overline{)768} \end{array}$$

Practice finding the mean (average). Round to the nearest tenth if necessary.

1. Dinners served:

   489 561 522 450

   Mean = _____

2. Prices paid for shirts:

   $4.89 $9.97 $5.90 $8.64

   Mean = _____

3. Piglets born:

   23 19 15 21 22

   Mean = _____

4. Student absences:

   6 5 13 8 9 12 7

   Mean = _____

5. Paychecks received:

   $89.56 $99.99 $56.54

   Mean = _____

6. Choir attendance:

   56 45 97 66 70

   Mean = _____

7. Long distance calls:

   33 14 24 21 19

   Mean = _____

8. Train boxcars:

   56 55 48 61 51

   Mean = _____

9. Cookies eaten:

   5 6 8 9 2 4 3

   Mean = _____

Find the mean (average) of the following word problems.

10. Val's science grades were 95, 87, 65, 94, 78, and 97. What was her average? _____

11. Ann runs a business from her home. The number of orders for the last 7 business days were 17, 24, 13, 8, 11, 15, and 9. What was the average number of orders per day? _____

12. Melissa tracked the number of phone calls she had per day: 8, 2, 5, 4, 7, 3, 6, 1. What was the average number of calls she received? _____

13. The Cheese Shop tracked the number of lunches they served this week: 42, 55, 36, 41, 38, 33, and 46. What was the average number of lunches served? _____

14. Leah drove 364 miles in 7 hours. What was her average miles per hour? _____

15. Tim saved $680 in 8 months. How much did his savings average each month? _____

16. Ken made 117 passes in 13 games. How many passes did he average per game? _____

FINDING DATA MISSING FROM THE MEAN

EXAMPLE: Mara knew she had an 88 average in her biology class, but she lost one of her papers. The three papers she could find had scores of 98%, 84%, and 90%. What was the score on her fourth paper?

Step 1: Figure the total score on four papers with an 88% average. $.88 \times 4 = 3.52$

Step 2: Add together the scores from the three papers you have. $.98 + .84 + .90 = 2.72$

Step 3: Subtract the scores you know from the total score. $3.52 - 2.72 = .80$ She had 80% on her fourth paper.

Find the data missing from the following problems.

1. Gabriel earned 87% on his first geography test. He wants to keep a 92% average. What does he need to get on his next test to bring his average up?

2. Rian earned $68.00 on Monday. How much money must he earn on Tuesday to have an average of $80 earned for the two days?

3. Haley, Chuck, Dana, and Chris entered a contest to see who could bake the most chocolate chip cookies in an hour. They baked an average of 75 cookies. Haley baked 55, Chuck baked 70, and Dana baked 90. How many did Chris bake?

4. Four wrestlers made a pact to lose some weight before the competition. They lost an average of 7 pounds each, over the course of 3 weeks. Carlos lost 6 pounds, Steve lost 5 pounds, and Greg lost 9 pounds. How many pounds did Wes lose?

5. Three boxes are ready for shipment. The boxes average 26 pounds each. The first box weighs 30 pounds; the second weighs 25 pounds. How much does the third box weigh?

6. The five jockeys running in the next race average 92 pounds each. Nicole weighs 89 pounds. Jon weighs 95 pounds. Jenny and Kasey weigh 90 pounds each. How much does Jordan weigh?

7. Jessica made three loaves of bread that weighed a total of 45 ounces. What was the average weight of each loaf?

8. Celeste made scented candles to give away to friends. She had 2 pounds of candle wax which she melted, scented, and poured into 8 molds. What was the average weight of each candle?

9. Each basketball player has to average a minimum of 5 points a game for the next three games to stay on the team. Ben is feeling the pressure. He scored 3 points in the first game and 2 points in the second game. How many points does he need to score in the third game to stay on the team?

MEDIAN

In a list of numbers ordered from lowest to highest, the **median** is the middle number. To find the **median,** first arrange the numbers in numerical order. If there is an odd number of items in the list, the **median** is the middle number. If there is an even number of items in the list, the **median** is the **average of the two middle numbers.**

EXAMPLE 1: Find the median of 42, 35, 45, 37, and 41.

Step 1: Arrange the numbers in numerical order: 35 37 ⑷1 42 45.

Step 2: Find the middle number. **The median is 41.**

EXAMPLE 2: Find the median of 14, 53, 42, 6, 14, and 46.

Step 1: Arrange the numbers in numerical order: 6 14 ⟨14 42⟩ 46 53.

Step 2: Find the average of the 2 middle numbers.
$(14 + 42) \div 2 = 28$. **The median is 28.**

Circle the median in each list of numbers.

1. 35, 55, 40, 30, and 45
4. 15, 16, 19, 25, and 20
7. 401, 758, and 254

2. 7, 2, 3, 6, 5, 1, and 8
5. 75, 98, 87, 65, 82, 88, and 100
8. 41, 23, 14, 21, and 19

3. 65, 42, 60, 46, and 90
6. 33, 42, 50, 22, and 19
9. 5, 8, 3, 10, 13, 1, and 8

10.	11.	12.	13.	14.	15.	16.
19	9	45	52	20	8	15
14	3	32	54	21	17	40
12	10	66	19	25	13	42
15	17	55	63	18	14	32
18	6	61	20	16	22	28

Find the median in each list of numbers.

17. 10, 8, 21, 14, 9, and 12   _____   20. 48, 13, 54, 82, 90, and 7   _____

18. 43, 36, 20, and 40   _____   21. 23, 21, 36, and 27   _____

19. 5, 24, 9, 18, 12, and 3   _____   22. 9, 4, 3, 1, 6, 2, 10, and 12   _____

23.	24.	25.	26.	27.	28.	29.
2	11	13	75	48	22	17
10	22	15	62	45	19	30
6	25	9	60	52	15	31
18	28	35	52	30	43	18
20	10	29	80	35	34	14
23	23	33	50	58	28	25

_____   _____   _____   _____   _____   _____   _____

MODE

In statistics, the **mode** is the number that occurs most frequently in a list of numbers.

EXAMPLE: Exam grades for a Math class were as follows:
70 88 92 85 99 85 70 85 99 100 88 70 99 88 88 99 88 92 85 88.

Step 1: Count the number of times each number occurs in the list.

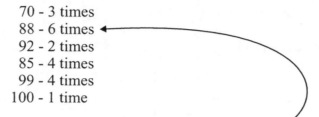

        70 - 3 times
        88 - 6 times
        92 - 2 times
        85 - 4 times
        99 - 4 times
       100 - 1 time

Step 2: Find the number that occurs most often.
          The mode is 88 because it is listed 6 times. No other number is listed as often.

Find the mode in each of the following lists of numbers.

1. 88	2. 54	3. 21	4. 56	5. 64	6. 5	7. 12
15	42	16	67	22	4	41
88	44	15	67	22	9	45
17	56	78	19	15	8	32
18	44	21	56	14	4	16
88	44	16	67	14	7	12
17	56	21	20	22	4	12

mode ___ mode ___ mode ___ mode ___ mode ___ mode ___ mode ___

8. 48, 32, 56, 32, 56, 48, 56   **mode** _____

9. 12, 16, 54, 78, 16, 25, 20   **mode** _____

10. 5, 4, 8, 3, 4, 2, 7, 8, 4, 2   **mode** _____

11. 11, 9, 7, 11, 7, 5, 7, 7, 5   **mode** _____

12. 84, 22, 79, 22, 87, 22, 22   **mode** _____

13. 95, 87, 65, 94, 78, 95   **mode** _____

14. 8, 2, 5, 4, 7, 2, 3, 6, 1   **mode** _____

15. 89, 7, 11, 89, 17, 56   **mode** _____

16. 15, 48, 52, 41, 8, 48   **mode** _____

17. 22, 45, 48, 12, 22, 41, 22   **mode** _____

18. 62, 44, 78, 62, 54, 44, 62   **mode** _____

19. 54, 22, 54, 78, 22, 78, 22   **mode** _____

20. 14, 17, 33, 21, 33, 17, 33   **mode** _____

21. 65, 51, 8, 21, 8, 65, 70, 8   **mode** _____

22. 17, 24, 13, 8, 11, 8, 15, 9   **mode** _____

23. 51, 45, 84, 51, 65, 74, 51   **mode** _____

24. 8, 74, 65, 15, 9, 10, 74   **mode** _____

25. 62, 54, 2, 7, 89, 2, 7, 54, 2   **mode** _____

APPLYING MEASURES OF CENTRAL TENDENCY

On the Ohio test, you will be asked to solve real-world problems involving Measures of Central Tendency.

EXAMPLE: Aida is shopping around for the best price on a 17" computer monitor. She travels to seven stores and finds the following prices: $199, $159, $249, $329, $199, $209, and $189. When Aida went to the eighth and final store, she found the price for the 17" monitor was $549. Which of the measures of central tendency, mean, median, or mode, will change the most as a result of the last price Aida found?

Step 1: **Solve for all three measures of the seven values**

Mean: $\dfrac{\$199+\$159+\$249+\$329+\$199+\$209+\$189}{7} = \$219$

Median: From least to greatest: $159, $189, $199, $199, $209, $249, $329.
The 4th value = $199
Mode: The number repeated the most is $199.

Step 2: **Find the mean, median, and Mode with the eighth value added.**

Mean: $\dfrac{\$199+\$159+\$249+\$329+\$199+\$209+\$189+\$549}{8} = \$260.25$

Median: $159, $189, $199, $199, $209, $249, $329, $549.
The avg. of 4th & 5th number = $204
Mode: The number still repeated the most is $199.

Answer: The measure which changed the most by adding the 8th value is the **mean**.

---

1. The Realty Teens Company has the selling prices for 10 houses sold during the month of July. The following prices are given in thousands of dollars:

   | 176 | 89 | 525 | 125 | 107 | 100 | 525 | 61 | 75 | 114 |

   Find the mean, median, and mode of the selling prices. Which measure is most representative for the selling price of such homes? Explain.

2. A soap manufacturing company wants to know if the weight of its product is on target, meaning 4.75 oz. With that purpose in mind, a quality control technician selects 30 bars of soap from production, 5 from each shift, and finds the following weights in oz.

   1st shift: 4.76, 4.75, 4.77, 4.77, 4.74
   2nd shift: 4.72, 4.72, 4.75, 4.76, 4.73
   3rd shift: 4.76, 4.76, 4.77, 4.76, 4.76

   a) What are the values for the measures of central tendency for the sample from each shift?
   b) Find the mean, median, and mode for the 24 hour production sample.
   c) Which is the most accurate measure of central tendency for the 24 hour production?
   d) Find the range of values for each shift. Is the range an effective tool for drawing a conclusion in this case? Why or why not?

STEM-AND-LEAF PLOTS

A **stem-and-leaf plot** is a way to organize and analyze statistical data. To make a stem-and-leaf plot, first draw a vertical line.

Final Math Averages
85 92 87 62 75 84 96 52
45 77 98 75 71 79 85 82
87 74 76 68 93 77 65 84
79 65 77 82 86 84 92 60
99 75 88 74 79 80 63 84
87 90 75 81 73 69 73 75
31 86 89 65 69 75 79 76

Stem	Leaves
3	1
4	5
5	2
6	0,2,3,5,5,5,8,9,9
7	1,3,3,3,4,4,5,5,5,5,5,5,5,6,6,7,7,7,9,9,9
8	0,1,2,2,4,4,4,4,5,5,6,6,7,7,7,8,9
9	0,2,2,3,6,8,9

On the left side of the line, list all the numbers that are in the tens place from the set of data. Next, list each number in the ones place on the right side of the line in ascending order. It is easy to see at a glance that most of the students scored in the 70's or 80's with a majority having averages in the 70's. It is also easy to see that the maximum average is 99, and the lowest average is 31. Stem-and-leaf plots are a way to organize data making it easy to read.

1. Make a stem-and-leaf plot from the data below, and then answer the questions that follow.

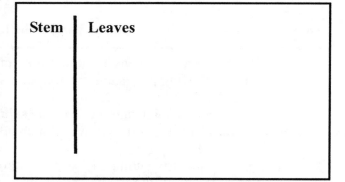

Speeds on Turner Road

CAR SPEED, mph
45 52 47 35 48 50 51 43
40 51 32 24 55 41 32 33
36 59 49 52 34 28 69 47
29 15 63 42 35 42 58 59
39 41 25 34 22 16 40 31
55 10 46 38 50 52 48 36
21 32 36 41 52 49 45 32
52 45 56 35 55 65 20 41

Stem	Leaves

2. What was the fastest speed recorded?

3. What was the slowest speed recorded?

4. Which speed was most often recorded?

5. If the speed limit is 45 miles per hour, how many were speeding?

6. If the speed limit is 45 miles per hour, how many were at least 20 mph over or under the speed limit?

MORE STEM-AND-LEAF PLOTS

Two sets of data can be displayed on the same stem-and-leaf plot.

EXAMPLE: The following is an example of a back-to-back stem-and-leaf plot.

Bryan's Math scores {60,65,72,78,85,90}
Bryan's English scores {78,88,89,89,92,95,100}

Math		English
5,0	6	
2,8	7	8
5	8	8,9,9
0	9	2,5
	10	0

2|7 means 72   8|9 means 89

Read the stem-and-leaf plot below and answer the questions that follow.

3rd grade Boys' Weights		3rd Grade Girls' Weights
8,7,5,3,2	4	0,2, 4, 7
6, 4, 1, 0	5	1,8,8,8, 9
5	6	0 6, 6, 8, 8
0	9	8

4|5 means 54   6|8 means 68

1. What is the median for the girls' weights?

2. What is the median for the boys' weights?

3. What is the mode for the girls' weights?

4. What is the weight of the lightest boy?

5. What is the weight of the heaviest boy?

6. What is the weight of the heaviest girl?

7. Create a stem-and-leaf plot for the data given below.

Automobile Speeds on I-85

60	65	80	75	92	81	63
65	67	75	78	79	77	69
62	57	64	65	68	71	69
71	73	56	69	69	70	74

Automobile Speeds on I-75

72	56	62	65	63	60	58
55	57	70	69	59	53	61
58	61	63	67	57	63	67
56	58	59	62	64	63	69

8. What is the median speed for I-75?

9. What is the median speed for I-85?

10. What is the mode speed for I-75?

11. What is the mode speed for I-85?

12. What was the fastest speed on either interstate?

QUARTILES AND EXTREMES

In statistics, large sets of data are separated into four equal parts. These parts are called **quartiles**. The **median** separates the data into two halves. Then, the median of the upper half is the **upper quartile**, and the median of the lower half is the **lower quartile**.

The **extremes** are the highest and lowest values in a set of data. The lowest value is called the **lower extreme**, and the highest value is called the **upper extreme**.

EXAMPLE 1: The following set of data shows the high temperatures (in degrees Fahrenheit) in cities across the United States on a particular autumn day. Find the median, the upper quartile, the lower quartile, the upper extreme, and the lower extreme of the data.

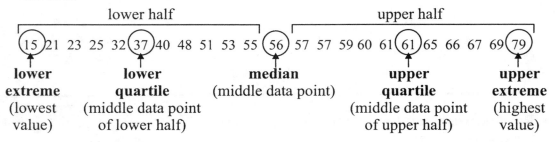

EXAMPLE 2: The following set of data shows the fastest race car qualifying speeds in miles per hour. Find the median, the upper quartile, the lower quartile, the upper extreme, and the lower extreme of the data.

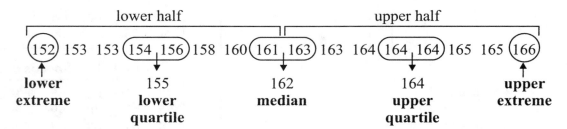

Note: When you have an even number of data points, the median is the average of the two middle points. The lower middle number is then included in the lower half of the data, and the upper middle number is included in the upper half.

Find the median, the upper quartile, the lower quartile, the upper extreme, and the lower extreme of each set of data given below.

1.   0 0 1 1 1 2 2 3 3 4 5

2.   15 16 18 20 22 22 23

3.   62 75 77 80 81 85 87 91 94

4.   74 74 76 76 77 78

5.   3 3 3 5 5 6 6 7 7 7 8 8

6.   190 191 192 192 194 195 196

7.   6 7 9 9 10 10 11 13 15

8.   21 22 24 25 27 28 32 35

BOX-AND-WHISKER PLOTS

Box-and-whisker plots are used to summarize data as well as to display data. A box-and-whisker plot summarizes data using the median, upper and lower quartiles, and the lower and upper extreme values. Consider the data below—a list of employees' ages at the Acme Lumber Company:

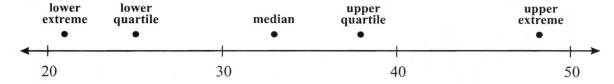

ⓐ21 22 23 24 24 24ⓑ26 27 28 29 30 32 32ⓒ33 33 33 34 35 36 37 37ⓓ38 39 40 40 41 44ⓔ

lower extreme   **lower quartile**   **median**   **upper quartile**   **upper extreme**

Step 1: Find the median, upper quartile, lower quartile, upper extreme, and lower extreme just like you did on the previous page.

Step 2: Plot the 5 data points found in step 1 above a number line as shown below.

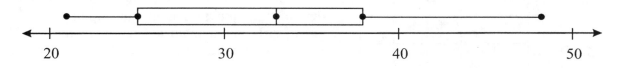

Step 3: Draw a box around the quartile values, and draw a vertical line through the median value. Draw whiskers from each quartile to the extreme value data points.

This box-and-whisker displays five types of information: lower extreme, lower quartile, median, upper quartile, and upper extreme.

Draw a box-and-whisker plot for the following sets of data.

1.
10 12 12 15 16 17 19 21 22 22 25 27 31 35 36 37 38 38 41 43 45 50 51 56 57 58 59

2.
5 5 6 7 9 9 10 11 12 15 15 16 17 18 19 19 20 22 24 26 27 27 30 31 31 35 37

SCATTER PLOTS

A **scatter plot** is a graph of ordered pairs involving two sets of data. These plots are used to detect whether two sets of data, or variables, are truly related.

In the example to the right, two variables, income and education, are being compared to see if they are related or not. Twenty people were interviewed, ages 25 and older, and the results were recorded on the chart.

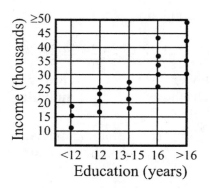

Imagine drawing a line on the scatter plot where half the points are above the line and half the points are below it. In the plot on the right, you will notice that this line slants upward and to the right. This line direction means there is a **positive** relationship between education and income. In general, for every increase in education, there is a corresponding increase in income.

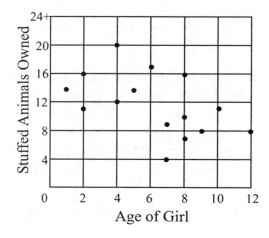

Now, examine the scatter plot on the left. In this case, 15 girls ages 2-12 were interviewed and asked, "How many stuffed animals do you currently have?" If you draw an imaginary line through the middle points, you will notice that the line slants downward and to the right. This plot demonstrates a **negative** relationship between the age of girls and their stuffed animal ownership. In general, as the girls' ages increase, the number of stuffed animals owned decreases.

Finally, look at the scatter plot shown on the right. In this plot, Rita wanted to see the relationship between the temperature in the classroom and the grades she received on tests she took at that temperature. As you look to your right, you will notice that the points are distributed all over the graph. Because this plot is not in a pattern, there is no way to draw a line through the middle of the points. This type of point pattern indicates there is **no** relationship between Rita's grades on tests and the classroom temperature.

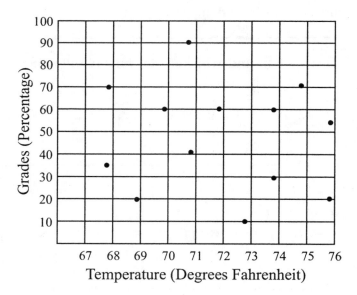

Examine each of the scatter plots below. On the line below each plot, write whether the relationship shown between the two variables is "positive", "negative", or "no relationship".

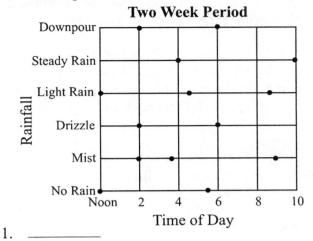

1. _____

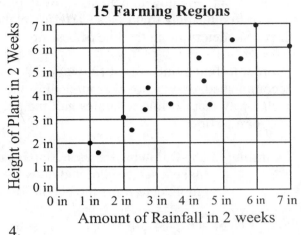

4. _____

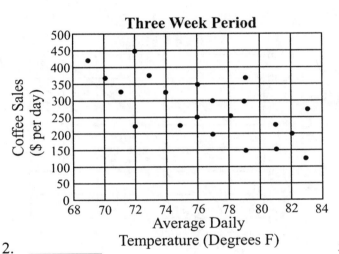

2. _____

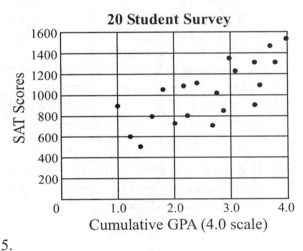

5. _____

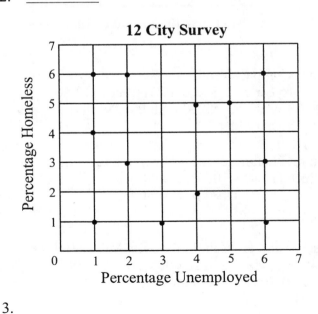

3. _____

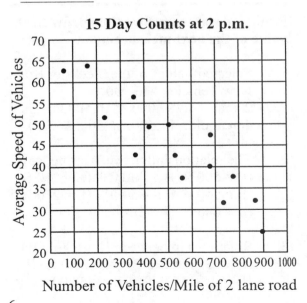

6. _____

THE LINE OF BEST FIT

At this point, you now understand how to plot points on a Cartesian plane. You also understand how to find the data trend on a Cartesian plane. These skills are necessary to accomplish the next task, determining the line of best fit.

In order to find a line of best fit, you must first draw a scatterplot of all data points. Once this is accomplished, draw an oval around all of the points plotted. Draw a line through the points in such a way that the line separates half the points from one another. You may now use this line to answer questions.

Example: The following data set contains the heights of children between 5 and 13 years old. Make a scatter plot and draw the line of best fit to represent the trend. Using the graph, determine the height for a 14 year-old child.

Age 5: 4'6", 4'4", 4' 5"   Age 8: 4'8", 4'6", 4'7"   Age 11: 5'0", 4'10"
Age 6: 4'7", 4'5", 4'6"   Age 9: 4'9", 4'7", 4'10"   Age 12: 5'1", 4'11", 5'0", 5'3"
Age 7: 4'9", 4'7", 4'6", 4'8"   Age 10: 4'9", 4'8", 4' 10"   Age 13: 5'3", 5'2", 5'0", 5'1"

In this example, the data points lay in a positive sloping direction. To determine the line of best fit, all data points were circled, then a line of best fit was drawn. Half of the points lay below, half above the line of best fit drawn bisecting the narrow length of the oval.

To find the height of a 14-year old, simply continue the line of best fit forward. In this case, the height is 62 inches.

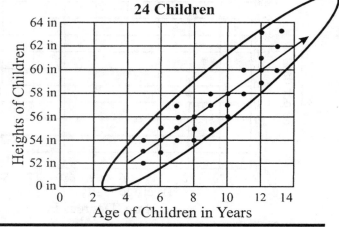

24 Children

Plot the data sets below, then draw the line of best fit. Next, use the line to estimate the value of the next measurement.

1. Selected Values of the Sleekster Brand Light Compact Vehicles:
    New Vehicle: $13,000.   1 year old: $12,000, $11,000, $12,500
    2 year old: $9,000, $10,500, $9,500   3 year old: $8,500, $8,000, $9,000
    4 year old: $7,500, $6,500, $6,000   5 year old: ?

2. The relationship between string length and kite height for the following kites:
    (L = 500 ft, H = 400 ft) (L = 250 ft, H = 150 ft) (L = 100 ft, H = 75 ft)
    (L = 500 ft, H = 350 ft) (L = 250 ft, H = 200 ft) (L = 100 ft, H = 50 ft)
    (L = 600 ft, H = ?)

3. Relationship between Household Incomes(HI) and Household Property Values (HPV):
    (HI = $30,000, HPV = $100,000) (HI = $45,000, HPV = $120,000) (HI = $60,000,
    HPV = $135,000) (HI = $50,000, HPV = 115,000) (HI = $35,000, HPV = 105,000) (HI =
    $65,000, HPV = $155,000) (HI = $90,000, HPV = ?)

HISTOGRAMS

A **histogram** is a bar graph of the data in a frequency table.

EXAMPLE: Draw a histogram for the customer sales data presented in the frequency table.

CUSTOMER SALES	
Total	**Frequency**
$0-5.00	6
$5.01-10.00	11
$10.01-15.00	12
$15.01-20.00	15
$20.01-25.00	3
$25.01-30.00	4
$30.01-35.00	4
$35.01-40.00	1

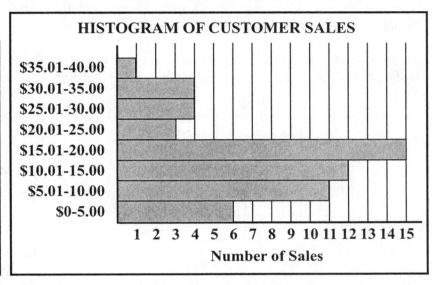

Use the frequency charts that you filled in on the previous page to draw histograms for the same data.

1.
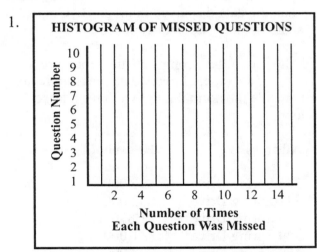

2.
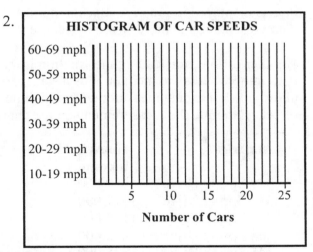

3.
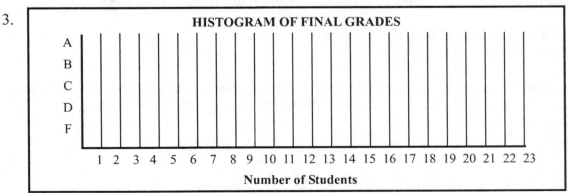

MISLEADING STATISTICS

As you read magazines and newspapers, you will see many charts and graphs which present statistical data. This data will illustrate how measurements change over time or how one measurement corresponds to another measurement. However, some charts and graphs are presented to make changes in data appear greater than they actually are. The people presenting the data create these distortions to make exaggerated claims.

There is one method to arrange the data in ways which can exaggerate statistical measurements. A statistician can create a graph in which the number line does not begin with zero.

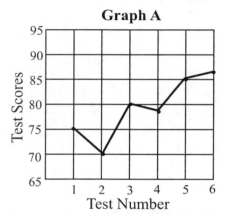

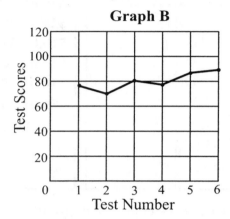

In the two graphs above, notice how each graph displays the same data. However, the way the data is displayed in graph A appears more striking than the data displayed in graph B. Graph A's data presentation is more striking because the test score numbers do not begin at zero.

Another form of misleading information is through the use of the wrong statistical measure to determine what is the median. For instance, the mean, or average, of many data measurements allows **outliers** (data measurements which lie well outside the normal range) to have a large effect. Examine the measurements in the chart below.

Address	Household Income	Address	Household Income
341 Spring Drive	$19,000	346 Spring Drive	$30,000
342 Spring Drive	$17,000	347 Spring Drive	$32,000
343 Spring Drive	$26,000	348 Spring Drive	$1,870,000
344 Spring Drive	$22,000	349 Spring Drive	$31,000
345 Spring Drive	$25,000	350 Spring Drive	$28,000

Average (Mean) Household Income: $210,000
Median Household Income: $27,000

In this example, the outlier, located at 348 Spring Drive, inflates the average household income on this street to the extent that it is over eight times the median income for the area.

Read the following charts and graphs, and then answer the questions below.

Graph A - Stasia's Weight Loss

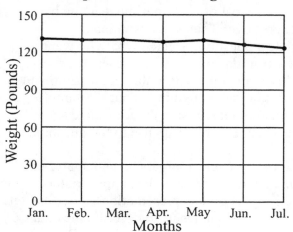

Graph B - Stasia's Weight Loss

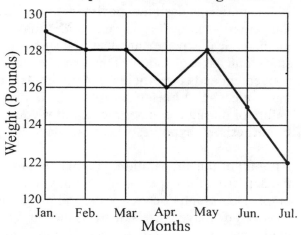

1.   Which graph above presents misleading statistical information? Why is the graph misleading?

Twenty teenagers were asked how many electronic and computer games they purchased per year. The following table shows the results.

Number of Games	0	1	2	3	4	5	58
Number of Teenagers	4	2	5	3	4	1	1

2.   Find the mean of the data.
3.   Find the median of the data.
4.   Find the mode of the data.
5.   Which measurement is most misleading?
6.   Which measurement would depict the data most accurately?
7.   Is the *mean* of a set of data affected by outliers? Justify your answer with the example above.

Examine the two bar graphs below.

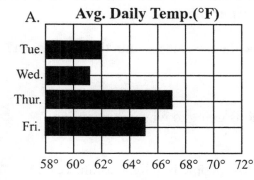

8.   Which graph is misleading? Why?

DESIGNING AN EXPERIMENT

Mathematicians design **experiments**, just like scientists. Most of the experiments done by mathematicians are for research and statistics. There are several steps in designing a mathematical experiment. The first step is to formulate a question. Decide what you want to study, and ask a question. The next step is to choose a **population**. In many cases, the most convenient and cost efficient population is the one closest to you. Within this population, you must select an **unbiased sample**, which means you cannot know anything about the sample before or during the experiment. After you have found an unbiased sample, formulate a **hypothesis**. A hypothesis is a statement that gives the best possible response to the question.

After all of this preparation, you may begin the experiment. Collect, organize, and analyze all the data from the experiment. Next, you must decide how to display the data appropriately. Line graphs, bar graphs, scatter plots, and pie graphs are examples of data presentation. After the data has been displayed, use statistics, such as a measure of central tendency, to describe the data mathematically. Last, make conclusions, and evaluate the results of the experiment. Prove or disprove your hypothesis.

EXAMPLE: Leon wants to find out why no students in his World History class are making an A. He decided to conduct an experiment. What steps should he take to make this a mathematical experiment?

Solution: The first step is to form a question, "Why is no one in Leon's World History class making an A?" The next step is to choose a population. In this case, the population is stated in the question, Leon's World History class. In order to make this an unbiased sample, Leon cannot include himself within the experiment. The next step is to form a hypothesis. An example is "No one in Leon's class is making an A because they don't study enough for the tests."
A possible way to collect information for this experiment is to take a survey of how many hours each student studies for each test. A survey should always have questions that pertain to the experiment. After the students take the next test, grades should be collected. Once the survey and the test performance data have been collected, display the data. An excellent way to display this kind of data would be in a scatter plot. This scatter plot would show if a relationship exists between hours studied and grades on the test. Once this has been done, make your conclusions from your data. Disprove or prove the hypothesis.

Answer the following questions about mathematical experiments.

1. After you have asked your question, what would be the next step within the experiment?

2. Name five different ways to display data.

3. Design an experiment based on the question, "Who is going to win the upcoming election?"

4. Design an experiment based on the hypothesis, "Most people buy light colored cars because they do not get as hot during the summer."

CHAPTER 16 REVIEW

Find the mean, median, and mode for each of the following sets of data. Fill in the table below.

❶ Miles Run by Track Team Members	
Jeff	24
Eric	20
Craig	19
Simon	20
Elijah	25
Rich	19
Marcus	20

❷ **1992 SUMMER OLYMPIC GAMES**
Gold Medals Won

Unified Team	45	Hungary	11
United States	37	South Korea	12
Germany	33	France	8
China	16	Australia	7
Cuba	14	Japan	3
Spain	13		

❸ Hardware Store Payroll June Week 2	
Erica	$280
Dane	$206
Sam	$240
Nancy	$404
Elsie	$210
Gail	$305
David	$280

Data Set Number	Mean	Median	Mode
❶			
❷			
❸			

4. Jenica bowled three games and scored an average of 116 points per game. She scored 105 on her first game and 128 on her second game. What did she score on her third game?

5. Concession stand sales for each game in the season were $320, $540, $230, $450, $280, and $580. What was the mean sales per game?

6. Cedrick D'Amitrano works Friday and Saturday delivering pizza. He delivers 8 pizzas on Friday. How many pizzas must he deliver on Saturday to average 11 pizzas per day?

7. Long cooked three Vietnamese dinners that weighed a total of 40 ounces. What was the average weight for each dinner?

8. The Swamp Foxes scored an average of 7 points per soccer game. They scored 9 points in the first game, 4 points in the second game, and 5 points in the third game. What was their score for their fourth game?

9. Shondra is 66 inches tall, and DeWayne is 72 inches. How tall is Michael if the average height of these three students is 77 inches?

Over the past 2 years, Coach Strive has kept a record of how many points his basketball team, the Bearcats, has scored in each game:

29 32 35 35 36 38 39 40 40 41 42 43 44 44 45 47 49 50 52 53 62

10. Create a stem-and-leaf plot for the data.

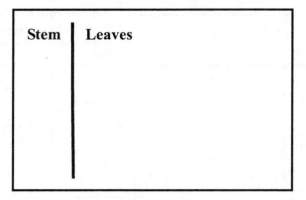

12. What is the median?

13. What is the upper quartile?

14. What is the lower quartile?

15. What is the upper extreme?

16. What is the lower extreme?

11. Create a box-and-whisker plot for the data.

The daily high temperatures (°F) of Laughlin over the month of February are given below.

65 67 69 75 76 79 80 81 85 85 85 85 86 86
87 87 88 88 89 90 90 91 91 92 93 95 97 98

17. Create a stem-and-leaf plot for the data.

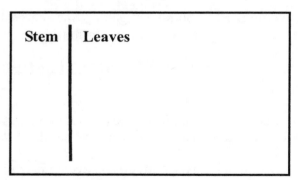

18. Create a box-and-whisker plot for the data. Label the median, the quartiles, and the extremes.

The Riveras and the Rogers families are meeting for a Fourth of July family reunion in the same park. The ages of the Rivera family members are 48, 79, 20, 2, 14, 84, 32, 61, 48, 92, 87, 54, 41, 27, 18, 21, 36, 44, 27, 66, 27, 16, 54, 48, 48, 6, and 4. The ages of the Roger's family members are 26, 84, 14, 7, 30, 50, 55, 41, 29, 33, 1, 15, 48, 16, and 20. Plot each of their ages on the stem-and-leaf plot below and answer the questions that follow.

19.

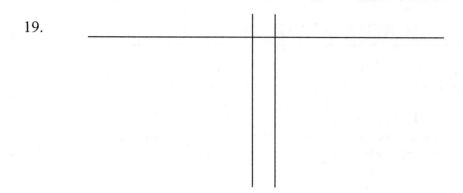

20. In the data above, which age is the mode of the data for the Rivera family?

21. Which age is the median in the Rogers family?

22. What ages are the two oldest Riveras?

23. What age are the two youngest Riveras?

24. Which family has the older median age?

On the line below each plot, write whether the relationship shown between the two variables is "positive", "negative", or "no relationship".

25.

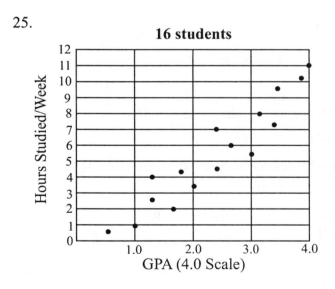

26.

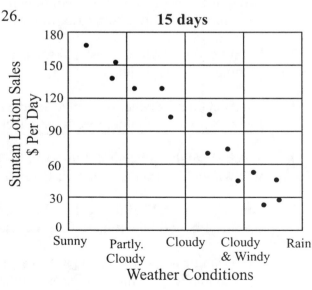

Chapter 17
Data Interpretation

READING TABLES

A **table** is a concise way to organize large quantities of information using rows and columns. **Read each table carefully, and then answer the questions that follow.**

Some employers use a tax table like the one below to figure how much Federal Income Tax should be withheld from a single person paid weekly. The number of withholding allowances claimed is also commonly referred to as the number of deductions claimed.

Federal Income Tax Withholding Table					
SINGLE Persons – WEEKLY Payroll Period					
If the wages are –		And the number of withholding allowances claimed is –			
		0	1	2	3
At least	But less than	The amount of income tax to be withheld is –			
$250	260	31	23	16	9
$260	270	32	25	17	10
$270	280	34	26	19	12
$280	290	35	28	20	13
$290	300	37	29	22	15

1. David is single, claims 2 withholding allowances, and earned $275 last week. How much Federal Income Tax was withheld? _____

2. Cecily claims 0 deductions, and she earned $297 last week. How much Federal Income Tax was withheld? _____

3. Sherri claims 3 deductions and earned $268 last week. How much Federal Income Tax was withheld from her check? _____

4. Mitch is single and claims 1 allowance. Last week, he earned $291. How much was withheld from his check for Federal Income Tax? _____

5. Ginger earned $275 this week and claims 0 deductions. How much Federal Income Tax will be withheld from her check? _____

6. Bill is single and earns $263 per week. He claims 1 withholding allowance. How much Federal Income Tax is withheld each week? _____

Study the table below about United States farming trends since 1900. Then answer the questions that follow.

CHANGES IN FARMING SINCE 1900

	1900	1930	1960	1990
Farm Population	29,875,000	30,529,000	15,699,000	4,591,000
Number of Farms	5,737,000	6,295,000	3,963,000	2,140,000
Average Size (acres)	153	157	297	461
Average Bushels per Acre	50	53	89	150
Annual Income per Farm	$1,306	$1,527	$9,737	$91,179

1. How much did the average bushels per acre increase from 1900 to 1990? _____

2. In which 30 year period did the farm population decrease the most? From _____ to _____

3. In which year were there the most people living on each farm? _____

4. By how many acres was the average farm larger in 1990 than in 1930? _____

5. How much was the increase in annual farm income from 1930 to 1990? _____

6. In which 30 year period was there the least growth in bushels per acre? From _____ to _____

7. In which year was there the largest number of farms? _____

8. How many times larger were the bushels per acre in 1990 than in 1900? _____

9. How many more acres was the average size farm in 1990 than in 1900? _____

10. There were about 5 people on each farm in 1900. To the nearest dollar, how much did they earn per person each year? _____

BAR GRAPHS

Bar graphs can be either vertical or horizontal. There may be just one bar or more than one bar for each interval. Sometimes each bar is divided into two or more parts. In this section, you will work with a variety of bar graphs. Be sure to read all titles, keys, and labels to completely understand all the data that is presented. **Answer the questions about each graph below.**

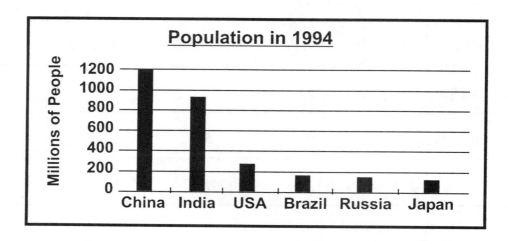

1. Which country has over 1 billion people? _____

2. How many countries have fewer than 200,000,000 people? _____

3. How many more people does India have than Japan? _____

4. If you added together the populations of the USA, Brazil, Russia, and Japan, would it come closer to the population of India or China? _____

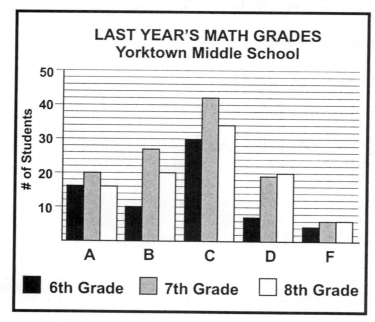

5. How many of last year's 6th graders made C's in math? _____

6. How many more math students made B's in the 7th grade than in the 8th grade? _____

7. Which letter grade is the mode of the data? _____

8. How many 8th graders took math last year? _____

9. How many students made A's in math last year? _____

222

LINE GRAPHS

The line graphs below are shown with a globe marking the lines of latitude to make the line graphs more understandable. Study the line graphs below, and then answer the questions that follow.

Number of Species of Birds
Central and North America

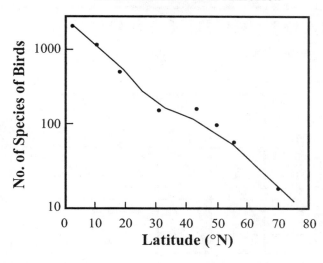

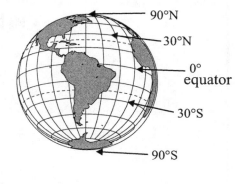

After reading the graph above, label each of the following statements as true or false.

1. There are more species of birds at the North Pole than at the equator. _____

2. There are more species of birds in Mexico than in Canada. _____

3. As the latitude increases, the number of species of birds decreases. _____

4. At 30°N there are over 100 species of birds. _____

5. The warmer the climate, the fewer kinds of birds there are. _____

These true or false statements, 6–10, refer to the graph on the left.

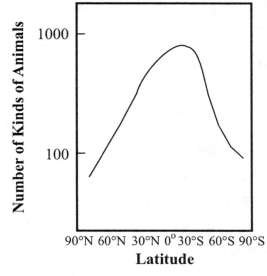

6. The further north and south you go from the equator, the greater the variety of animals there are. _____

7. The closer you get to the equator, the greater the variety of animals to be found. _____

8. There are fewer kinds of animals at 30°S than at 60°S latitude. _____

9. The number of kinds of animals increases as the latitude decreases. _____

10. The number of kinds of animals increases at the poles. _____

MULTIPLE LINE GRAPHS

Multiple line graphs are a way to present a large quantity of data in a small space. It would often take several paragraphs to explain in words the same information that one graph could.

On the graph below, there are three lines. You will need to read the **key** to understand the meaning of each.

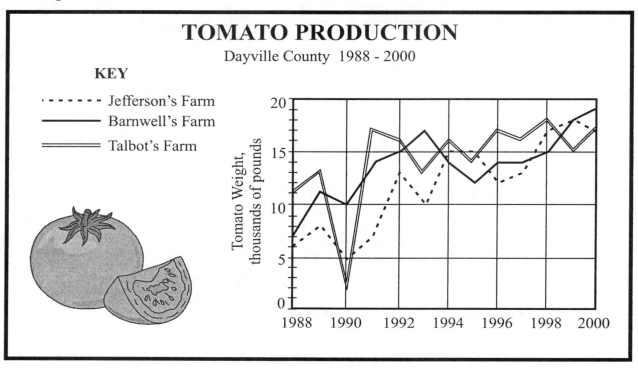

TOMATO PRODUCTION

Dayville County 1988 - 2000

KEY

· · · · · · Jefferson's Farm

——— Barnwell's Farm

═══ Talbot's Farm

Tomato Weight, thousands of pounds

Study the graph, and then answer the questions below.

1. In what year did Barnwell's Farm produce 8,000 pounds of tomatoes more than Talbot's Farm?   _____

2. In which year did Dayville County produce the most pounds of tomatoes?   _____

3. In 1993, how many more pounds of tomatoes did Barnwell's Farm produce than Talbot's Farm?   _____

4. How many pounds of tomatoes did Dayville County's three farms produce in 1992?   _____

5. In which year did Dayville County produce the fewest pounds of tomatoes?   _____

6. Which farm had the most dramatic increase in production from one year to the next?   _____

7. How many more pounds of tomatoes did Jefferson's Farm produce in 1992 than in 1988?   _____

8. Which farm produced the most pounds of tomatoes in 1995?   _____

CIRCLE GRAPHS

Circle graphs represent data expressed in percentages of a total. The parts in a circle graph should always add up to 100%. Circle graphs are sometimes called **pie graphs** or **pie charts**.

To figure the value of a percent in a circle graph, multiply the percent by the total. Use the circle graphs below to answer the questions. The first question is worked for you as an example.

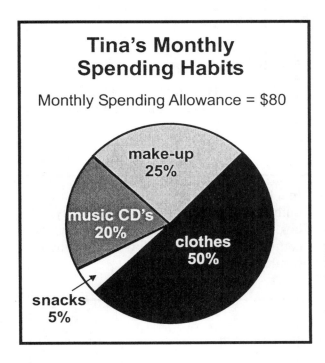

Tina's Monthly Spending Habits

Monthly Spending Allowance = $80

make-up 25%
music CD's 20%
clothes 50%
snacks 5%

1. How much did Tina spend each month on music CD's?

   $80 × 0.20 = $16.00

   <u>$16.00</u>

2. How much did Tina spend each month on make-up?

   _____

3. How much did Tina spend each month on clothes?

   _____

4. How much did Tina spend each month on snacks?

   _____

Fill in the following chart.

Favorite Activity	Number of Students
5. watching TV	
6. talking on the phone	
7. playing video games	
8. surfing the Internet	
9. playing sports	
10. reading	

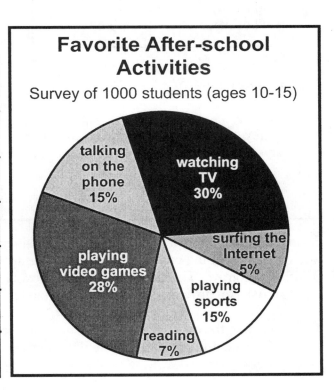

Favorite After-school Activities

Survey of 1000 students (ages 10-15)

talking on the phone 15%
watching TV 30%
surfing the Internet 5%
playing video games 28%
playing sports 15%
reading 7%

CHAPTER 17 REVIEW

KNIGHTS BASKETBALL Points Scored				
Player	game 1	game 2	game 3	game 4
Joey	5	2	4	8
Jason	10	8	10	12
Brandon	2	6	5	6
Ned	1	3	6	2
Austin	0	4	7	8
David	7	2	9	4
Zac	8	6	7	4

1. How many points did the Knights basketball team score in game 1?

_____

2. How many more points did David score in game 3 than in game 1?

_____

3. How many points did Jason score in the first 4 games?

_____

Jessica Bloodsoe and Katie Turick are climbing Mt. Fuji in Japan which is 12,388 ft. high. The higher they go, the slower their climb due to lack of oxygen. The chart below shows their progress.

Days Ascending	Altitude
End of day 1	4,000 feet
End of day 2	7,200 feet
End of day 3	9,600 feet

4. If the weather holds, what will be their altitude on day 5?

_____

5. If they can keep the same rate, how many days would it take them to get to the top?

_____

In a large city of 200,000, there was an outbreak of tuberculosis. Immediately, health care workers began an immunization campaign. The chart below records their results.

	No. of People Immunized	No. of TB Cases
Year 1	20,000	60
Year 2	60,000	45
Year 3	100,000	30

6. About how many cases of TB would you predict for year 4?

_____

Exotic goldfish are kept in different size containers of water. The larger the container, the bigger the size the goldfish can grow. The chart on the right shows how big one goldfish can grow in different size containers.

7. Based on the chart, how large would you predict a goldfish could grow in a 140 gallon container?

_____

Fish Size	Container Size
1 inch	20 gallon or less
$2\frac{1}{2}$ inches	50 gallon
5 inches	100 gallon

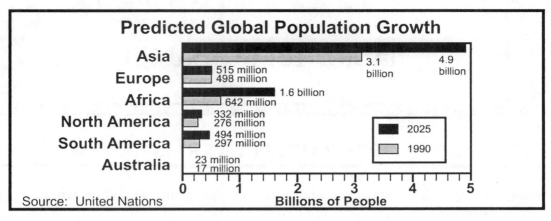

Predicted Global Population Growth

Asia — 515 million / 498 million ... 3.1 billion ... 4.9 billion
Europe
Africa — 1.6 billion / 642 million
North America — 332 million / 276 million
South America — 494 million / 297 million
Australia — 23 million / 17 million

Legend: ■ 2025   ▨ 1990

Source: United Nations   Billions of People   0 1 2 3 4 5

8. By how many is Asia's population predicted to increase between 1990 and 2025?

9. In 1990, how much larger was Africa's population than Europe's? _____

10. Where is the population expected to more than double between 1990 and 2025? _____

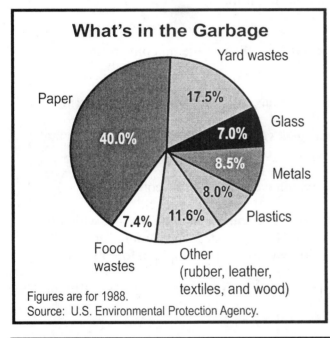

What's in the Garbage

Yard wastes 17.5%
Paper 40.0%
Glass 7.0%
Metals 8.5%
Plastics 8.0%
Other (rubber, leather, textiles, and wood) 11.6%
Food wastes 7.4%

Figures are for 1988.
Source: U.S. Environmental Protection Agency.

11. In 1988, the United States produced 160 million metric tons of garbage. According to the pie chart, how much glass was in the garbage?

_____

12. Out of the 160 million metric tons of garbage, how much was glass, plastic, or metal?

_____

13. If in 1990, the garbage reached 200 million metric tons, and the percentage of wastes remained the same as in 1988, how much food would have been in the 1990 garbage?

_____

14. In the space below, draw a line graph showing a population increasing over time.

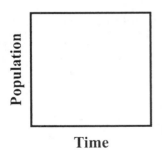

Population

Time

15. In the space below, draw a line graph of a population headed for extinction.

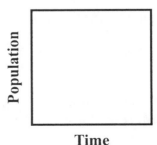

Population

Time

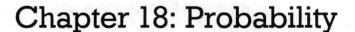

Chapter 18: Probability

PROBABILITY TERMS

Probability - the branch of mathematics that calculates the chance something will or will not happen.

Simple Event - one event. Tossing of one coin is an example.

Compound Event - multiple events. Tossing a coin more than once or rolling a die more than once are two examples.

Independent Events - the outcome of one event does not influence the outcome of the second event.

Dependent Events - the outcome of the first event does influence the outcome of the second event.

Equally Likely Outcomes - all outcomes of the event have the same chance of occurring.

Law of Large Numbers - As the number of trials gets very large, the mean of experimental outcomes approaches the theoretical probability.

Population - an entire group or collection about which we wish to draw conclusions.

Sample - units selected to study from the population. The sample may be **biased**, which means that some knowledge of the sample is gained in advance. The sample can also be **unbiased**, which means that nothing is known about the sample before the study.

Rank - the number of a value in a list arranged in decreasing order. For example, a fifth number in a list.

Frequency - the number of times a value occurs in data that has been divided into classes.

$P(A)$ - notation used to mean the probability of outcome 'A' occurring.

$P'(A)$ - notation used to mean the probability that outcome 'A' does not occur.

PROBABILITY

Probability is the chance something will happen and is a theoretical result. An experimental result is what actually happens. Although the outcome (the experimental result) of a random event is uncertain, probability (the theoretical result) suggests a pattern that will emerge after many repetitions of the given event. Probability is most often expressed as a fraction, a decimal, a percent, or can also be written out in words.

EXAMPLE 1: Billy had 3 red marbles, 5 white marbles, and 4 blue marbles on the floor. His cat came along and batted one marble under the chair. What is the **probability** it was a red marble?

Step 1: The number of red marbles will be the top number of the fraction. $\longrightarrow$ $\dfrac{3}{12}$

Step 2: The total number of marbles is the bottom number of the fraction. $\longrightarrow$

The answer may be expressed in lowest terms. $P(A) = \dfrac{3}{12} = \dfrac{1}{4}$

EXAMPLE 2: Determine the probability that the pointer will stop on a shaded wedge or the number 1.

Step 1: Count the number of possible wedges that the spinner can stop on to satisfy the above problem. There are 5 wedges that satisfy it (4 shaded wedges and one number 1). The top number of the fraction is 5.

Step 2: Count the total number of wedges, 7. The bottom number of the fraction is 7.

$P(A) = \dfrac{5}{7}$ or **five out of seven**.

EXAMPLE 3: Refer to the spinner above. If the pointer stops on the number 7, what is the probability that it will **not** stop on 7 on the next spin?

Step 1: Ignore the information that the pointer stopped on the number 7 on the previous spin. The probability of the next spin does not depend on the outcome of the previous spin. Simply find the probability that the spinner will **not** stop on 7. Remember, if P is the probability of an event occurring, 1− P is the probability of an event **not** occurring. In this example, the probability of the spinner landing on 7, is $\frac{1}{7}$.

Step 2: The probability that the spinner will not stop on 7 is $1 - \dfrac{1}{7}$ which equals $\dfrac{6}{7}$.

$P'(A) = \dfrac{6}{7}$ or **six out of seven**.

Find the probability of the following problems. Express the answer as a percent.

1. A computer chose a random number between 1 and 50. What is the probability of guessing the same number that the computer chose in 1 try?

    _____

2. There are 24 candy-coated chocolate pieces in a bag. Eight have defects in the coating that can be seen only with close inspection. What is the probability of pulling out a defective piece without looking?

    _____

3. Seven sisters have to choose which day each will wash the dishes. They put equal size pieces of paper each labeled with a day of the week in a hat. What is the probability that the first sister who draws will choose a weekend day?

    _____

4. For his garden, Clay has a mixture of 12 white corn seeds, 24 yellow corn seeds, and 16 bi-color corn seeds. If he reaches for a seed without looking, what is the probability that Clay will plant a bi-color corn seed first?

    _____

5. Mom just got a new department store credit card in the mail. What is the probability that the last digit is an odd number?

    _____

6. Alex has a paper bag of cookies that includes 8 chocolate chip, 4 peanut butter, 6 butterscotch chip, and 12 ginger. Without looking, his friend John reaches in the bag for a cookie. What is the probability that the cookie is peanut butter?

    _____

7. An umpire at a little league baseball game has 14 balls in his pockets. Five of the balls are brand A, 6 are brand B, and 3 are brand C. What is the probability that the next ball he throws to the pitcher is a brand C ball?

    _____

8. What is the probability that the spinner arrow will land on an even number?

    _____

9. The spinner in the problem above stopped on a shaded wedge on the first spin and stopped on the number 2 on the second spin. What is the probability that it will not stop on a shaded wedge or on the 2 on the third spin?

    _____

10. A company is offering 1 grand prize, 3 second place prizes, and 25 third place prizes based on a random drawing of contest entries. If you entered one of the 500 total entries, what is the probability you will win a third place prize?

    _____

11. In the contest problem above, what is the probability that you will win either the grand prize or a second place prize?

    _____

12. A box of a dozen donuts has 3 lemon cream-filled, 5 chocolate cream-filled, and 4 vanilla cream-filled. If the donuts look identical, what is the probability of picking a lemon cream-filled?

    _____

230

INDEPENDENT AND DEPENDENT EVENTS

In mathematics, the outcome of a first event may or may not influence the outcome of a second event. If the outcome of a first event does not influence the outcome of the second event, these events are **independent**. However, if the first event has an influence on the second event, the events are **dependent**. When someone needs to determine the probability of two events occurring, he or she will need to use an equation. These equations will change depending on whether the events are independent or dependent in relation to each other.

When finding the probability of two **independent** events, multiply the probability of each favorable outcome together.

EXAMPLE 1: One bag of marbles contains 1 white, 1 yellow, 2 blue, and 3 orange marbles. A second bag of marbles contains 2 white, 3 yellow, 1 blue, and 2 orange marbles. What is the probability of drawing a blue marble from each bag?

Solution: Probability of Favorable Outcomes

Bag 1: $\frac{2}{7}$

Bag 2: $\frac{1}{8}$

Probability of blue marble from each bag: $\frac{2}{7} \times \frac{1}{8} = \frac{2}{56} = \frac{1}{28}$

In order to find the probability of two **dependent** events, you will need to use a different set of rules. For the first event, you must divide the number of favorable outcomes by the number of possible outcomes. For the second event, you must subtract one from the number of favorable outcomes <u>only</u> if the favorable outcome is the <u>same</u>. However, you must subtract one from the number of total possible outcomes. Finally, you must multiply the probability of event one by the probability of event two.

EXAMPLE 2: One bag of marbles contains 3 red, 4 green, 7 black, and 2 yellow marbles. What is the probability of drawing a green marble, removing it from the bag, and then drawing another green marble?

	Favorable Outcomes	Total Possible Outcomes
Draw 1	4	16
Draw 2	3	15
Draw 1 × Draw 2	12	240

Answer: $P(A) = \frac{12}{240}$ or $\frac{1}{20}$

EXAMPLE 3: Using the same bag of marbles, what is the probability of drawing a red marble and then drawing a black marble?

	Favorable Outcomes	Total Possible Outcomes
Draw 1	3	16
Draw 2	7	15
Draw 1 × Draw 2	21	240

Answer: $P(A) = \frac{21}{240}$ or $\frac{7}{80}$

Find the probability of the following problems. Express the answer as a fraction.

1. Prithi has two boxes. Box 1 contains 3 red, 2 silver, 4 gold, and 2 blue combs. She also has a second box containing 1 black and 1 clear brush. What is the probability that Prithi selected a red brush from box 1 and a black brush from box 2?

2. Terrell cast his line into a pond containing 7 catfish, 8 bream, 3 trout, and 6 northern pike. He immediately caught a bream. What are the chances that Terrell will catch a second bream when he casts his line?

3. Gloria Quintero entered a contest in which the person who draws his or her initials out of a box containing all 26 letters of the alphabet wins the grand prize. Gloria reaches in and draws a "G", keeps it, then draws another letter. What is the probability that Gloria will next draw a "Q"?

4. Steve Marduke had two spinners in front of him. The first one was numbered 1–6, and the second was numbered 1–3. If Steve spins each spinner once, what is the probability that the first spinner will show an odd number and the second spinner will show a "1"?

5. Carrie McCallister flipped a coin twice and got heads both times. What is the probability that Carrie will get tails the third time she flips the coin?

6. Vince Macaluso is pulling two socks out of a washing machine in the dark. The washing machine contains three tan, one white, and two black socks. If Vince reaches in and pulls the socks out one at a time, what is the probability that Vince will pull out two tan socks in his first two tries?

7. John Salome has a bag containing 2 yellow plums, 2 red plums, and 3 purple plums. What is the probability that he reaches in without looking and pulls out a yellow plum, eats it, reaches in again without looking, and pulls out a red plum to eat?

8. Artie Drake turns a spinner which is evenly divided into 11 sections numbered 1–11. On the first spin, Artie's pointer lands on "8." What is the probability that the spinner lands on an even number the second time he turns the spinner?

9. Leanne Davis played a game with a street entertainer. In this game, a ball was placed under one of three coconut halves. The vendor shifted the coconut halves so quickly that Leanne could no longer tell which coconut half contained the ball. She selected one and missed. The entertainer then shifted them around once more and asked Leanne to pick again. What is the probability that Leanne will select the coconut half containing the ball?

10. What is the probability that Jane Robelot reaches into a bag containing 1 daffodil and 2 gladiola bulbs and pulls out a daffodil bulb, and then reaches into a second bag containing 6 tulip, 3 lily, and 2 gladiola bulbs and pulls out a lily bulb?

MORE PROBABILITY

EXAMPLE: You have a cube with one number, 1, 2, 3, 4, 5, or 6 painted on each face of the cube. What is the probability that if you throw the cube 3 times, you will get the number 2 each time?

If you roll the cube once, you have a 1 in 6 chance of getting the number 2. If you roll the cube a second time, you again have a 1 in 6 chance of getting the number 2. If you roll the cube a third time, you again have a 1 in 6 chance of getting the number 2. The probability of rolling the number 2 three times in a row is:

$$P(A) = \frac{1}{6} \times \frac{1}{6} \times \frac{1}{6} = \frac{1}{216}$$

Find the probability that each of the following events will occur.

There are 10 balls in a box, each with a different digit on it: 0, 1, 2, 3, 4, 5, 6, 7, 8, or 9. A ball is chosen at random and then put back in the box.

1. What is the probability that if you picked out a number ball 3 times, you would get the number 7 each time?

2. What is the probability you would pick a ball with 5, then 9, and then 3?

3. What is the probability that if you picked out a ball four times, you would always get an odd number?

4. A couple has 4 children ages 9, 6, 4, and 1. What is the probability that they are all girls?

There are 26 letters in the alphabet, allowing a different letter to be on each of 26 cards. The cards are shuffled. After each card is chosen at random, it is put back in the stack of cards, and the cards are shuffled again.

5. What is the probability that when you pick 3 cards, one at a time, that you will draw first a "y," then an "e," and then an "s"?

6. What is the probability that you will draw 4 cards and get the letter "z" each time?

7. What is the probability that you will draw twice and get a letter that is in the word "random" both times?

8. If you flipped a coin 3 times, what is the probability you would get heads every time?

9. Marie is clueless about 4 of her multiple-choice answers. The possible answers are A, B, C, D, E, or F. What is the probability that she will guess all four answers correctly?

TREE DIAGRAMS

Drawing a **tree diagram** is another method of determining the probability of events occurring.

EXAMPLE: If you toss two six-sided numbered cubes that have 1, 2, 3, 4, 5, or 6 on each side, what is the probability you will get two cubes that add up to 9? One way to determine the probability is to make a tree diagram.

Cube 1	Cube 2	Cube 1 plus Cube 2
1	1	2
	2	3
	3	4
	4	5
	5	6
	6	7
2	1	3
	2	4
	3	5
	4	6
	5	7
	6	4
3	1	8
	2	5
	3	6
	4	7
	5	8
	6	⑨
4	1	5
	2	6
	3	7
	4	8
	5	⑨
	6	10
5	1	6
	2	7
	3	8
	4	⑨
	5	10
	6	11
6	1	7
	2	8
	3	⑨
	4	10
	5	11
	6	12

Alternative method

Write down all of the numbers on both cubes which would add up to 9.

Cube 1	Cube 2
4	5
5	4
6	3
3	6

Numerator = 4 combinations

For denominator: Multiply the number of sides on one cube times the number of sides on the other cube.

$6 \times 6 = 36$

Numerator:
Denominator: $\dfrac{4}{36} = \dfrac{1}{9}$

There are 36 possible ways the cubes could land. Out of those 36 ways, the two cubes add up to 9 only 4 times. The probability you will get two cubes that add up to 9 is $\dfrac{4}{36}$ or $\dfrac{1}{9}$.

Read each of the problems below. Then, answer the questions.

1. Jake has a spinner. The spinner is divided into eight equal regions numbered 1–8. In two spins, what is the probability that the numbers added together will equal 12?

2. Charlie and Libby each spin one spinner one time. The spinner is divided into 5 equal regions numbered 1–5. What is the probability that these two spins added together would equal 7?

3. Gail spins a spinner twice. The spinner is divided into 9 equal regions numbered 1–9. In two spins, what is the probability that the difference between the two numbers will equal 4?

4. Diedra throws two 10-sided numbered cubes. What is the probability that the difference between the two numbers will equal 7?

5. Cameron throws two six-sided numbered cubes. What is the probability that the difference between the two numbers will equal 3?

6. Tesla spins one spinner twice. The spinner is divided into 11 equal regions numbered 1–11. What is the probability that the two numbers added together will equal 11?

7. Samantha decides to roll two five-sided numbered cubes. What is the probability that the two numbers added together will equal 4?

8. Mary Ellen spins a spinner twice. The spinner is divided into 7 equal regions numbered 1–7. What is the probability that the product of the two numbers equals 10?

9. Conner decides to roll two six-sided numbered cubes. What is the probability that the product of the two numbers equals 4?

10. Tabitha spins one spinner twice. The spinner is divided into 9 equal regions numbered 1–9. What is the probability that the sum of the two numbers equals 10?

11. Darnell decides to roll two 15-sided numbered cubes. What is the probability that the difference between the two numbers is 13?

12. Inez spins one spinner twice. The spinner is divided into 12 equal regions numbered 1–12. What is the probability that the sum of two numbers equals 10?

13. Gina spins one spinner twice. The spinner is divided into 8 equal regions numbered 1–8. What is the probability that the two numbers added together equals 9?

14. Celia rolls two six-sided numbered cubes. What is the probability that the difference between the two numbers is 2?

15. Brett spins one spinner twice. The spinner is divided into 4 equal regions numbered 1–4. What is the probability that the difference between the two numbers will be 3?

SIMULATIONS

A **simulation** is usually generated by a computer program. It automatically produces the results of an experiment. To find probabilities, the simulation generates the results from a series of trials. The probabilities that are found from simulations are experimental and are not always accurate.

EXAMPLE: The chart below represents a computer simulation. It shows the frequencies of the results of flipping two coins. The two coins were flipped at the same time 100 times.

Outcome	TT	TH	HT	HH
Frequency	23	35	23	19

Find the theoretical probability of flipping one tail and one head, and find the experimental probability of flipping one tail and one head based on the computer simulation, then compare the two values.

Step 1: Find the theoretical probability. The probability of flipping a tail with coin one is $\frac{1}{2}$, and the probability of flipping a head with coin two is $\frac{1}{2}$. To find the probability of flipping a tail with coin one and flipping a head with coin two, you must multiply the two probabilities together, $\frac{1}{2} \times \frac{1}{2} = \frac{1}{4}$. The probability of flipping a head with coin one and a tail with coin two is $\frac{1}{2} \times \frac{1}{2} = \frac{1}{4}$. Since it does not matter which coin is tails and which is heads, add the two probabilities together.

$$\tfrac{1}{4} + \tfrac{1}{4} = \tfrac{1}{2}$$

The theoretical probability is 50%.

Step 2: Find the experimental probability. The frequency of TH is 35, so out of 100 flips, the probability is $\frac{35}{100}$. The frequency of HT is 23, so out of 100 flips, the probability is $\frac{23}{100}$. To find the theoretical probability of flipping one head and one tail, you need to add the two probabilities together.

$$\tfrac{35}{100} + \tfrac{23}{100} = \tfrac{58}{100} = \tfrac{29}{50}$$

The experimental probability based on the simulation is 58%.

Step 3: The difference between the theoretical probability and the experimental probability is 8%. Eight percent is not a huge difference. Since the two values are not too far apart, this means that the computer accurately simulates tossing of two coins.

Use the simulations to find your answers.

1. A computer program simulated tossing three coins 500 times. The results are shown below.

HHH	50	HTT	66
HTH	76	THT	57
HHT	62	TTH	69
THH	64	TTT	56

a) Based on the computer simulation, what is the experimental probability of tossing two heads and a tail?

b) What is the theoretical probability of tossing two heads and one tail?

c) Based on the computer simulation, what is the experimental probability of tossing three tails?

d) What is the theoretical probability of tossing three tails?

e) Compare your answers from part a with part b, and compare your answer from part c with part d. Based on this comparison, is this an accurate simulation of tossing three coins?

2. Below is a computer simulation of rolling one six-sided cube 50 times.

Outcome	1	2	3	4	5	6
Frequency	8	6	12	11	5	7

a) What is the theoretical probability of rolling a 3 or a 4?

b) Calculate the theoretical probability of rolling a 6.

c) Determine what the experimental probability of rolling a six based on the simulation.

d) Compare the theoretical and experimental probabilities of rolling a six from parts b and c. What are your conclusions?

CHAPTER 18 REVIEW

1. There are 50 students in the school orchestra in the following sections:

    25 string section
    15 woodwind
    5   percussion
    5   brass

    One student will be chosen at random to present the orchestra director with an award. What is the probability the student will be from the woodwind section?

2. Fluffy's cat treat box contains 6 chicken-flavored treats, 5 beef-flavored treats, and 7 fish-flavored treats. If Fluffy's owner reaches in the box without looking and chooses one treat, what is the probability that Fluffy will get a chicken-flavored treat?

3. The spinner on the right stopped on the number 5 on the first spin. What is the probability that it will not stop on the number 5 on the second spin?

4. Three cakes are sliced into 20 pieces each. Each cake contains 1 gold ring. What is the probability that one person who eats one piece of cake from each of the 3 cakes will find 3 gold rings?

5. Brianna tossed a coin 4 times. What is the probability she got all tails?

6. Sherri turned the spinner on the right 3 times.
    What is the probability that the pointer always landed on a shaded number?

    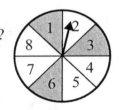

7. A box of a dozen donuts has 3 lemon cream-filled, 5 chocolate cream-filled, and 4 vanilla cream-filled. If the donuts look identical, what is the probability that if you pick a donut at random, it will be chocolate cream-filled?

8. Erica got a new credit card in the mail. What is the probability that the last four digits are all 5's?

9. There are 26 letters in the alphabet. What is the probability that the first two letters of your new license plate will be your initials?

10. Mary has 4 green mints and 8 white mints the same size in her pocket. If she pulls one out, what is the probability it will be green?

Read the following, and answer questions 11–15.

There are 9 slips of paper in a hat, each with a number from 1 to 9. The numbers correspond to a group of students who must answer a question when the number for their group is drawn. Each time a number is drawn, the number is put back in the hat.

11. What is the probability that the number 6 will be drawn twice in a row?

12. What is the probability that the first 5 numbers drawn will be odd numbers?

13. What is the probability that the second, third, and fourth numbers drawn will be even numbers?

14. What is the probability that the first five times a number is drawn it will be the number 5?

15. What is the probability that the first five numbers drawn will be 1, 2, 3, 4, 5 in that order?

Answer the following probability questions.

16. If you toss two six-sided numbered cubes, what is the probability they will add up to 7? (Make a tree diagram.)

17. Make a tree diagram to show the probability of a couple with 3 children having a boy and two girls.

Solve the following word problems. Then, write whether the problem is "dependent" or "independent."

18. Felix Perez reaches into a 10 piece puzzle and pulls out one piece at random. This piece has two places where it could connect to other pieces. What is the probability that he will select another piece which fits the first one if he selects the next piece at random?

19. Barbara Stein is desperate for a piece of chocolate candy. She reaches into a bag which contains 8 peppermint, 5 butterscotch, 7 toffee, 3 mint, and 6 chocolate pieces and pulls out a toffee piece. Disappointed, she throws it back into the bag and then reaches back in and pulls out one piece of candy. What is the probability that Barbara pulled out a chocolate piece on the second try?

Match each term with the correct definition.

20. compound event

21. law of large numbers

22. probability

23. $P(A)$

24. unbiased sample

25. frequency

26. $P'(A)$

27. independent events

28. population

29. rank

30. equally likely outcomes

31. simple event

32. dependent events

A. a theoretical result

B. one event

C. multiple events

D. the outcome of one event does not influence the outcome of the second event

E. the outcome of one event does influence the outcome of the second event

F. all outcomes of the event have the same chance of occurring

G. units selected to study that are unknown

H. the number of a value in a list arranged in decreasing order

I. notation used to mean the probability of outcome 'A' occurring

J. the mean of experimental outcomes that approach the theoretical probability as the number of trials gets very large.

K. an entire group or collection about which we wish to draw conclusions.

L. the number of times a value occurs in data that has been divided into classes.

M. notation used to mean the probability that outcome 'A' does not occur.

240

Chapter 19: Permutations and Combinations

PERMUTATIONS

A **permutation** is an arrangement of items in a specific order. The formula $_nP_r = \frac{n!}{(n-r)!}$ is the formula for permutations. n is the number you have to choose from, and r is the number of objects you want to arrange. If a problem asks how many ways you can arrange 6 books on a bookshelf, it is asking you how many permutations there are for 6 items.

EXAMPLE 1: Ron has 4 items: a model airplane, a trophy, an autographed football, and a toy sports car. How many ways can he arrange the 4 items on a shelf?

Solution: The diagram below shows the permutations for arranging the 4 items on a shelf if he chooses to put the trophy first.

1st item   2nd item   3rd item   4th item

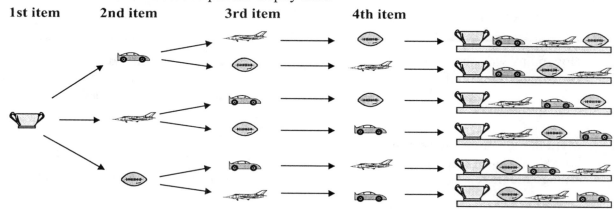

There are 6 permutations. Next, you could construct a tree diagram of permutations choosing the model car first. That tree diagram would also have 6 permutations. Then, you could construct a tree diagram choosing the airplane first. Finally, you could construct a pyramid choosing the football first. You would then have a total of 4 tree diagrams, each having 6 permutations. The total number of permutations is $6 \times 4 = 24$. There are 24 ways to arrange the 4 items on a bookshelf.

You probably don't want to draw tree diagrams for every permutation problem. For the problem above, Ron has 4 items to arrange. Therefore, multiply $4 \times 3 \times 2 \times 1 = 24$. Another way of expressing this calculation is 4!, stated as 4 factorial. $4! = 4 \times 3 \times 2 \times 1$.

Note: To find the permutation using the formula, $_nP_r = \frac{n!}{(n-r)!}$. n is the number you have to choose from, 4, and r is the number of objects you want to arrange, 4.
$$_4P_4 = \frac{4!}{(4-4)!} = \frac{4!}{0!} = \frac{4!}{1} = 4! = 4 \times 3 \times 2 \times 1 = 24.$$
(Remember that $0! = 1$.)

EXAMPLE 2: How many ways can you line up 6 students?

Solution: The number of permutations for 6 students = $6! = 6 \times 5 \times 4 \times 3 \times 2 \times 1 = 720$. There are 6 choices for the first position, 5 for the second, 4 for the third, 3 for the fourth, 2 for the fifth, and 1 for the sixth.

Note: The number of permutations for 6 students $= {}_6P_6 = \dfrac{6!}{(6-6)!} = \dfrac{6!}{0!} = \dfrac{6!}{1} = 6! = 6 \times 5 \times 4 \times 3 \times 2 \times 1 = 720$.

EXAMPLE 3: Shelley and her mom, dad, and brother are having cake for her birthday. Since it is Shelley's birthday, she gets a piece first. How many ways are there to pass out the pieces of cake?

Solution: Since Shelley gets the first piece, the first spot is fixed. The second, third, and fourth spots are not fixed, and anyone left can be in one of the three spots.

Spot	1	2	3	4
Choices of people	1	3	2	1

Now, multiply the choices together, $1 \times 3 \times 2 \times 1 = 6$ ways to pass out cake.

Note: You can also use the permutation formula, but fix the first spot and just arrange the last three spots. $1 \times {}_3P_3 = 1 \times \dfrac{3!}{(3-3)!} = \dfrac{3!}{0!} = \dfrac{3!}{1} = 3! = 3 \times 2 \times 1 = 6$ ways

---

1. How many ways can you arrange five books on a bookshelf?

2. Myra has six novels to arrange on a bookshelf. How many ways can she arrange the novels?

3. Seven sprinters signed up for the 100-meter dash. How many ways can the seven sprinters line up on the start line?

4. Keri wants an ice cream cone with one scoop of chocolate, one scoop of vanilla, and one scoop of strawberry. How many ways can the scoops be arranged on the cone if the top flavor is chocolate?

5. At Sam's party, the DJ has four song requests. In how many different orders can he play the four songs?

6. Yvette has five comic books. How many different ways can she stack the comic books?

7. Sandra's couch can hold three people. How many ways can she and her two friends sit on the couch?

8. How many ways can you arrange the numbers 1, 2, 3, 4, 5, 6, 7, 8, 9, 10 and always have 3 at position 1 and 10 at position 5?

MORE PERMUTATIONS

The formula $_nP_r = \dfrac{n!}{(n-r)!}$ can also be used if you are trying to arrange a specific number of objects, but have more than you want to arrange. n is the number you have to choose from, and r is the number of objects you want to arrange.

EXAMPLE: If there are 6 students, how many ways can you line up any 4 of them?

Step 1: Find all your variables. The formula is $_nP_r = \dfrac{n!}{(n-r)!}$.
n (the number you have to choose from) = 6
r (the number of objects you want to arrange) = 4

Step 2: Plug into the formula.
$$_6P_4 = \frac{6!}{(6-4)!} = \frac{6!}{2!} = \frac{6 \times 5 \times 4 \times 3 \times \cancel{2} \times \cancel{1}}{\cancel{2} \times \cancel{1}} = 6 \times 5 \times 4 \times 3 = 360.$$
There are 360 ways to line up 4 of the 6 students.

Find the number of permutations for each of the problems below.

1. How many ways can you arrange four out of eight books on a shelf?

2. How many 3 digit numbers can be made using the numbers 2, 3, 5, 8, and 9?

3. How many ways can you line up four students out of a class of twenty?

4. Kim worked in the linen department of a store. Eight new colors of towels came in. Her job was to line up the new towels on a long shelf. How many ways could she arrange the eight colors?

5. Terry's CD player holds 5 CDs. Terry owns 12 CDs. How many different ways can he arrange his CDs in the CD player?

6. Erik has eleven shirts he wears to school. How many ways can he choose a different shirt to wear on Monday, Tuesday, Wednesday, Thursday, and Friday?

7. Deb has a box of twelve markers. The art teacher told her to choose three markers and line them up on her desk. How many ways can she line up three markers from the twelve?

8. Jeff went into an ice cream store serving 32 flavors of ice cream. He wanted a cone with two different flavors. How many ways could he order two scoops of ice cream, one on top of the other?

9. In how many ways can you arrange any three letters from the 26 letters in the alphabet?

COMBINATIONS

In a **combination**, the order does not matter. In a **permutation**, if someone picked two letters of the alphabet, **k, m** and **m, k**, they would be considered 2 different permutations. In a **combination**, **k, m** and **m, k** would be the same combination. A different order does not make a new combination. The formula for combinations is $_nC_r = \frac{n!}{(n-r)!\,r!}$ where n is the total number of objects you choose from and r is the number that you choose to arrange.

EXAMPLE: How many combinations of three letters from the set {a, b, c, d, e} are there?

Step 1: Find the **permutation** of 3 out of 5 objects.
Step 2: Divide by the permutation of the **number of objects** to be chosen from the total (3). This step eliminates the duplicates in finding the permutations.
Step 3: Cancel common factors and simplify.

$$\frac{5 \times \overset{2}{\cancel{4}} \times \cancel{3}}{\cancel{3} \times \cancel{2} \times 1} = 10$$

Note: Using the formula, find all your variables. The formula is $_nC_r = \frac{n!}{(n-r)!\,r!}$.
n (the number you choose from) = 5, r (the number of objects arranged) = 3
Now, plug into the formula.
$$_5C_3 = \frac{5!}{(5-3)!\,3!} = \frac{5!}{2!\,3!} = \frac{5 \times 4 \times \cancel{3 \times 2 \times 1}}{(2 \times 1)\,(\cancel{3 \times 2 \times 1})} = \frac{20}{2} = 10.$$
There can be 10 combinations of three letters from the set {a, b, c, d, e}.

Find the number of combinations for each problem below.

1. How many combinations of 4 numbers can be made from the set of numbers {2, 4, 6, 7, 8, 9}?

2. Johnston Middle School wants to choose 3 students at random from the 7th grade to take an opinion poll. There are 124 seventh graders in the school. How many different groups of 3 students could be chosen? (Use a calculator for this one.)

3. How many combinations of 3 students can be made from a class of 20?

4. Fashion Ware catalog has a sweater that comes in 8 colors. How many combinations of 2 different colors does a shopper have to choose from?

5. Angelo's Pizza offers 10 different pizza toppings. How many different combinations can be made of pizzas with four toppings?

6. How many different combinations of 5 flavors of jelly beans can you make from a store that sells 25 different flavors of jelly beans?

7. The track team is running the relay race in a competition this Saturday. There are 14 members of the track team. The relay race requires 4 runners. How many combinations of 4 runners can be formed from the track team?

8. Kerri got to pick 2 prizes from a grab bag containing 12 prizes. How many combinations of 2 prizes are possible?

MORE COMBINATIONS

Another kind of combination involves selection from several categories.

EXAMPLE: At Joe's Deli, you can choose from 4 kinds of bread, 5 meats, and 3 cheeses when you order a sandwich. How many different sandwiches can be made with Joe's choices for breads, meats, and cheeses if you choose 1 kind of bread, 1 meat, and 1 cheese for each sandwich?

JOE'S SANDWICHES

Breads	**Meats**	**Cheeses**
White	Roast Beef	Swiss
Pumpernickel	Corned Beef	American
Light rye	Pastrami	Mozzarella
Whole wheat	Roast Chicken	
	Roast Turkey	

Solution: Multiply the number of choices in each category. There are 4 breads, 5 meats, and 3 cheeses, so $4 \times 5 \times 3 = 60$. There are 60 combinations of sandwiches.

Find the number of combinations that can be made in each of the problems below.

1. Angie has 4 pairs of shorts, 6 shirts, and 2 pairs of tennis shoes. How many different outfit combinations can be made with Angie's clothes?

   _____

2. Raymond has 7 baseball caps, 2 jackets, 10 pairs of jeans, and 2 pairs of sneakers. How many combinations of the 4 items can he make?

   _____

3. Claire has 6 kinds of lipstick, 4 eye shadows, 2 kinds of lip liner, and 2 mascaras. How many combinations can she use to make up her face?

   _____

4. Clarence's dad is ordering a new truck. He has a choice of 5 exterior colors, 3 interior colors, 2 kinds of seats, and 3 sound systems. How many combinations does he have to pick from?

   _____

5. A fast food restaurant has 8 kinds of sandwiches, 3 kinds of french fries, and 5 kinds of soft drinks. How many combinations of meals could you order if you ordered a sandwich, fries, and a drink?

   _____

6. In summer camp, Tyrone can choose from 4 outdoor activities, 3 indoor activities, and 3 water sports. He has to choose one of each. How many combinations of activities can he choose?

   _____

7. Jackie won a contest at school and gets to choose one pencil and one pen from the school store and an ice cream from the lunch room. There are 5 colors of pencils, 3 colors of pens, and 4 kinds of ice-cream. How many combinations of prize packages can she choose?

   _____

CHAPTER 19 REVIEW

Answer the following permutation and combination problems.

1. Daniel has 7 trophies he won playing soccer. How many different ways can he arrange them in a row on his bookshelf?

2. Missy has 12 colors of nail polish. She wears 1 color each day, 7 different colors a week. How many combinations of 7 colors can she make before she has to repeat the same 7 colors in a week?

3. Eileen has a collection of 12 antique hats. She plans to donate 5 of the hats to a museum. How many combinations of hats are possible for her donation?

4. Julia has 5 porcelain dolls. How many ways can she arrange 3 of the dolls on a display shelf?

5. Ms. Randal has 10 students. Every day she randomly draws the names of 2 students out of a bag to turn in their homework for a test grade. How many combinations of 2 students can she draw?

6. In the lunch line, students can choose 1 out of 3 meats, 1 out of 4 vegetables, 1 out of 3 desserts, and 1 out of 5 drinks. How many lunch combinations are there?

7. Andrea has 7 teddy bears in a row on a shelf in her room. How many ways can she arrange the bears in a row on her shelf?

8. Adrianna has 4 hats, 8 shirts, and 9 pairs of pants. Choosing one of each, how many different clothes combinations can she make?

9. The buffet line offers 5 kinds of meat, 3 different salads, a choice of 4 desserts, and 5 different drinks. If you chose one food from each category, from how many combinations would you have to choose?

10. How many pairs of students can Mrs. Smith choose to go to the library if she has 20 students in her class?

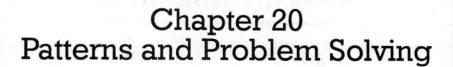

Chapter 20
Patterns and Problem Solving

NUMBER PATTERNS

In each of the examples below, there is a sequence of data that follows a pattern. Think of the given sequence like the output for a function. You must find the pattern that holds true for each number in the data. Once you determine the pattern, you can write out a function that fits the data and figure out any other number in the sequence.

	Sequence	Pattern	Next Number	20th number in the sequence
EXAMPLE 1:	3, 4, 5, 6, 7	$n + 2$	$f(n) = n + 2 = 8$	$f(20) = 20 + 2 = 22$

In number patterns, the sequence is the output. The input can be the set of whole numbers starting with 1. But, you must determine the "rule" or pattern. Look at the table below.

input	sequence
1 →	3
2 →	4
3 →	5
4 →	6
5 →	7

What pattern or "rule" can you come up with that gives you the first number in the sequence, 3, when you input 1? $n + 2$ will work because when $n = 1$, the first number in the sequence = 3. Does this pattern hold true for the rest of the numbers in the sequence? Yes, it does. When $n = 2$, the second number in the sequence = 4. When $n = 3$, the third number in the sequence = 5, and so on. Therefore, $n + 2$ is the pattern. Even without knowing the algebraic form of the pattern, you could figure out that 8 is the next number in the sequence. The function describing this pattern would be $f(n) = n + 2$. To find the 20th number in the pattern, use $n = 20$ to get 22.

	Sequence	Pattern	Next Number	20th number in the sequence
EXAMPLE 2:	1, 4, 9, 16, 25	n^2	$f(n) = n^2 = 36$	400
EXAMPLE 3:	−2, −4, −6, −8, −10	$−2n$	$f(n) = −2n = −12$	−40

Find the pattern and the next number in each of the sequences below.

	Sequence	Pattern	Next Number	20th number in the sequence
1.	−2, −1, 0, 1, 2	_____	_____	_____
2.	5, 6, 7, 8, 9	_____	_____	_____
3.	3, 7, 11, 15, 19	_____	_____	_____
4.	−3, −6, −9, −12, −15	_____	_____	_____
5.	3, 5, 7, 9, 11	_____	_____	_____
6.	2, 4, 8, 16, 32	_____	_____	_____
7.	1, 8, 27, 64, 125	_____	_____	_____
8.	0, −1, −2, −3, −4	_____	_____	_____
9.	2, 5, 10, 17, 26	_____	_____	_____
10.	4, 6, 8, 10, 12	_____	_____	_____

MAKING PREDICTIONS

Use what you know about number patterns to answer the following questions.

Corn plants grow as tall as they will get in about 20 weeks. Study the chart of the rate of corn plant growth below, and answer the questions that follow.

Corn Growth	
Beginning Week	**Height (inches)**
2	9
7	39
11	63
14	??

1. If the growth pattern continues, how high will the corn plant be beginning week 14?

2. If the growth pattern was constant (at the same rate from week to week), how high was the corn in the beginning of the 8th week?

Peter Nichols is staining furniture for a furniture manufacturer. He stains large pieces of furniture that take longer to dry in the beginning of the day and smaller pieces of furniture as the day progresses.

Time	# Pieces Completed per Hour
Hour 1	3
Hour 3	5
Hour 6	8

3. How many pieces of furniture did Peter stain during his second hour of work?

4. How many pieces of furniture will Peter have stained by the end of an 8 hour day?

Brian Bailey is bass fishing down the Humbolt River. He has selected six locations to fish. Using his car, he drives to the first location near Golconda. His final location is near Valmy. As he travels south, he notices that the bass catches are getting larger.

Fishing Direction	Fishing Location	Number of bass caught
North	1	4
	2	unrecorded
	3	10
	4	unrecorded
South	5	16

5. How many bass would he likely catch in the sixth location?

6. If he fishes six locations, how many bass is he likely to catch altogether?

INDUCTIVE REASONING AND PATTERNS

Humans have always observed what happened in the past and used these observations to predict what would happen in the future. This is called **inductive reasoning**. Although mathematics is referred to as the "deductive science," it benefits from inductive reasoning. We observe patterns in the mathematical behavior of a phenomenon, then find a rule or formula for describing and predicting its future mathematical behavior. There are lots of different kinds of predictions that may be of interest.

EXAMPLE 1: Nancy is watching her nephew, Drew, arrange his marbles in rows on the kitchen floor. The figure below shows the progression of his arrangement.

Row 1
Row 2
Row 3
Row 4

QUESTION 1: Assuming this pattern continues, how many marbles would Drew place in a fifth row?

ANSWER 1: It appears that Drew doubles the number of marbles in each successive row. In the 4th row he had 8 marbles, so in the 5th row we can predict 16 marbles.

QUESTION 2: How many marbles will Drew place in the nth row?

ANSWER 2: To find a rule for the number of marbles in the nth row, we look at the pattern suggested by the table below.

Which row	1st	2nd	3rd	4th	5th
Number of marbles	1	2	4	8	16

Observing closely, you will notice that the nth row contains 2^{n-1} marbles.

QUESTION 3: Suppose Nancy tells you that Drew now has 6 rows of marbles on the floor. What is the total number of marbles in his arrangement?

ANSWER 3: Again, organizing the data in a table could be helpful.

Number of rows	1	2	3	4	5
Total number of marbles	1	3	7	15	31

With careful observation, one will notice that the total number of marbles is always 1 less than a power of 2; indeed, for n rows there are $2^n - 1$ marbles total.

QUESTION 4: If Drew has 500 marbles, what is the maximum number of *complete* rows he can form?

ANSWER 4: With 8 complete rows, Drew will use $2^8 - 1 = 255$ marbles, and to form 9 complete rows he would need $2^9 - 1 = 511$ marbles; thus, the answer is 8 complete rows.

EXAMPLE 2: Manuel drops a golf ball from the roof of his high school while Carla videos the motion of the ball. Later, the video is analyzed, and the results are recorded concerning the height of each bounce of the ball.

QUESTION 1: What height do you predict for the fifth bounce?

Initial height	1st bounce	2nd bounce	3rd bounce	4th bounce
30 ft	18 ft	10.8 ft	6.48 ft	3.888 ft

ANSWER 1: To answer this question, we need to be able to relate the height of each bounce to the bounce immediately preceding it. Perhaps the best way to do this is with **ratios** as follows:

$$\frac{\text{Height of 1st bounce}}{\text{Initial bounce}} = 0.6 \qquad \frac{\text{Height of 2nd bounce}}{\text{Height of 1st bounce}} = 0.6 \qquad \frac{\text{Height of 4th bounce}}{\text{Height of 3rd bounce}} = 0.6$$

Since the ratio of the height of each bounce to the bounce before it appears constant, we have some basis for making predictions.

Using this, we can reason that the fifth bounce will be equal to 0.6 of the fourth bounce

Thus, we predict the fifth bounce to have a height of $\mathbf{0.6 \times 3.888 = 2.3328}$ **ft.**

QUESTION 2: Which bounce will be the last one with a height of one foot or greater?

ANSWER 2: For this question, keep looking at predicted bounce heights until a bounce less than 1 foot is reached.

The sixth bounce is predicted to be 1.39968 ft.
The seventh bounce is predicted to be 0.839808 ft.

Thus, the last bounce with a height greater than 1 foot is predicted to be the sixth one.

Read each of the following questions carefully. Use inductive reasoning to answer each question. You may wish to make a table or a diagram to help you visualize the pattern in some of the problems. Show your work.

George is stacking his coins as shown below.

1. How many coins do you predict he will place in the fourth stack?

2. How many coins in an *n*th row?

3. If George has exactly 6 "complete" stacks, how many coins does he have?

4. If George has 2,000 coins, how many complete stacks can he form?

Bob and Alice have designed and created a website for their high school. The first week they had 5 visitors to the site; during the second week, they had 10 visitors; and during the third week, they had 20 visitors.

5. If current trends continue, how many visitors can they expect in the fifth week?

6. How many in the *n*th week?

7. How many weeks will it be before they get more than 500 visitors in a single week?

8. In 1979 (the first year of classes), there were 500 students at Brookstone High. In 1989, there were 1000 students. In 1999, there were 2000 students. How many students would you predict at Brookstone in 2009 if this pattern continues (and no new schools are built)?

9. The number of new driver's licenses issued in the city of Boomtown, USA was 512 in 1992, 768 in 1994, 1,152 in 1996, and 1,728 in 1998. Estimate the number of new driver's licenses that will be issued in 2000.

10. The average combined (math and verbal) SAT score for seniors at Brookstone High was 1,000 in 1996, 1,100 in 1997, 1,210 in 1998, and 1331 in 1999. Predict the combined SAT score for Brookstone seniors in 2000.

Juan wants to be a medical researcher, inspired in part by the story of how penicillin was discovered as a mold growing on a laboratory dish. One morning, Juan observes a mold on one of his lab dishes. Each morning thereafter, he observes and records the pattern of growth. The mold appeared to cover about 1/32 of the dish surface on the first day, 1/16 on the second day, and 1/8 on the third day.

11. If this rate of growth continues, on which day can Juan expect the entire dish to be covered with mold?

12. Suppose that whenever the original dish gets covered with mold Juan transfers half of the mold to another dish. How long will it be before *both* dishes are covered again?

13. Every year on the last day of school, the Brookstone High cafeteria serves the principal's favorite dish – Broccoli Surprise. In 1988, 1024 students chose to eat Broccoli Surprise on the last day of school, 512 students in 1992, and 256 students in 1996. Predict how many will choose Broccoli Surprise on the last day of school in 2000.

Part of testing a new drug is determining the rate at which it will break down (*decay*) in the blood. The decay results for a certain antibiotic after a 1000 milligram injection are given in the table below.

12:00 PM	1:00 PM	2:00 PM
1000 mg	800 mg	640 mg

14. Predict the number of milligrams that will be in the patient's bloodstream at 3:00 PM.

15. At which hour can the measurer expect to record a result of less than 300 mg?

16. Marie has a daylily in her mother's garden. Every Saturday morning in the spring, she measures and records its height in the table below. What height do you predict for Marie's daylily on April 29? (Hint: Look at the *change* in height each week when looking for the pattern.)

April 1	April 8	April 15	April 22
12 in	18 in	21 in	22.5 in

17. Bob puts a glass of water in the freezer and records the temperature every 15 minutes. The results are displayed in the table below. If this pattern of cooling continues, what will be the temperature at 2:15 PM? (Hint: Again, look at the *changes* in temperature in order to see the pattern.)

1:00 PM	1:15 PM	1:30 PM	1:45 PM
92°F	60°F	44°F	36°F

Suppose you cut your hand on a rusty nail that deposits 25 bacteria cells into the wound. Suppose also that each bacterium splits into two bacteria every 15 minutes.

18. How many bacteria will there be after two hours?

19. How many 15-minute intervals will pass before there are over a million bacteria?

20. Elias performed a psychology experiment at his school. He found that when someone is asked to pass information along to someone else, only about 70% of the original information is actually passed on to the recipient. Suppose Elias gives the information to Brian, Brian passes it along to George, and George passes it to Montel. Using Elias's results from past experiments, what percentage of the original information does Montel actually receive?

FINDING A RULE FOR PATTERNS

EXAMPLE: Mr. Applegate wants to put desks together in his math class so that students can work in groups. The diagram below shows how he wishes to do it.

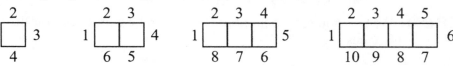

With 1 table he can seat 4 students, with 2 tables he can seat 6, with 3 tables 8, and with 4 tables 10.

QUESTION 1: How many students can he seat with 5 tables?

ANSWER 1: With 5 tables he could seat 5 students along the sides of the tables and 1 student on each end; thus, a total of 12 students could be seated.

QUESTION 2: Write a rule that Mr. Applegate could use to tell how many students could be seated at n tables. Explain how you got the rule.

ANSWER 2: For n tables, there would be n students along each of 2 sides and 2 students on the ends (1 on each end); thus, a total of $2n + 2$ students could be seated at n tables.

EXAMPLE 2: When he isn't playing football for the Brookstone Bears, Tim designs web pages. A car dealership paid Tim $500 to start a site with photos of its cars. The dealer also agreed to pay Tim $50 for each customer who buys a car first viewed on the web site.

QUESTION 1: Write and explain a rule that tells how much the dealership will pay Tim for the design of the web site and sale of n cars from his web site.

ANSWER 1: Tim's payment will be the initial $500 plus $50 for each sale. Translated into mathematical language, if Tim sells n cars he will be paid a total of $500 + 50n$ dollars.

QUESTION 2: How many cars have to be sold from his site in order for Tim to get $1,000 from the dealership?

ANSWER 2: He earned $500 just by establishing the site, so he only needs to earn an additional $500, which at $50 per car requires the sale of only 10 cars. (Note: Another way to solve this problem is to use the rule found in the first question. In that case, you simply solve the equation $500 + 50n = 1000$ for the variable n.)

253

EXAMPLE 3: Eric is baking muffins to raise money for the Homecoming dance. He makes 18 muffins with each batch of batter, but he must give one muffin each to his brother, his sister, his dog, and himself (of course!) each time a batch is finished baking.

QUESTION 1: Write a rule for the number of muffins Eric produces for the fundraiser with n batches.

ANSWER 1: He bakes 18 with each batch, but only 14 are available for the fundraiser. Thus, with n batches he will produce $14n$ muffins for the Homecoming. **The rule $= 14n$**

QUESTION 2: Use your rule to determine how many muffins he will contribute if he makes 7 batches.

ANSWER 2: The number of batches, n, equals 7. Therefore, he will produce $14 \times 7 = 98$ muffins with 7 batches.

QUESTION 3: Determine how many batches he must bake in order to contribute at least 150 muffins.

ANSWER 3: Ten batches will produce $10 \times 14 = 140$ muffins. Eleven batches will produce $11 \times 14 = 154$ muffins. To produce at least 150 muffins, he must bake at least 11 batches.

QUESTION 4: Determine how many muffins he would actually bake in order to contribute 150 muffins.

ANSWER 4: Since Eric actually bakes 18 muffins per batch, 11 batches would result in Eric baking $11 \times 18 = 198$ muffins.

Carefully read and solve the problems below. Show your work.

Tito is building a picket fence along both sides of the driveway leading up to his house. He will have to place posts at both ends and at every 10 feet along the way because the rails come in prefabricated ten-foot sections.

1. How many posts will he need for a 180 foot driveway?

2. Write and explain a rule for determining the number of posts needed for n ten-foot sections.

3. How long of a driveway can he fence with 32 posts?

Linda is working as a bricklayer this summer. She lays the bricks for a walkway in *sections* according to the pattern depicted below.

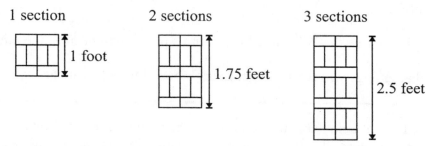

4. Write a formula for the number of bricks needed to lay n sections.

5. Write a formula for the number of feet covered by n sections.

6. How many bricks would it take to lay a walk that is 10 feet long?

Dakota's beginning pay at his new job is $300 per week. For every three months, he continues to work there he will get a $10 per week raise.

7. Write a formula for Dakota's weekly pay after n three-month periods.

8. After n years?

9. How long will he have to work before his pay gets to $400 a week?

Amanda is selling shoes this summer. In addition to her hourly wages, Amanda got a $100 bonus just for accepting the position, and she gets a $2 bonus for each pair of shoes she sells.

10. Write and explain a rule that tells how much she will make in bonuses if she sells n pairs of shoes.

11. How many pairs of shoes must she sell in order to make $200 in bonuses?

A certain teen telephone chat line, which sells itself as a benefit to teens but which is actually a money-making scheme, is a 900 telephone number that charges $2.00 for the first minute and $0.95 for each additional minute.

12. Write a formula for the cost of speaking n minutes on this line.

13. How many minutes does it take to accumulate charges of more than $50.00?

Laura's (unsharpened) pencil was initially 8 inches long. After the first sharpening, it was 7 inches long. Each sharpening thereafter, Laura noticed the pencil would be ½ inch shorter after sharpening than before.

14. Write and explain a rule that tells how long Laura's pencil will be after the nth sharpening.

15. How many sharpenings will it take to get Laura's pencil to only 3 inches long?

Ritchie's dad is tired of not being able to use his own phone whenever he wants, so he started measuring time on the phone and devised a plan for encouraging Ritchie to talk less. Ritchie will receive his ordinary allowance of $20 each week, but for each minute over two hours that Ritchie was on the phone that week, his dad deducts $0.25 from the allowance.

16. Write a rule for the allowance Ritchie receives if he talks on the phone for n minutes a week. (Hint: You actually have two rules: One for less than 120 minutes and one for 120 minutes or more.)

Every time Bob (the used car salesman) sells a car he makes a $150 commission. However, he must pay the owner of the car lot (Mike) a $32 "membership fee" for each car sold. Bob wishes to earn $1,235 for a new riding lawn mower.

17. Write a rule for the net pay that Bob earns after n sales.

18. How many cars will he have to sell in order to purchase his new mower?

Roberta works at the Oakwood movie theater. The first row in the theater has 14 seats, and each row (except the first) has four more seats than the row before it.

19. Write and explain a rule for the number of seats in the nth row at Roberta's theater.

20. Which is the first row to have more than 100 seats?

The table below displays data relating temperature in degrees Farenheit to the number of chirps per minute for a cricket.

Temp (°F)	50	52	55	58	60	64	68
Chirps/min.	40	48	60	72	80	96	112

21. Write a formula or rule that predicts the number of chirps per minute when the temperature is n degrees.

ALGORITHMS

An **algorithm** is a sequence of actions to accomplish a task. It is the process of performing specific steps to solve a problem. Long division is an example of an algorithm. A **flowchart** is a visual way of presenting an algorithm.

EXAMPLE: Use the images below to carry out the algorithm.

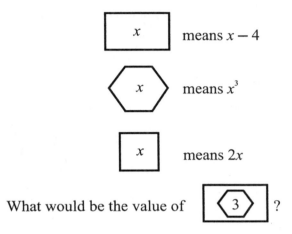

What would be the value of ?

Solution: The first step is to locate the 3. The three is directly in a hexagon, which is in a rectangle. The algorithm must be solved beginning with the shape that the number, 3, is directly in. Since it is in the hexagon, you must look at what the hexagon symbolizes. The hexagon symbolizes x^3, so substitute 3 in for x. $(3)^3 = 27$. The hexagon is in a rectangle, so now you must perform the operation of the rectangle, $x - 4$, on the result from the hexagon's operation. $27 - 4 = 23$. So the value of the algorithm is **23**.

Use the images below to solve the algorithms.

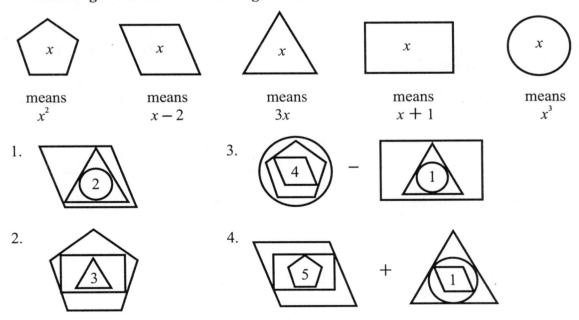

DEPUCTIVE AND INDUCTIVE ARGUMENTS

In general, there are two types of logical arguments: **deductive** and **inductive**. Deductive arguments tend to move from general statements or theories to more specific conclusions. Inductive arguments tend to move from specific observations to general theories.

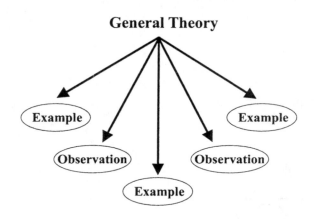

Deductive Reasoning

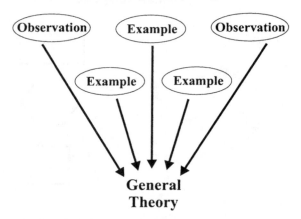

Inductive Reasoning

Compare the two examples below:

Deductive Argument

Premise 1	All men are mortal.
Premise 2	Socrates is a man.
Conclusion	Socrates is mortal.

Inductive Argument

Premise 1	The sun rose this morning.
Premise 2	The sun rose yesterday morning.
Premise 3	The sun rose two days ago.
Premise 4	The sun rose three days ago.
Conclusion	The sun will rise tomorrow.

An inductive argument cannot be proved beyond a shadow of a doubt. For example, it's a pretty good bet that the sun will come up tomorrow, but the sun not coming up presents no logical contradiction.

On the other hand, a deductive argument can have logical certainty, but it must be properly constructed. Consider the examples below.

True Conclusion for an Invalid Argument

All men are mortal.
Socrates is mortal.
Therefore, Socrates is a man.

Even though the above conclusion is true, the argument is based on invalid logic. Both men and women are mortal. Therefore, Socrates could be a woman.

False Conclusion from a Valid Argument

All astronauts are men.
Julia Roberts is an astronaut.
Therefore, Julia Roberts is a man.

In this case, the conclusion is false because the premises are false. However, the logic of the argument is valid because *if* the premises were true, then the conclusion would be true.

EXAMPLE 1: Which argument is valid?

If you speed on Hill Street, you will get a ticket.
If you get a ticket, you will pay a fine.

A. I paid a fine, so I was speeding on Hill Street.
B. I got a ticket, so I was speeding on Hill Street.
C. I exceeded the speed limit on Hill Street, so I paid a fine.
D. I did not speed on Hill Street, so I did not pay a fine.

Answer: C is valid.
A is incorrect. I could have paid a fine for another violation.
B is incorrect. I could have gotten a ticket for some other violation.
D is incorrect. I could have paid a fine for speeding somewhere else.

EXAMPLE 2: Assume the given proposition is true. Then, determine if each statement is true or false.

Given: If a dog is thirsty, he will drink.

A. If a dog drinks, then he is thirsty.   T or F
B. If a dog is not thirsty, he will not drink.   T or F
C. If a dog will not drink, he is not thirsty.   T or F

Answer: A is false. He is not necessarily thirsty; he could just drink because other dogs are drinking or drink to show others his control of the water. This statement is the converse of the original.
B is false. The reasoning from A applies. This statement is the inverse of the original.
C is true. It is the **contrapositive,** or the complete opposite of the original.

For numbers 1–5, what conclusion can be drawn from each proposition?

1. All squirrels are rodents. All rodents are mammals. Therefore,

2. All fractions are rational numbers. All rational numbers are real numbers. Therefore,

3. All squares are rectangles. All rectangles are parallelograms. All parallelograms are quadrilaterals. Therefore,

4. All Chevrolets are made by General Motors. All Luminas are Chevrolets. Therefore,

5. If a number is even and divisible by three, then it is divisible by six. Eighteen is divisible by six. Therefore,

For numbers 6–9, assume the given proposition is true. Then, determine if the statements following it are true or false.

All squares are rectangles.

6. All rectangles are squares.   T or F
7. All non-squares are non-rectangles.   T or F
8. No squares are non-rectangles.   T or F
9. All non-rectangles are non-squares.   T or F

CHAPTER 20 REVIEW

Find the pattern for the following number sequences, and then find the *n*th number requested.

1. 0, 1, 2, 3, 4   pattern _____

2. 0, 1, 2, 3, 4   20th number _____

3. 1, 3, 5, 7, 9   pattern _____

4. 1, 3, 5, 7, 9   25th number _____

5. 3, 6, 9, 12, 15   pattern _____

6. 3, 6, 9, 12, 15   30th number _____

Olivia starts, maintains, and sells ant farms as a hobby. She had 500 ants in 1996, 2,000 in 1997, and 8,000 in 1998.

7. If she continues to grow as she has since 1996, how many ants will she have in 2000?

8. How many in the *n*th year after 1996?

9. In what year would she have more than 100,000 ants?

10. Sean is studying bacteria and antibiotics. Using standard measurement and estimation techniques, he records a reading of about 100,000 bacteria on a lab dish. He then applies a drop of antibiotic and does another bacteria count every 30 minutes. He finds 90,000 after 30 minutes, 81,000 after 60 minutes, 72,900 after 90 minutes, and 65,610 after 120 minutes. How many do you predict he will find 150 minutes after applying the antibiotic?

Justin has just got a bill from his Internet Service Provider. The first four months of charges for his service are recorded in the table below.

	January	February	March	April
Hours	0	10	5	25
Charge	$4.95	$14.45	$9.70	$28.70

11. Write a formula for the cost of *n* hours of Internet service.

12. What is the greatest number of hours he can get on the Internet and still keep his bill under $20.00?

Lisa is baking cookies for the Fall Festival. She bakes 27 cookies with each batch of batter. However, she has a defective oven, which results in 5 cookies in each batch being burnt.

13. Write a formula for the number of cookies available for the festival as a result of Lisa baking n batches of cookies.

14. How many batches does she need in order to produce 300 cookies for the festival?

15. How many cookies (counting burnt ones) will she actually bake?

Use the images below to solve the algorithms.

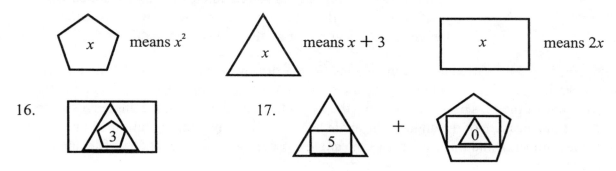

16.

17.

Chapter 21: Angles

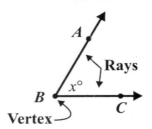

Angles are made up of two rays with a common endpoint. Rays are named by the endpoint B and another point on the ray. Ray $\overrightarrow{BA}$ and ray $\overrightarrow{BC}$ share a common endpoint.

Angles are usually named by three capital letters. The middle letter names the vertex. The angle to the left can be named ∠ABC or ∠CBA. An angle can also be named by a lower case letter between the sides, ∠x, or by the vertex alone, ∠B.

A protractor, ⌓, is used to measure angles. The protractor is divided evenly into a half circle of 180 degrees (180°). When the middle of the bottom of the protractor is placed on the vertex, and one of the rays of the angle is lined up with 0°, the other ray of the angle crosses the protractor at the measure of the angle. The angle below has the ray pointing left lined up with 0° (the outside numbers), and the other ray of the angle crosses the protractor at 55°. The angle measures 55°.

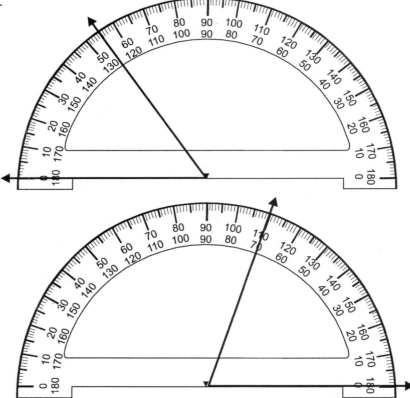

The angle above has the ray pointing right lined up with 0° using the inside numbers. The other ray crosses the protractor and measures the angle at 70°.

262

TYPES OF ANGLES

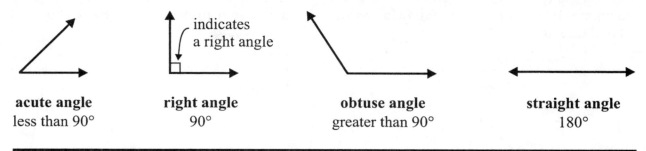

acute angle
less than 90°

right angle
90°

indicates
a right angle

obtuse angle
greater than 90°

straight angle
180°

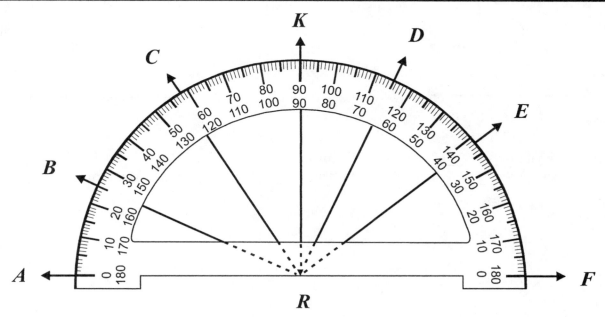

Using the protractor above, find the measure of the following angles. Then, tell what type
of angle it is: acute, right, obtuse, or straight.

	Measure	Type of Angle
1. What is the measure of angle *ARF*?	_____	_____
2. What is the measure of angle *CRF*?	_____	_____
3. What is the measure of angle *BRF*?	_____	_____
4. What is the measure of angle *ERF*?	_____	_____
5. What is the measure of angle *ARB*?	_____	_____
6. What is the measure of angle *KRA*?	_____	_____
7. What is the measure of angle *CRA*?	_____	_____
8. What is the measure of angle *DRF*?	_____	_____
9. What is the measure of angle *ARD*?	_____	_____
10. What is the measure of angle *FRK*?	_____	_____

MEASURING ANGLES

Estimate the measure of the following angles. Then, use your protractor to record the actual measure.

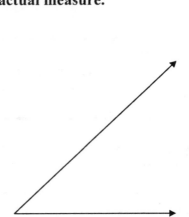  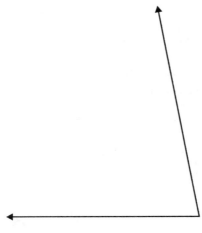

1.   Estimate = _____ °
      Measure = _____ °

4.   Estimate = _____ °
      Measure = _____ °

7.   Estimate = _____ °
      Measure = _____ °

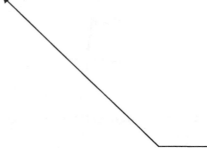 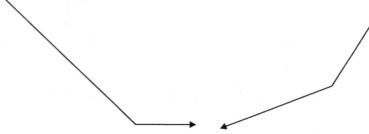 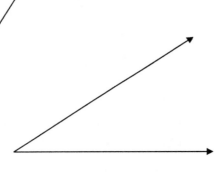

2.   Estimate = _____ °
      Measure = _____ °

5.   Estimate = _____ °
      Measure = _____ °

8.   Estimate = _____ °
      Measure = _____ °

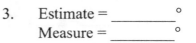

3.   Estimate = _____ °
      Measure = _____ °

6.   Estimate = _____ °
      Measure = _____ °

9.   Estimate = _____ °
      Measure = _____ °

CENTRAL ANGLES

In this chapter, you will learn about central angles and why they are important when making circle graphs.

A central angle is the angle formed by each "piece of the pie." The vertex of a central angle is in the center of the circle. Look at the diagram on the right.

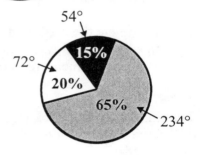

In circle graphs, the percentages have to add up to 100%, and the angles for each "piece of pie" must add up to 360°. Notice the pie graph to the right. Each percent of the pie is marked with a corresponding angle measure.

EXAMPLE: Consider the following data:

Survey of fiction reading preferences among 300 high school students	
Romance novels	70
Science fiction	60
Fantasy	90
Historical novels	40
Poetry	10
Mysteries	30

Step 1: First, you need to find what percent of the total each type of fiction represents. Divide each item in the survey by the total number of students. For example, according to the chart, 70 out of 300 students prefer romance novels, so to find the percent, divide 70 by 300. Rounding to the nearest percent, you get 23%. Repeat for each type of fiction.

Step 2: Multiply the percent of each type of fiction by 360° to figure out how many degrees each "piece of pie" should be. For romance novels, 23% of 360° is 83° (rounded to the nearest degree).

	Number of Students	% of total	Central angle of the circle
Romance novels	70	23%	83°
Science fiction	60	20%	72°
Fantasy	90	30%	108°
Historical novels	40	13%	47°
Poetry	12	4%	14°
Mysteries	30	10%	36°
	300	100%	360°

Complete the following exercises on central angles.

A dartboard has been divided into wedges according to the following color percentages.

blue	30%
red	25%
yellow	10%
green	35%

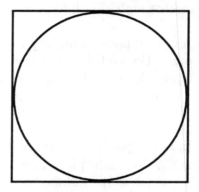

1.   Find the central angle measurements of each color.

2.   Complete the dartboard by drawing each color wedge to scale. Label each color on the dartboard and indicate the measure of each central angle.

The students at Maverick High School voted on Teacher-of-the-Year. The Student Council tallied the 720 total votes and created a pie chart.

Mr. Perry	252
Mrs. Nance	180
Miss Murphy	144
Mr. Bard	87
Mr. Olson	36
All Others	21

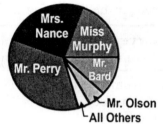

3.   Calculate the percent of the votes that each teacher received.

4.   Calculate the measures of each central angle on the pie chart.

Other central angle type questions involve a clock. These are very similar to the pie chart.

EXAMPLE: The second hand on a clock goes from the 11 to the 2. How many degrees has the second hand traveled?

Step 1:   You know that there are 60 seconds in a minute. The second hand traveled 15 seconds out of 60 as it went from the 11 to the 2. $15 \div 60 = .25$ or 25%.

Step 2:   Multiply the percent by 360° just like you did for the pie chart. $.25 \times 360 = 90°$. So, the second hand traveled 90°.

Calculate how many degrees the second hand travels for the following:

5.   12 to 3   _____   8.   6 to 3   _____
6.   9 to 11   _____   9.   12 to 1   _____
7.   4 to 10   _____   10.   3 to 5   _____

ADJACENT ANGLES

Adjacent angles are two angles that have the same vertex and share one ray. They do not share space inside the angles.

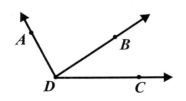

In this diagram, $\angle ADB$ is **adjacent** to $\angle BDC$.

However, $\angle ADB$ is **not adjacent** to $\angle ADC$ because adjacent angles do not share any space inside the angle.

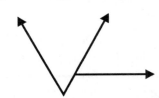

These two angles are **not adjacent.** They share a common ray but do not share the same vertex.

For each diagram below, name the angle that is adjacent to it.

1.

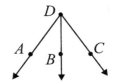

$\angle CDB$ is adjacent to $\angle$ _____

2.

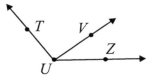

$\angle TUV$ is adjacent to $\angle$ _____

3.

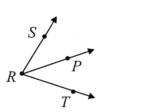

$\angle SRP$ is adjacent to $\angle$ _____

4.

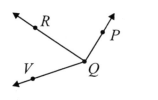

$\angle PQR$ is adjacent to $\angle$ _____

5.

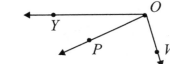

$\angle YOP$ is adjacent to $\angle$ _____

6.

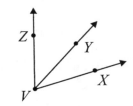

$\angle XVY$ is adjacent to $\angle$ _____

7.

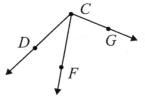

$\angle DCF$ is adjacent to $\angle$ _____

8.

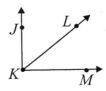

$\angle JKL$ is adjacent to $\angle$ _____

VERTICAL ANGLES

When two lines intersect, two pairs of vertical angles are formed. Vertical angles are not adjacent. Vertical angles have the same measure.

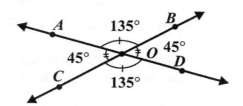

∠AOB and ∠COD are vertical angles. ∠AOC and ∠BOD are vertical angles. **Vertical angles** are **congruent**. Congruent means they have the same measure.

In the diagrams below, name the second angle in each pair of vertical angles.

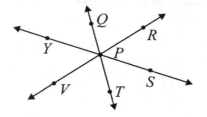

1. ∠YPV _____   4. ∠VPT _____

2. ∠QPR _____   5. ∠RPT _____

3. ∠SPT _____   6. ∠VPS _____

7. ∠MLN _____   10. ∠GLM _____

8. ∠KLH _____   11. ∠KLM _____

9. ∠GLN _____   12. ∠HLG _____

Use the information given to find the measure of each unknown vertical angle.

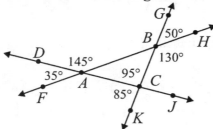

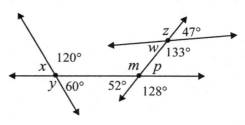

13. ∠CAF = _____   19. ∠x = _____

14. ∠ABC = _____   20. ∠y = _____

15. ∠KCJ = _____   21. ∠z = _____

16. ∠ABG = _____   22. ∠w = _____

17. ∠BCJ = _____   23. ∠m = _____

18. ∠CAB = _____   24. ∠p = _____

COMPLEMENTARY AND SUPPLEMENTARY ANGLES

Two angles are **complementary** if the sum of the measures of the angles is 90°.
Two angles are **supplementary** if the sum of the measures of the angles is 180°.

The angles may be adjacent but do not need to be.

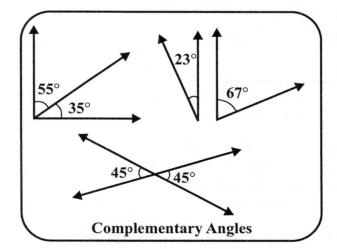

Complementary Angles

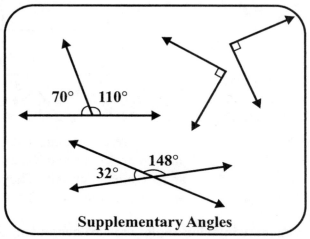

Supplementary Angles

Calculate the measure of each unknown angle.

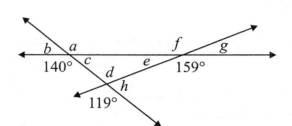

1. ∠a = _____   5. ∠e = _____

2. ∠b = _____   6. ∠f = _____

3. ∠c = _____   7. ∠g = _____

4. ∠d = _____   8. ∠h = _____

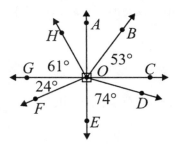
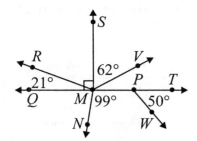
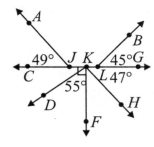

9. ∠AOB = _____   13. ∠RMS = _____   17. ∠AJK = _____

10. ∠COD = _____   14. ∠VMT = _____   18. ∠CKD = _____

11. ∠EOF = _____   15. ∠QMN = _____   19. ∠FKH = _____

12. ∠AOH = _____   16. ∠WPQ = _____   20. ∠BLC = _____

CORRESPONDING, ALTERNATE INTERIOR, AND ALTERNATE EXTERIOR ANGLES

If two parallel lines are intersected by a **transversal**, a line passing through both parallel lines, the **corresponding angles** are congruent.

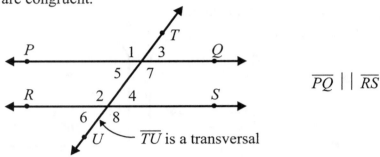

$\overline{PQ} \parallel \overline{RS}$

$\overline{TU}$ is a transversal

∠1 and ∠2 are congruent. They are corresponding angles.
∠3 and ∠4 are congruent. They are corresponding angles.
∠5 and ∠6 are congruent. They are corresponding angles.
∠7 and ∠8 are congruent. They are corresponding angles.

Alternate interior angles are also congruent. They are on opposite sides of the transversal and inside the parallel lines.

∠5 and ∠4 are congruent. They are alternate interior angles.
∠7 and ∠2 are congruent. They are alternate interior angles.

Alternate exterior angles are also congruent. They are on opposite sides of the transversal and above and below the parallel lines.

∠1 and ∠8 are congruent. They are alternate exterior angles.
∠3 and ∠6 are congruent. They are alternate exterior angles.

Look at the diagram below. For each pair of angles, state whether they are corresponding (C), alternate interior (I), alternate exterior (E), vertical (V), or supplementary angles (S).

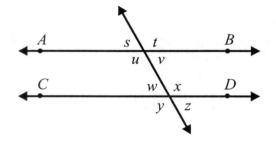

$\overline{AB}$ and $\overline{CD}$ are parallel.

1. ∠u , ∠x _____
2. ∠w , ∠s _____
3. ∠t , ∠y _____
4. ∠s , ∠t _____
5. ∠w , ∠y _____

6. ∠t , ∠x _____
7. ∠w , ∠z _____
8. ∠v , ∠w _____
9. ∠v , ∠z _____
10. ∠s , ∠z _____

11. ∠t , ∠u _____
12. ∠w , ∠x _____
13. ∠w , ∠s _____
14. ∠s , ∠v _____
15. ∠x , ∠z _____

270

ANGLE RELATIONSHIPS

When two lines meet at a point, they form an angle. On the Ohio test, you will be asked to apply knowledge of angle relationships to real-world situations. You will also apply these skills in later classes in mathematics.

Example: Make a graphic relationship between a clock and a Cartesian plane. Draw and explain two congruent triangles using the digits on the clock.

    1.   Use the center of a clock as the origin of the Cartesian plane.
    2.   The x-axis aligns with the hours 3 and 9. The y-axis aligns with the hours 12 and 6.
    3.   The clock can be divided into four quadrants, each of 90 degrees on the Cartesian plane.

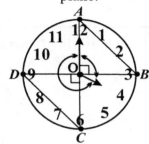

Point $A = 12$. Point $B = 3$. Point $C = 6$. Point $D = 9$. O is the center.

    1. $\overline{OA} = \overline{OB} = \overline{OC} = \overline{OD}$. Points on the circumference are equal distance from the center.
    2. $\angle AOB = \angle COD$. First and third quadrants of the Cartesian plane.
    3. $\triangle AOB \cong \triangle COD$.

---

1.   Find the measure of the two angles formed in each case by the hands of the clock, a) at 7:00 a.m. and b) at 2:00 p.m.

2.   A grandfather clock, that is supposed to strike a bell at every hour, does not work properly when the hands of the clock form angles in which one angle formed is twice the measure of the opposite angle. Is there a time when this event would happen? If so, find the two times.

3.   Given: $\overline{PQ} \parallel \overline{MN}$
    $\overline{AB}$ intersects $\overline{PQ}$ at R, and $\overline{MN}$ at S
    $\angle ARP = 5x$ and $\angle ASN = 13x$
    Find the measures of all angles in degrees.

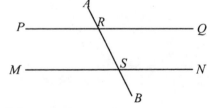

4.   If two parallel lines are cut by a transversal, find the measures of:
    a.   Two alternate exterior angles represented by $x + 14$ and $2x - 39$
    b.   Two corresponding angles represented by $4x + 10$ and $5x - 5$
    c.   Two exterior angles on the same side of the transversal whose values are $3x$ and $7x$.

5.   Given $\overline{MN}$ and $\overline{OP}$ are parallel and the measures of some of the angles shown in the figures, find the value of the remaining angles.

    a. $\angle B = 62°$ and $\angle G = 103°$ b. $\angle C = 76°$ and $\angle F = 34°$

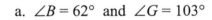

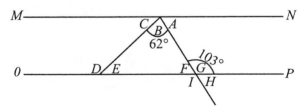

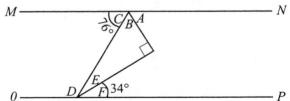

SUM OF INTERIOR ANGLES OF A POLYGON

Given a polygon, you can find the sum of the measures of the interior angles using the following formula:

Sum of the measures of the interior angles = $180°(n - 2)$
where n is the number of sides of the polygon.

EXAMPLE: Find the sum of the measures of the interior angles of the following polygon:

The figure has 8 sides. Using the formula we have $180°(8 - 2) = 180°(6) = 1080°$.

Using the formula, $180°(n - 2)$, find the sum of the interior angles of the following figures.

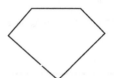 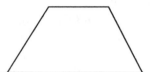

1. _____   4. _____   7. _____   10. _____

  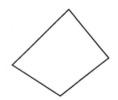 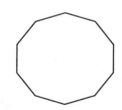

2. _____   5. _____   8. _____   11. _____

  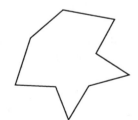 

3. _____   6. _____   9. _____   12. _____

272

CONGRUENT FIGURES

Two figures are **congruent** when they are exactly the same size and shape. If the corresponding sides and angles of two figures are congruent, then the figures themselves are congruent. For example, look at the two triangles below.

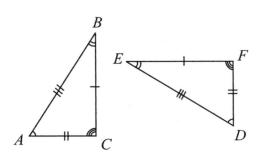

Compare the lengths of the sides of the triangles. The slash marks indicate that $\overline{AB}$ and $\overline{ED}$ have the same length. Therefore, they are congruent, which can be expressed as $AB \cong ED$. We can also see that $BC \cong EF$ and $AC \cong FD$. In other words, the corresponding sides are congruent. Now, compare the corresponding angles. The arc markings show that the corresponding angles have the same measure and are, therefore, congruent: $\angle A \cong \angle D$, $\angle B \cong \angle E$, and $\angle C \cong \angle F$. Because the corresponding sides and angles of the triangles are congruent, we say that the triangles are congruent: $\triangle ABC \cong \triangle DEF$.

EXAMPLE 1: Decide whether the figures in each pair below are congruent or not.

PAIR 1

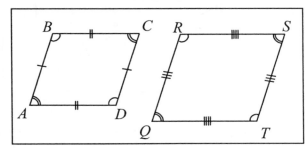

PAIR 2

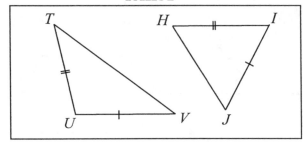

In Pair 1, the two parallelograms have congruent corresponding angles. However, because the corresponding sides of the parallelogram are not the same size, the figures are not congruent.

In Pair 2, the two triangles have two corresponding sides which are congruent. However, the hypotenuses of these triangles are not congruent (indicated by the lack of a triple hash mark), so the triangles are not congruent.

PAIR 3

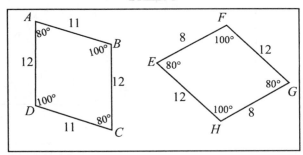

PAIR 4

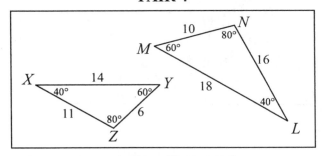

In Pair 3, all of the corresponding angles of these parallelograms are congruent; however, the corresponding sides are not congruent. Therefore, these figures are not congruent.

In Pair 4, the triangles share congruent corresponding angles, but the measures for all three corresponding sides of the triangles are not congruent. Therefore, the triangles are not congruent.

273

Examine the pairs of corresponding figures below. On the first line below the figures, write whether the figures are congruent or not congruent. On the second line, write a brief explanation of how you chose your answer.

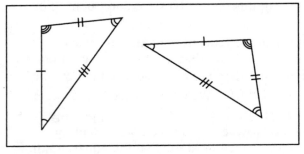

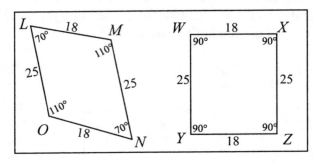

1. _____

4. _____

_____

_____

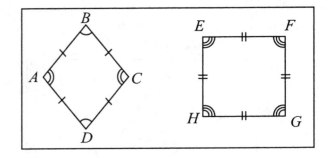

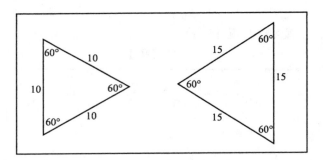

2. _____

5. _____

_____

_____

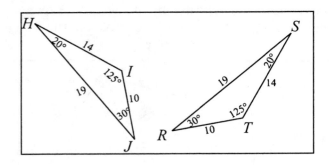

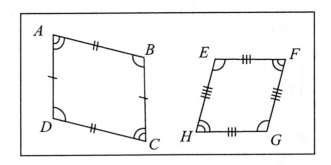

3. _____

6. _____

_____

_____

ANGLE APPLICATIONS

Using rules for angles, workers in diverse fields can develop new innovations, complete creative projects, and maintain uniform designs.

EXAMPLE 1: An architect examined the drawing below. Using the ancient Incan building system of interlocking similar trapezoidal blocks, the architect hopes to create a wall which is resistant to earthquakes. What is the degree angle of the region labeled *x*?

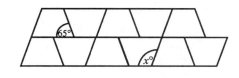

Solution: Using the rules of supplementary angles, we find that the corresponding angle is $180° - 65° = 115°$. Using the rules of alternate interior angles, we find the $115°$ angle to be the same as $m\angle x$.

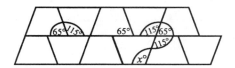

Examine the problems below. Using the rules you have learned in this chapter, solve for *x*.

1. Mr. Ramirez was installing a new slide at the city park. In order to be certain the slide is welded properly, he will need to know the angle where the supporting beams meet the slide. Knowing the sum of the angle measures of a triangle, which of the following statements is true?

    A. The right angle plus $m\angle x = 135°$
    B. The right angle minus $m\angle x = 30°$
    C. $30° + m\angle x = 45°$
    D. $30° +$ the right angle $= 110°$

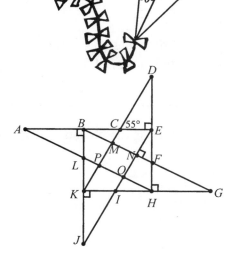

2. Danny and Eddie were trying to come up with the ideal model for a high flying kite. Knowing the sum of the angle measures of a triangle and the laws of congruent shapes, which of the following statements is correct?

    A. $\angle d = \angle b$
    B. $\angle a + \angle c = 90°$
    C. $\angle c = 45°$
    D. $\angle d - \angle a = 15°$

3. Examine the quilt pattern on the right. Using the rule of vertical angles and knowing the sum of the angle measures of a triangle, which of the following statements is correct?

    A. $m\angle LAB + m\angle LPK = 135°$
    B. $m\angle KHL + m\angle HLB = 90°$
    C. $m\angle KHF - m\angle NEF = 25°$
    D. $m\angle MCE - m\angle IOH = 35°$

275

CHAPTER 21 REVIEW

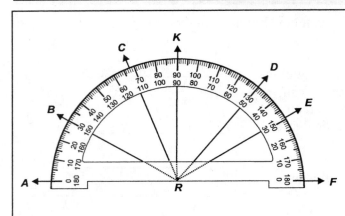

1. What is the measure of ∠DRA?

   _____

2. What is the measure of ∠CRF?

   _____

3. What is the measure of ∠ARB?

   _____

4. Which angle is a supplementary angle to ∠EDF?

   _____

5. What is the measure of angle ∠GDF?

   _____

6. Which 2 angles are right angles?

   _____ and _____

7. What is the measure of ∠EDF?

   _____

8. Which angle is adjacent to ∠BAD?

   _____

9. Which angle is a complementary angle to ∠HAD?

   _____

10. What is the measure of ∠HAB?

    _____

11. What is the measure of ∠CAD?

    _____

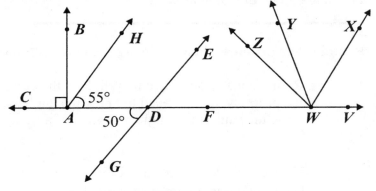

12. What kind of angle is ∠FDA?

    _____

13. What kind of angle is ∠GDA?

    _____

14. Which angles are adjacent to ∠EDA?

    _____ and _____

15. Measure ∠VWX with a protractor.

    _____

16. Measure ∠FWY with a protractor.

    _____

17. Measure ∠VWY with a protractor.

    _____

276

Look at the diagram below. For each pair of angles, state whether they are corresponding (C), alternate interior (I), alternate exterior (E), vertical (V), or supplementary angles (S).

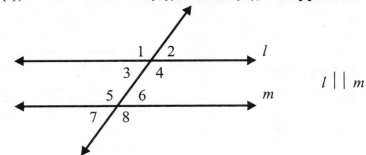

18. ∠1 and ∠4 _____

19. ∠2 and ∠6 _____

20. ∠1 and ∠3 _____

21. ∠5 and ∠8 _____

22. ∠5 and ∠7 _____

23. ∠6 and ∠5 _____

24. ∠2 and ∠7 _____

25. ∠1 and ∠2 _____

26. ∠4 and ∠5 _____

27. ∠6 and ∠8 _____

28. ∠3 and ∠6 _____

29. ∠4 and ∠8 _____

30. ∠1 and ∠5 _____

31. ∠2 and ∠3 _____

32. The second hand on a clock moves from the 6 to the 9. How many degrees has the second hand traveled?

33. If you constructed a pie chart for J & K's budget, what would be the central angle measure for office expenses?

34. If you constructed a pie chart for J & K's budget, what would be the central angle measure for advertising?

J & K Manufacturing Company 2 million dollar spending budget	
Cost of Goods Sold	$750,000
Advertising	$500,000
Payroll and Benefits	$350,000
Warehouse Supplies	$160,000
Office Expenses	$150,000
Utilities	$56,000
Other	$34,000

35. Lem wanted to cut a rusted stop sign into quarters in his shop class. Which of the following statements is factual?

A. $m\angle ABF = 67.5°$
B. $m\angle CBF + m\angle BAH = 135°$
C. $m\angle HGF = 67.5°$
D. $m\angle BAH - m\angle HIF = 35°$

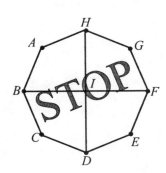

36. A railroad track cuts through two parallel roads. If angle 1 and angle 2 are congruent, which of the following statements is factual?

A. $m\angle 1 + m\angle 2 = 180°$
B. $m\angle 1 - m\angle 2 = 0$
C. $m\angle 1 + m\angle 2 = 90°$
D. $m\angle 1 - m\angle 2 = 90°$

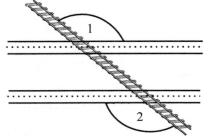

37. Peter is building a stained glass window for his bathroom. If the blue triangle is isosceles and is also congruent to the yellow triangle, which of the following statements is factual?

A. $m\angle 1 + m\angle 2 = 180°$
B. $m\angle 1 - m\angle 2 = 90°$
C. $m\angle 1 - m\angle 2 = 30°$
D. $m\angle 1 + m\angle 2 = 90°$

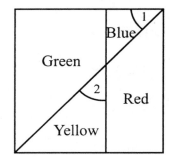

38. What is the sum of the measures of the interior angles in the figure below?

_____

Chapter 22: Triangles

INTERIOR ANGLES OF A TRIANGLE

The three interior angles of a triangle always add up to be 180°.

EXAMPLE 1:

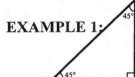

$$45° + 45° + 90° = 180°$$

$$30° + 60° + 90° = 180°$$

$$60° + 60° + 60° = 180°$$

EXAMPLE 2: Find the missing angle in the triangle.

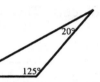

Solution:

$$20° + 125° + x = 180°$$
$$\underline{-20° \quad -125° \qquad -20° -125°}$$
$$x = 180° - \ 20° - \ 125°$$
$$x = 35°.$$

Subtract 20° and 125° from both sides to get x by itself.

The missing angle is 35°.

Find the missing angle in the triangles.

1.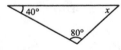

4.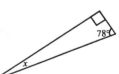

7.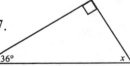

2.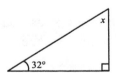

5.

8.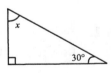

3.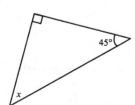

6.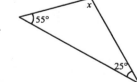

9.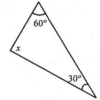

SIMILAR TRIANGLES

Two triangles are similar if the measurements of the three angles in both triangles are the same. If the three angles are the same, then their corresponding sides are proportional.

CORRESPONDING SIDES - The triangles below are similar. Therefore, the two shortest sides from each triangle, *c* and *f*, are corresponding. The two longest sides from each triangle, *a* and *d*, are corresponding. The two medium length sides, *b* and *e*, are corresponding.

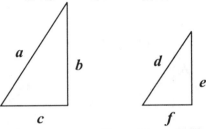

PROPORTIONAL - The corresponding sides of similar triangles are proportional to each other. This means if we know all the measurements of one triangle, and we only know one measurement of the other triangle, we can figure out the measurements of the other two sides with proportion problems. The two triangles below are similar.

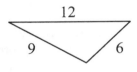 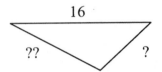

Note: **To set up the proportion correctly, it is important to keep the measurements of each triangle on opposite sides of the equal sign.**

To find the short side:	**To find the medium length side:**
Step 1: Set up the proportion.	**Step 1:** Set up the proportion.
$\dfrac{long\ side}{short\ side}$ $\dfrac{12}{6} = \dfrac{16}{?}$	$\dfrac{long\ side}{medium}$ $\dfrac{12}{9} = \dfrac{16}{??}$
Step 2: Solve the proportion as you did on the previous page.	**Step 2:** Solve the proportion as you did on the previous page.
$16 \times 6 = 96$ $96 \div 12 = 8$	$16 \times 9 = 144$ $144 \div 12 = 12$

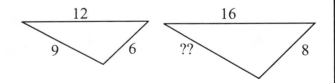 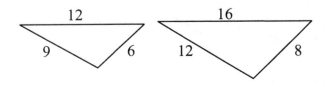

MORE SIMILAR TRIANGLES

Find the missing side from the following similar triangles.

1.

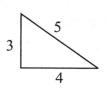

2.

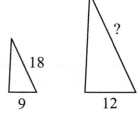

3.

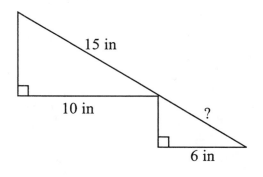

4.

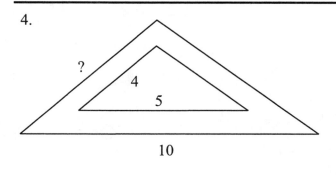

5.

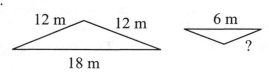

6.

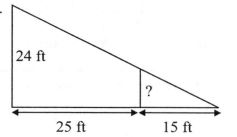

7.

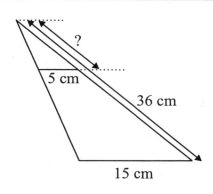

8.

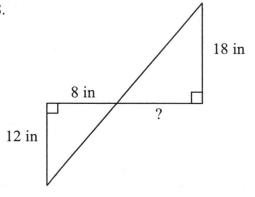

281

PYTHAGOREAN THEOREM

Pythagoras was a Greek mathematician and philosopher who lived around 600 B.C. He started a math club among Greek aristocrats called the Pythagoreans. Pythagoras formulated the **Pythagorean Theorem** which states that in a **right triangle**, the sum of the squares of the legs of the triangle are equal to the square of the hypotenuse. Most often you will see this formula written as $a^2 + b^2 = c^2$. **This relationship is only true for right triangles.**

EXAMPLE: Find the length of side c.

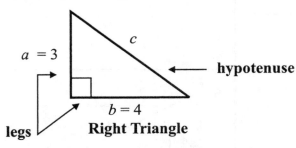

Formula: $a^2 + b^2 = c^2$
$$3^2 + 4^2 = c^2$$
$$9 + 16 = c^2$$
$$25 = c^2$$
$$\sqrt{25} = \sqrt{c^2}$$
$$5 = c$$

Find the hypotenuse of the following triangles. Round the answers to two decimal places.

1.

$c =$ _____

4.

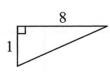

$c =$ _____

7.

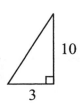

$c =$ _____

2.

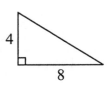

$c =$ _____

5.

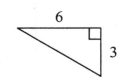

$c =$ _____

8.

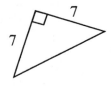

$c =$ _____

3.

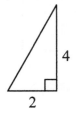

$c =$ _____

6.

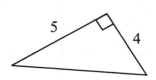

$c =$ _____

9.

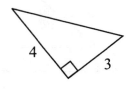

$c =$ _____

FINDING THE MISSING LEG OF A RIGHT TRIANGLE

In the right triangle shown, the measurement of the hypotenuse is known as well as one of the legs. To find the measurement of the other leg, use the Pythagorean Theorem by filling in the known measurements, and then solve for the unknown side.

In the formula, $a^2 + b^2 = c^2$, a and b are the legs, and c is always the hypotenuse. $9^2 + b^2 = 41^2$. Now solve for b algebraically.

$$81 + b^2 = 1681$$
$$b^2 = 1681 - 81$$
$$b^2 = 1600$$
$$\sqrt{b^2} = \sqrt{1600}$$
$$b = 40$$

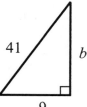

Practice finding the measure of the missing leg in each right triangle below.

1.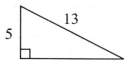

_____

2.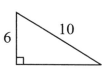

_____

3.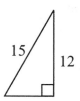

_____

4.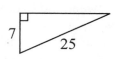

_____

5.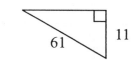

_____

6.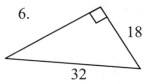

_____

7.

_____

8.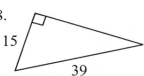

_____

9.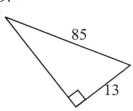

_____

APPLICATIONS OF THE PYTHAGOREAN THEOREM

The Pythagorean Theorem can be used to determine the distance between two points in some situations. Recall that the formula is written $a^2 + b^2 = c^2$.

EXAMPLE: Find the distance between point B and point A given that the length of each square is 1 inch long and 1 inch wide.

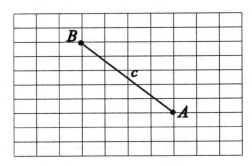

Step 1: Draw a straight line between the two points. We will call this side c.

Step 2: Draw two more lines, one from point B and one from point A. These lines should make a 90° angle. The two new lines will be labeled a and b. We do this to make a right triangle, so we can use the Pythagorean Theorem to find the distance.

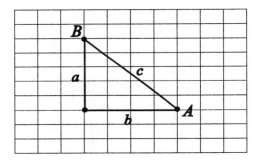

Step 3: Find the length of a and c by counting the number of squares each line has. We find that $a = 5$ inches and $b = 4$ inches. Now, substitute the values found into the Pythagorean Theorem.

$$a^2 + b^2 = c^2$$
$$5^2 + 4^2 = c^2$$
$$25 + 16 = c^2$$
$$41 = c^2$$
$$\sqrt{41} = \sqrt{c^2}$$
$$\sqrt{41} = c$$

Use the Pythagorean Theorem to find the distances asked. Round your answers to two decimal points.

Below is a diagram of the mall. Use the grid to help answer questions 1 and 2. Each square is 25 feet × 25 feet.

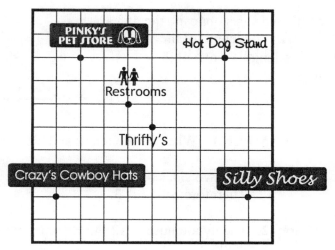

1. Marty walks from Pinky's Pet Store to the restrooms to wash his hands. How far did he walk?

2. Betty needs to meet her friend at Silly Shoes, but she wants to get a hot dog first. If Betty is at Thrifty's, how far will she walk to meet her friend?

Below is a diagram of a football field. Use the grid on the football field to help find the answers to questions 3 and 4. Each square is 10 yards × 10 yards.

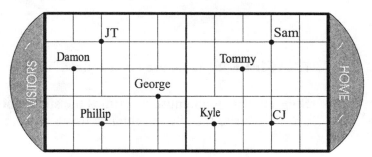

3. George must throw the football to a teammate before he is tackled. If CJ is the only person open, how far must George be able to throw the ball?

4. Damon has the football and is about to make a touchdown. If Phillip tries to stop him, how far must he run to reach Damon?

SPECIAL RIGHT TRIANGLES

Two right triangles are special right triangles if they have fixed ratios among their sides.

45-45-90 Triangles

In a 45-45-90 triangle, the two sides opposite the 45°
angles will always be equal. The length of the
hypotenuse is $\sqrt{2}$ times the length of one of the
sides opposite a 45° angle.

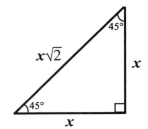

EXAMPLE 1: What are the lengths of sides a and b?

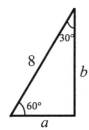

Step 1: The two sides opposite the 45° angles are equal.
Therefore, side $b = 3$.

Step 2: The hypotenuse is $\sqrt{2}$ times the length of a side opposite a 45°
angle.
Therefore, $a = 3 \times \sqrt{2}$
Simplify: $a = 3\sqrt{2}$

30-60-90 Triangles

In a 30-60-90 triangle, the side opposite the 30° angle
is the shortest leg. The side opposite the 60° angle is
$\sqrt{3}$ times as long as the shortest leg, and the hypotenuse
is twice as long as the shortest leg.

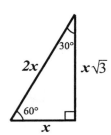

EXAMPLE 2: What are the lengths of sides a and b?

Step 1: The hypotenuse is 2 times the side opposite the 30° angle.
Write the above sentence using algebra and then solve.

$$8 = 2a$$
$$\frac{8}{2} = \frac{2a}{2}$$
$$4 = a$$

Step 2: Now that we know that the shortest leg has a length of 4,
the side opposite the 60° angle can be calculated easily.

$$b = a \times \sqrt{3}$$
$$b = 4 \times \sqrt{3}$$
$$b = 4\sqrt{3}$$

Find the missing leg of each of the special right triangles. Simplify your answers.

1.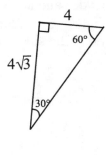
4

60°

4√3

30°

_____

3.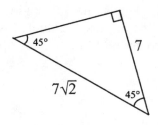
45°

7

7√2

45°

_____

5.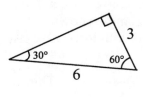
3

30°

60°

6

_____

2.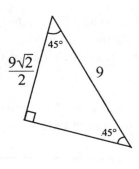
45°

$\frac{9\sqrt{2}}{2}$

9

45°

_____

4.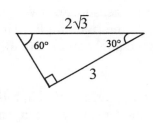
2√3

60°

30°

3

_____

6.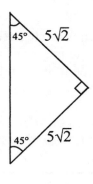
45°

5√2

45°

5√2

_____

Find the lengths of sides *a* and *b* in each of the special right triangles.

7.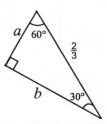
a

60°

$\frac{2}{3}$

b

30°

$a =$ _____ $b =$ _____

9.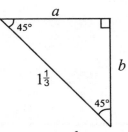
a

45°

$1\frac{1}{3}$

b

45°

$a =$ _____ $b =$ _____

11.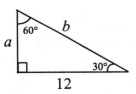
60°

b

a

30°

12

$a =$ _____ $b =$ _____

8.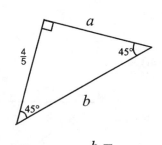
a

$\frac{4}{5}$

45°

45°

b

$a =$ _____ $b =$ _____

10.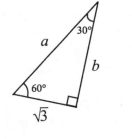
30°

a

b

60°

√3

$a =$ _____ $b =$ _____

12.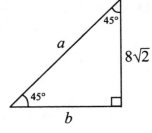
45°

a

8√2

45°

b

$a =$ _____ $b =$ _____

BASIC TRIGONOMETRIC RATIOS

Trigonometry is a mathematical topic that applies the relationships between sides and angles in right triangles. Recall that a right triangle has one 90° angle and two acute angles. Consider the right triangle shown below. Note that the angles are labeled with capital letters. The sides are labeled with lowercase letters that correspond to the angles opposite them.

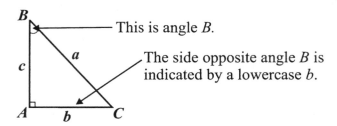

— This is angle B.

The side opposite angle B is indicated by a lowercase b.

Trigonometric ratios are ratios of the measures of two sides of a right triangle and are related to the acute angles of a right triangle, not the right angle. The value of a trigonometric ratio is dependent only on the size of the acute angle and is not affected by the lengths of the sides of the triangle.

We will consider the three basic trigonometric ratios in this section: **sine, cosine, and tangent.** Definitions and descriptions of the sine, cosine, and tangent functions are presented below.

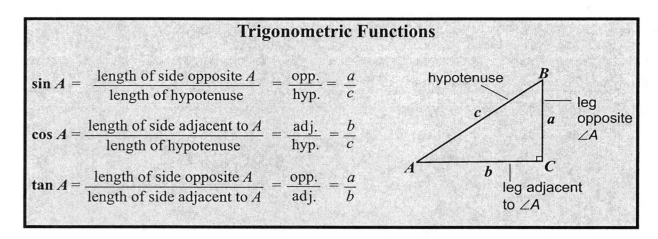

Trigonometric Functions

$$\sin A = \frac{\text{length of side opposite } A}{\text{length of hypotenuse}} = \frac{\text{opp.}}{\text{hyp.}} = \frac{a}{c}$$

$$\cos A = \frac{\text{length of side adjacent to } A}{\text{length of hypotenuse}} = \frac{\text{adj.}}{\text{hyp.}} = \frac{b}{c}$$

$$\tan A = \frac{\text{length of side opposite } A}{\text{length of side adjacent to } A} = \frac{\text{opp.}}{\text{adj.}} = \frac{a}{b}$$

EXAMPLE 1: For right triangle ABC, find $\sin A$, $\cos A$, $\tan A$, $\sin C$, $\cos C$, and $\tan C$.

$$\sin A = \frac{\text{opp.}}{\text{hyp.}} = \frac{3}{5} = 0.6 \qquad \sin C = \frac{\text{opp.}}{\text{hyp.}} = \frac{4}{5} = 0.8$$

$$\cos A = \frac{\text{adj.}}{\text{hyp.}} = \frac{4}{5} = 0.8 \qquad \cos C = \frac{\text{adj.}}{\text{hyp.}} = \frac{3}{5} = 0.6$$

$$\tan A = \frac{\text{opp.}}{\text{adj.}} = \frac{3}{4} = 0.75 \qquad \tan C = \frac{\text{opp.}}{\text{adj.}} = \frac{4}{3} = 1.\overline{3}$$

Find sin *A*, cos *A*, tan *A*, sin *B*, cos *B*, and tan *B* in each of the following right triangles. Express answers as fractions and as decimals rounded to three decimal places.

1.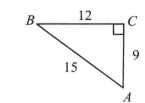

4.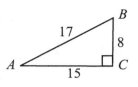

7.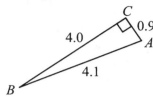

2.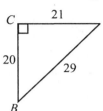

5.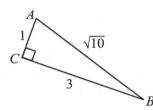

8.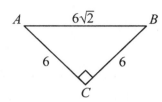

3.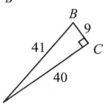

6.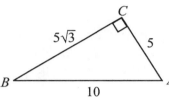

9.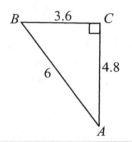

Once the values of the trigonometric ratios are found, then the values of the angles within the triangle can be found using the arcsine and arccosine. The arcsine, arccosine, and arctangent can also be written as sin^{-1}, cos^{-1}, and tan^{-1}. The arc functions' identities can be defined as:

$$\text{arcsin}(\sin(A)) = A$$
$$\text{arccos}(\cos(A)) = A$$
$$\text{arctan}(\tan(A)) = A$$

EXAMPLE 2: For right triangle *ABC*, where sin *A* = .6, find the values of angles *A* and *C*. Round to the nearest whole number.

Step 1: Using your calculator, arcsine is sin^{-1}. **
sin *A* = .6
sin^{-1}(sin *A*) = sin^{-1}(.6)   Take the arcsine of both sides.
A = 37°

Step 2: Since all the angles in a triangle add up to 180°, and *A* = 37° and *B* = 90°, then
A + *B* + *C* = 180°
37° + 90° + *C* = 180°
C = 180° − 37° − 90° = 53°
Therefore, *A* = 37°, *B* = 90°, and *C* = 53°

** To find the arcsine or arccosine using a TI-83 calculator, you must press the 2nd button, then press the trig function, SIN, COS, or TAN. After this, sin^{-1}, cos^{-1}, or tan^{-1} will appear onto the screen and you can enter the trig ratio, such as .6 from the example above. When finding an angle using a TI-83, you must always remember to be in degree mode. To check this, press MODE and make sure that Degree is highlighted, not Radian. If Degree is not highlighted, then go down and over to Degree and press ENTER. This will highlight Degree. To get out of this menu, hit 2nd, then MODE.
In other simpler scientific calculators, you might have to type the trig ratio, .6, first, then type 2nd SIN, 2nd COS, or 2nd TAN. If there isn't a 2nd button, you will have to type the trig ratio, then press the inverse button and the SIN, COS, or TAN button. The inverse button is usually abbreviated INV.

Find the values of the angles given the trigonometric function. Round your answers to the nearest degree.

1. $\sin A = .4$

2. $\tan x = 1$

3. $\sin b = .7$

4. $\cos C = \frac{\sqrt{2}}{2}$

5. $\tan A = -1.5$

6. $\cos y = -1$

7. $\sin B = -.6$

8. $\cos A = 0$

9. $\tan z = 2.6$

10. $\tan c = 50$

11. $\sin x = \frac{\sqrt{2}}{2}$

12. $\cos x = .1$

13. $\tan y = 0$

14. $\cos a = -.4$

15. $\sin C = 1$

The values of the trigonometric functions can also be determined if one or both of the measures of the acute angles is given.

EXAMPLE 3: Find the values of the sine, cosine, and tangent functions of both acute angles in the right triangle ABC shown at right.

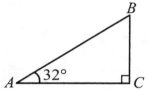

Step 1: Find the third angle.
$A + B + C = 180°$
$32° + B + 90° = 180°$
$B = 180° - 32° - 90° = 58°$

Step 2: Plug the angle values into $\sin A$, $\cos A$, $\tan A$, $\sin B$, $\cos B$, and $\tan B$.

$\sin A = \sin 32° = \textbf{.5299}$ $\sin B = \sin 58° = \textbf{.8480}$
$\cos A = \cos 32° = \textbf{.8480}$ $\cos B = \cos 58° = \textbf{.5299}$
$\tan A = \tan 32° = \textbf{.6249}$ $\tan B = \tan 58° = \textbf{1.600}$

Find $\sin A$, $\cos A$, $\tan A$, $\sin B$, $\cos B$, and $\tan B$ in each of the following right triangles. Express answers as decimals rounded to three decimal places.

1.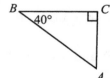

2.

3.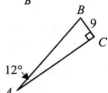

4.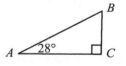

5.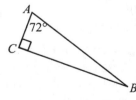

6.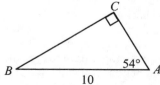

7.

8.

9.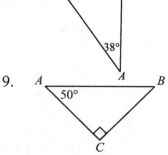

290

When given one acute angle and one side in a triangle, the other angle and two sides can be found using trigonometric functions.

EXAMPLE 4:   Find the third angle and the other two sides of the triangle.

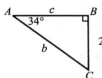

Step 1:   Find the third angle. Since all the angles in a triangle add up to 180°, and $A = 34°$ and $B = 90°$, then

$A + B + C = 180°$
$34° + 90° + C = 180°$
$C = 180° - 34° - 90° = 56°$

Step 2:   Find the missing sides. This can be done many different ways using sine, cosine, or tangent. We are going to use sine to find b and tangent to find c.

$\sin A = \frac{\text{opp.}}{\text{hyp.}}$ $\tan A = \frac{\text{opp.}}{\text{adj.}}$

$\sin 34° = \frac{2}{b}$ $\tan 34° = \frac{2}{c}$

$.5592 = \frac{2}{b}$ $.6745 = \frac{2}{c}$

$\frac{.5592b}{.5592} = \frac{2}{.5592}$ $\frac{.6745c}{.6745} = \frac{2}{.6745}$

$b = 3.58$ $c = 2.97$

$C = 56°$, $b = 3.58$, and $c = 2.97$

NOTE: After you have calculated the second side using one of the trigonometric ratios, you can use the Pythagorean Theorem to find the third side.
$2^2 + c^2 = 3.58^2 \longrightarrow c^2 = 3.58^2 - 2^2 \longrightarrow c^2 = 8.8164 \longrightarrow c = 2.97$

Find the missing sides and angles using the information given.

1.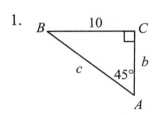

3.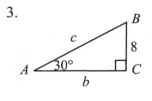

5.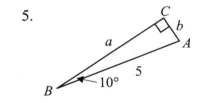

2.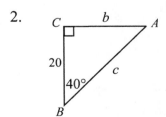

4.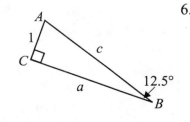

6.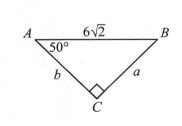

Use the pictures to help solve the problems.

1.   An F-22 is flying over two control towers. There is a point above the two towers where the fighter pilot can get a clean signal to both the towers. If he is 120 feet from tower one and is making a 59° angle with the two towers, find the distance, x, the F-22 is from the second tower, and find the distance, y, between the two towers.

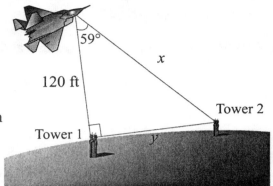

2.   Sandra is trying to use her cell phone to call her best friend. She can be no more than 3 miles from a tower in order to get a signal for her phone. If the telephone tower is 252 feet tall, find the angle of elevation, m, when Sandra's phone is the maximum 3 miles from the tower.
     HINT: Convert 3 miles to feet before solving. 1 mile = 5280 ft

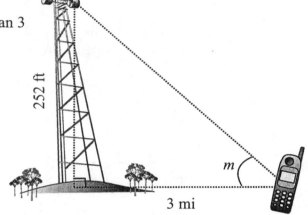

3.   Sir Stephen is returning from fighting a war. His first concern on his homecoming journey is to see if his family's banner still flies above their castle. If the flag rises 95 feet above his head, and he emerges from the forest 185 feet from the tower, at what angle, m, is his line of sight to the banner?

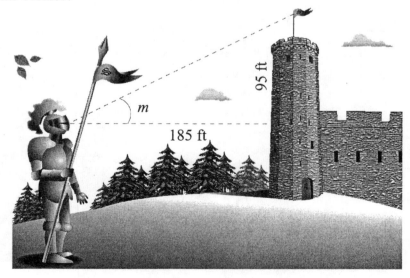

292

1. Find the missing angle.

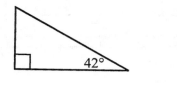

_____

2. What is the length of line segment $\overline{WY}$?

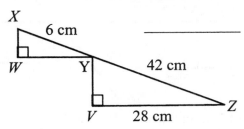

_____

3. Find the missing side.

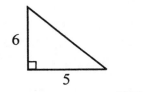

_____

4. Find the measure of the missing leg of the right triangle below.

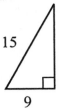

_____

5. The following two triangles are similar. Find the length of the missing side.

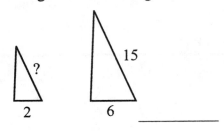

_____

For questions 6 and 7, find the value of angle x.

6. $\sin x = .5$

7. $\tan x = -1$

For questions 8 and 9, find the missing angle and sides.

8.

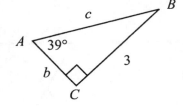

9.

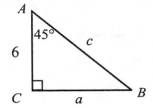

10. Chris walked east from his house to the gas station, which was 1.2 miles away. Then, he walked south from the gas station to his piano teacher's house. His piano teacher lives 2,112 feet from the gas station.

   a) Use the Pythagorean theorem to find the direct distance in miles from Chris's house to his piano teacher's house.

   b) Use a trigonometric ratio to find the angle measure between the direct path from Chris's house to the gas station and the direct path from Chris's house to his piano teacher's house.

The following terms are important for understanding the concepts that are presented in this chapter. Most of you have already been introduced to these terms. Rather than defining them in words, they are presented here by example as a refresher.

LINES AND LINE SEGMENTS

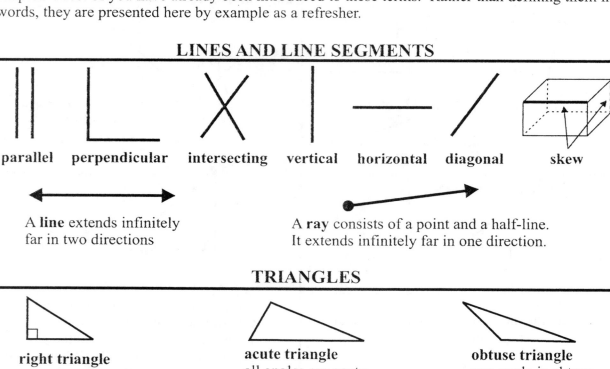

parallel **perpendicular** **intersecting** **vertical** **horizontal** **diagonal** **skew**

A **line** extends infinitely far in two directions

A **ray** consists of a point and a half-line. It extends infinitely far in one direction.

TRIANGLES

right triangle
contains 1 right ∠

acute triangle
all angles are acute
(less than 90°)

obtuse triangle
one angle is obtuse
(greater than 90°)

equilateral triangle
all three sides equal
all angles are 60°

scalene triangle
no sides equal
no angles equal

isosceles triangle
two sides equal
two angles equal

POLYGONS

square
equal sides
90° ∠s

rectangle
opposite sides
parallel, 90° ∠s

parallelogram
opposite sides
parallel

pentagon
5 sides

hexagon
6 sides

octagon
8 sides

PERIMETER

The **perimeter** is the distance around a polygon. To find the perimeter, add the lengths of the sides. On the Ohio Graduation Test in Mathematics, the lengths of the sides may be an algebraic expression.

EXAMPLES:

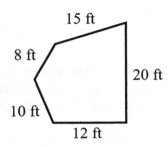

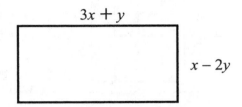

$$P = (3x + y) + (3x + y) + (x - 2y) + (x - 2y)$$
group like terms together and simplify
$$P = 3x + 3x + x + x + y + y - 2y - 2y$$
$$P = 8x - 2y$$

$$P = 15 + 20 + 12 + 10 + 8$$
$$P = 65 \text{ ft}$$

Find the perimeter of the following polygons.

1.

8 in
5 in

_____

4.

6 ft
6 ft

_____

7.

$x - 2y$
$2x + 3y$

_____

2.

3 ft
2 ft   2 ft
5 ft   5 ft

_____

5.

12 in
8 in   8 in
16 in

_____

8.

x
$2x - 3y$
y

_____

3.

13 cm   15 cm
10 cm

_____

6.

$x - 2$
$x + 6$

_____

9.

$x + 2$
$4x + 1$

_____

AREA OF SQUARES AND RECTANGLES

Area - area is always expressed in square units such as in^2, cm^2, ft^2, and m^2.

The area, (A), of squares and rectangles equals length (l) times width (w). $A = l\,w$

EXAMPLE 1:

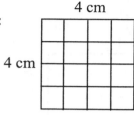

4 cm

4 cm

$A = l\,w$
$A = 4 \times 4$
$A = 16\ \text{cm}^2$

If a square has an area of 16 cm², it means that it will take 16 squares that are 1 cm on each side to cover the area of a square that is 4 cm on each side.

EXAMPLE 2: Using the same formula, find the area when the sides are algebraic expressions.

$h - 2$

$h + 1$

$A = l\,w$
$A = (h - 2)(h + 1) = h^2 - 2h + h - 2$
$A = h^2 - h - 2$

Find the area of the following squares and rectangles, using the formula $A = l\,w$.

1. 10 ft
    10 ft
    _____

2. 5 − 2m
    2 + m
    _____

3. 4 + 2h
    9 − h
    _____

4. 9 + n
    1 − n
    _____

5. 6 ft
    6 ft
    _____

6. 10 cm
    5 cm
    _____

7. 4 ft
    2 ft
    _____

8. 5 − n
    8 − 4n
    _____

9. 12 ft
    12 ft
    _____

10. 7 + 2b
    2 + b
    _____

11. n
    n + 8
    _____

12. 6 − 3f
    4 + f
    _____

AREA OF TRIANGLES

EXAMPLE: Find the area of the following triangle.

The formula for the area of a triangle is written below:

$A = \frac{1}{2} \times b \times h$

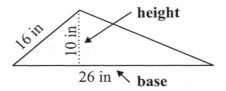

A = area
b = base
h = height

Step 1 Insert measurements from the triangle into the formula: $A = \frac{1}{2} \times 26 \times 10$

Step 2 Cancel and multiply.

$A = \frac{1}{\cancel{2}} \times \frac{\overset{13}{\cancel{26}}}{1} \times \frac{10}{1} = 130 \text{ in}^2$

Note: **Area is always expressed in square units such as in^2, ft^2, cm^2, or m^2.**

Find the area of the following triangles. Remember to include units.

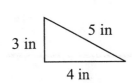

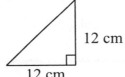

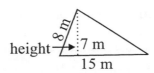

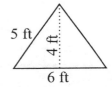

1. _____ in^2 4. _____   7. _____   10. _____

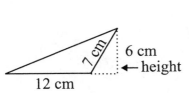

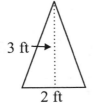

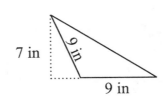

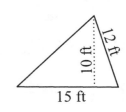

2. _____   5. _____   8. _____   11. _____

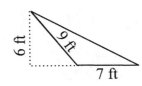

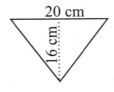

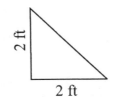

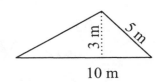

3. _____   6. _____   9. _____   12. _____

AREA OF TRAPEZOIDS AND PARALLELOGRAMS

EXAMPLE 1: Find the area of the following parallelogram.

The formula for the area of a parallelogram is $A = bh$.

A = **area**
b = **base**
h = **height**

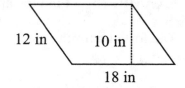

Step 1: Insert measurements from the parallelogram into the formula: $A = 18 \times 10$.

Step 2: Multiply. $18 \times 10 = 180 \text{ in}^2$

EXAMPLE 2: Find the area of the following trapezoid.

The formula for the area of a trapezoid is $A = \frac{1}{2}h\,(b_1 + b_2)$. A trapezoid has two bases that are parallel to each other. When you add the length of the two bases together and then multiply by $\frac{1}{2}$, you find their average length.

A = **area**
b = **base**
h = **height**

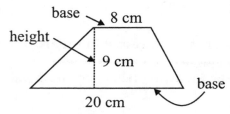

Insert measurements from the trapezoid into the formula and solve–
$\frac{1}{2} \times 9\,(8 + 20) = 126 \text{ cm}^2$.

Find the area of the following parallelograms and trapezoids.

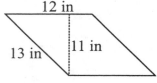

1. _____ in^2

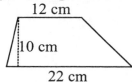

4. _____ cm^2

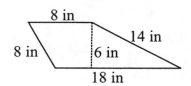

7. _____ in^2

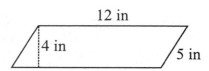

2. _____ in^2

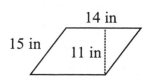

5. _____ in^2

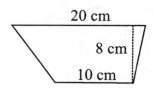

8. _____ cm^2

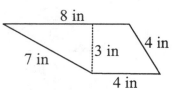

3. _____ in^2

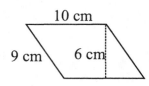

6. _____ cm^2

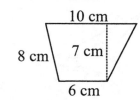

9. _____ cm^2

CIRCUMFERENCE

Circumference, *C* - the distance around the outside of a circle
Diameter, *d* - a line segment passing through the center of a circle from one side to the other
Radius, *r* - a line segment from the center of a circle to the edge of the circle
Pi, π - the ratio of the circumference of a circle to its diameter $\pi = \mathbf{3.14}$ or $\pi = \frac{22}{7}$

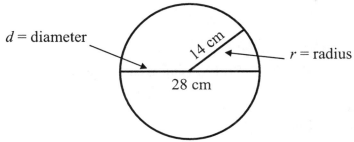

The formula for the circumference of a circle is $C = 2\pi r$ or $C = \pi d$. (The formulas are equal because the diameter is equal to twice the radius, $d = 2r$.)

EXAMPLE:

Find the circumference of the circle above.

$C = \pi d$ Use $= 3.14$
$C = 3.14 \times 28$
$C = 87.92$ cm

EXAMPLE:

Find the circumference of the circle above.

$C = 2\pi r$
$C = 2 \times 3.14 \times 14$
$C = 87.92$ cm

Use the formulas given above to find the circumference of the following circles.
Use π = 3.14.

1. 8 in

2. 14 ft

3. 2 cm

4. 6 m

5. 8 ft

$C = $ _____ $C = $ _____ $C = $ _____ $C = $ _____ $C = $ _____

Use the formulas given above to find the circumference of the following circles.
Use π = $\frac{22}{7}$.

6. 3 ft

7. 12 in

8. 6 m

9. 5 cm

10. 16 in

$C = $ _____ $C = $ _____ $C = $ _____ $C = $ _____ $C = $ _____

AREA OF A CIRCLE

The formula for the area of a circle is $A = \pi r^2$. The area is how many square units of measure would fit inside a circle.

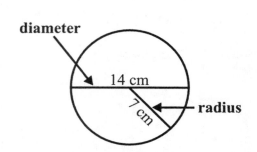

$$\pi = \frac{22}{7} \qquad \text{or} \qquad \pi = 3.14$$

EXAMPLE: Find the area of the circle, using both values for π.

Let $\pi = \dfrac{22}{7}$

$A = \pi r^2$

$A = \dfrac{22}{7} \times 7^2$

$A = \dfrac{22}{\cancel{7}} \times \dfrac{\cancel{49}^{\,7}}{1} = 154 \text{ cm}^2$

Let $\pi = 3.14$

$A = \pi r^2$

$A = 3.14 \times 7^2$

$A = 3.14 \times 49 = 153.86 \text{ cm}^2$

Find the area of the following circles. Remember to include units.

$\pi = 3.14 \qquad \pi = \dfrac{22}{7}$

1.
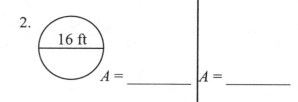
5 in

$A = \underline{\hspace{1.5cm}}$ $A = \underline{\hspace{1.5cm}}$

2.
16 ft

$A = \underline{\hspace{1.5cm}}$ $A = \underline{\hspace{1.5cm}}$

3.
8 cm

$A = \underline{\hspace{1.5cm}}$ $A = \underline{\hspace{1.5cm}}$

4.
3 m

$A = \underline{\hspace{1.5cm}}$ $A = \underline{\hspace{1.5cm}}$

Fill in the chart below. Include appropriate units.

	Radius	Diameter	Area $\pi = 3.14$	Area $\pi = \frac{22}{7}$
5.	9 ft			
6.		4 in		
7.	8 cm			
8.		20 ft		
9.	14 m			
10.		18 cm		
11.	12 ft			
12.		6 in		

300

TWO-STEP AREA PROBLEMS

Solving the problems below will require two steps. You will need to find the area of two figures, and then either add or subtract the two areas to find the answer. **Carefully read the EXAMPLES below.**

EXAMPLE 1:

Find the area of the living room below.

Figure 1

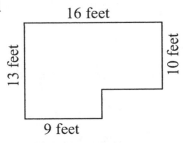

Step 1: Complete the rectangle as in Figure 2, and figure the area as if it were a complete rectangle.

Figure 2

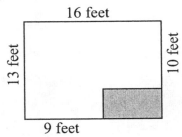

$A = $ length $\times$ width
$A = 16 \times 13$
$A = 208$ ft^2

Step 2: Figure the area of the shaded part.

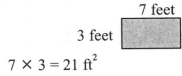

7 feet
3 feet

$7 \times 3 = 21$ ft^2

Step 3: Subtract the area of the shaded part from the area of the complete rectangle.

$208 - 21 = 187$ ft^2

EXAMPLE 2:

Find the area of the shaded sidewalk.

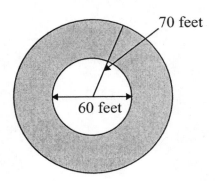

70 feet

60 feet

Step 1: Find the area of the outside circle.
$\pi = 3.14$
$A = 3.14 \times 70 \times 70$
$A = 15,386$ ft^2

Step 2: Find the area of the inside circle.
$\pi = 3.14$
$A = 3.14 \times 30 \times 30$
$A = 2,826$ ft^2

Step 3: Subtract the area of the inside circle from the area of the outside circle.

$15,386 - 2,826 = 12,560$ ft^2

Find the area of the following figures.

1.

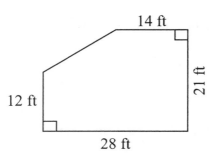

_____

2.

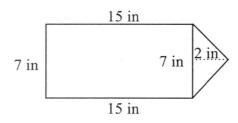

_____

3. What is the area of the shaded circle? Use π = 3.14, and round the answer to the nearest whole number.

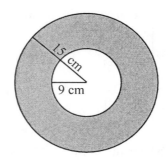

_____

4.

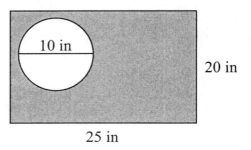

_____

5. What is the area of the rectangle that is shaded? Use π = 3.14, and round to the nearest whole number.

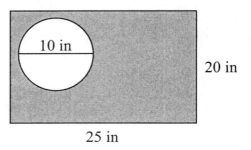

_____

6. What is the area of the shaded part?

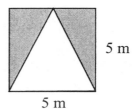

_____

7. What is the area of the shaded part?

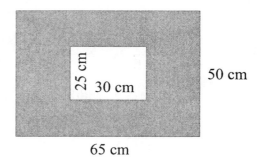

_____

8. 6 m

_____

GEOMETRIC RELATIONSHIPS OF PLANE FIGURES

Some problems on the Ohio Graduation Test in Mathematics may call for an understanding of what happens to the area of a figure when one or more of the dimensions is doubled or tripled.

EXAMPLE 1: Sam drew a square that was 2 inches on each side for art class. His teacher said the square needed to be twice as big. When Sam doubled each side to 4 inches, what happened to the area?

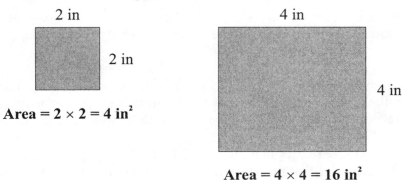

The area of the second square is 4 times larger than the first.

EXAMPLE 2: Sonya drew a circle with a radius of 3 inches for a school project. She also needed to make a larger circle with a radius of 9 inches. When Sonya drew the bigger circle, what was the difference in area?

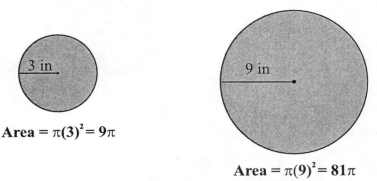

The area of the second circle is 9 times larger than the first.

From these two examples, we can determine that for every doubling or tripling of both sides or of the radius of a planar object, the total area increases by a squared value.

In other words, when both sides of the square doubled, the area was 2^2 or 4 times larger. When the radius of the circle became 3 times larger, the area became 3^2 or 9 times larger.

Carefully read each problem below and solve.

1. Ken drew a circle with a radius of 5 cm. He then drew a circle with a radius of 10 cm. How many times larger was the area of the second circle?

2. Dan drew a square with each side measuring 6 inches. He then drew a rectangle with a width of 6 inches and a length of 12 inches. How many times larger is the area of the rectangle than the area of the square? (**Hint:** The increase is *not* equal in both directions.)

3. Bob drew a square 3 inches on each side. Then he drew a bigger square that was 6 inches on each side. How many times larger is the area of the second square than the area of the first square?

4. Leslie draws a triangle with a base of 5 inches and a height of 3 inches. To use her triangle pattern for a bulletin board design, it needs to be 3 times bigger. If she increases the base and the height by multiplying each by 3, how much will the area of the triangle increase?

5. Heather is using 100 square tiles that measure 1 foot by 1 foot to cover a 10 feet by 10 feet floor. If she had used tiles that measured 2 feet by 2 feet, how many tiles would she have needed?

6. The area of circle B is 9 times larger than the area of circle A. If the radius of circle A is represented by x, how would you represent the radius of circle B?

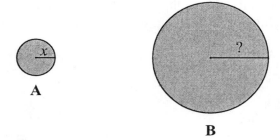

7. How many squares will it take to fill the rectangle below?

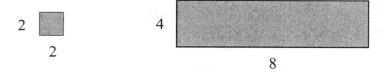

8. If the area of diamond B is one-fourth the area of diamond A, what are the dimensions of diamond B?

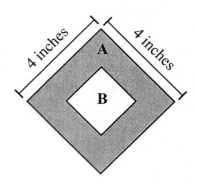

304   Copyright © American Book Company

CHAPTER 23 REVIEW

1. Find the area of the shaded region of the figure below.

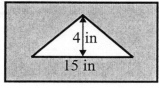

20 in

$A =$ _____

2. Calculate the perimeter of the following figure.

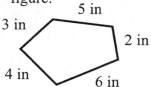

$P =$ _____

Calculate the perimeter and area of the following figures.

3.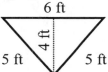

$P =$ _____

$A =$ _____

4. 7 in.

4 in.

$P =$ _____

$A =$ _____

5. What is the area of a square which measures 8 inches on each side?

$A =$ _____

6. If the radius of a circle is doubled, how is the area of the circle affected?

Calculate the circumference and the area of the following circles.

7.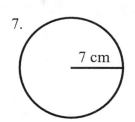

Use $\pi = \frac{22}{7}$

$C =$ _____

$A =$ _____

8.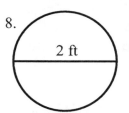

Use $\pi = 3.14$

$C =$ _____

$A =$ _____

9. Use $\pi = 3.14$ to find the area of the shaded part. Round your answer to the nearest whole number.

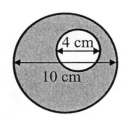

$A =$ _____

10. Tara is using 6-inch squares to make a quilt. The quilt dimensions are 5 feet by 12 feet. How many 6-inch squares will she need to complete the quilt?

_____

11. John has a small frisbee with a diameter of 6 inches. He has a larger frisbee with a diameter of 18 inches. How much larger is the area of the 18 inch frisbee compared to the 6 inch frisbee?

_____

Chapter 24: Solid Geometry

In this chapter, you will learn about the following three-dimensional shapes.

SOLIDS

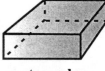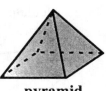

| cube | rectangular prism | cone | cylinder | sphere | pyramid |

UNDERSTANDING VOLUME

Volume - Measurement of volume is expressed in cubic units such as in^3, ft^3, m^3, cm^3, or mm^3. The volume of a solid is the number of cubic units that can be contained in the solid.

First, let's look at rectangular solids.

EXAMPLE: How many 1 cubic centimeter cubes will it take to fill up the figure below?

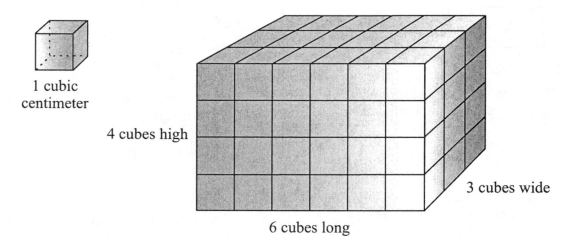

1 cubic centimeter

4 cubes high

3 cubes wide

6 cubes long

To find the volume, you need to multiply the length, times the width, times the height.

Volume of a rectangular solid = length $\times$ width $\times$ height $(V = l\,w\,h)$.

$V = 6 \times 3 \times 4 = 72$ cm^3

VOLUME OF RECTANGULAR PRISMS

You can calculate the volume (V) of a rectangular prism (box) by multiplying the length (l) by the width (w) by the height (h), as expressed in the formula $V = (l \times w \times h)$.

EXAMPLE: Find the volume of the box pictured on the right.

Step 1: Insert measurements from the figure into the formula.

Step 2: Multiply to solve. $\qquad 10 \times 4 \times 2 = 80 \text{ ft}^3$

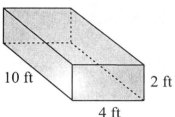

NOTE: Volume is always expressed in cubic units such as in^3, ft^3, m^3, cm^3, or mm^3.

Find the volume of the following rectangular prisms (boxes).

1.

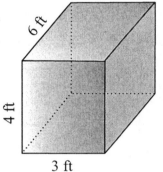

$V =$ _____

4.

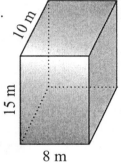

$V =$ _____

7.

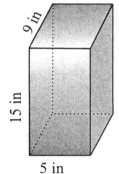

$V =$ _____

2.

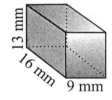

$V =$ _____

5.

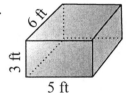

$V =$ _____

8.

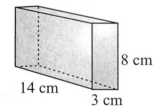

$V =$ _____

3.

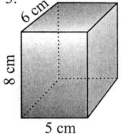

$V =$ _____

6.

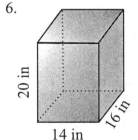

$V =$ _____

9.

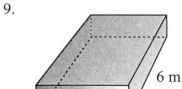

$V =$ _____

VOLUME OF CUBES

A **cube** is a special kind of rectangular prism (box). Each side of a cube has the same measure. So, the formula for the volume of a cube is $V = s^3$ ($s \times s \times s$).

EXAMPLE: Find the volume of the cube pictured at the right.

Step 1: Insert measurements from the figure into the formula.

Step 2: Multiply to solve. $5 \times 5 \times 5 = 125 \text{ cm}^3$

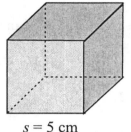

$s = 5$ cm

Note: **Volume is always expressed in cubic units such as in^3, ft^3, m^3, cm^3, or mm^3.**

Answer each of the following questions about cubes.

1. If a cube is 3 centimeters on each edge, what is the volume of the cube?

   _____

2. If the measure of the edge is doubled to 6 centimeters on each edge, what is the volume of the cube?

   _____

3. What if the edge of a 3 centimeter cube is tripled to become 9 centimeters on each edge? What will the volume be?

   _____

4. How many cubes with edges measuring 3 centimeters would you need to stack together to make a solid 12 centimeter cube?

   _____

5. What is the volume of a 2 centimeter cube?

   _____

6. Jerry built a 2 inch cube to hold his marble collection. He wants to build a cube with a volume 8 times larger. How much will each edge measure?

   _____

Find the volume of the following cubes.

7.

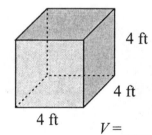

$s = 7$ in

$V =$ _____

8.

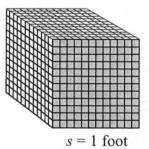

4 ft

4 ft

4 ft

$V =$ _____

9. 12 inches = 1 foot

$s = 1$ foot

How many cubic inches are in a cubic foot? _____

VOLUME OF SPHERES, CONES, CYLINDERS, AND PYRAMIDS

To find the volume of a solid, insert the measurements given for the solid into the correct formula and solve. Remember, volumes are expressed in cubic units such as in³, ft³, m³, cm³, or mm³.

Sphere	**Cone**	**Cylinder**
$V = \frac{4}{3}\pi r^3$	$V = \frac{1}{3}\pi r^2 h$	$V = \pi r^2 h$

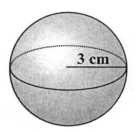
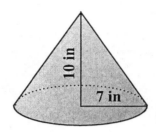
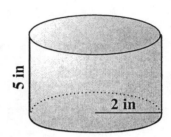

$V = \frac{4}{3}\pi r^3 \quad \pi = 3.14$

$V = \frac{4}{3} \times 3.14 \times 27$

$V = 113.04 \text{ cm}^3$

$V = \frac{1}{3}\pi r^2 h \quad \pi = 3.14$

$V = \frac{1}{3} \times 3.14 \times 49 \times 10$

$V = 512.87 \text{ in}^3$

$V = \pi r^2 h \quad \pi = \frac{22}{7}$

$V = \frac{22}{7} \times 4 \times 5$

$V = 62\frac{6}{7} \text{ in}^3$

Pyramids

$V = \frac{1}{3}Bh$ **B = area of rectangular base** $V = \frac{1}{3}Bh$ **B = area of triangular base**

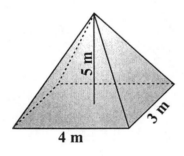
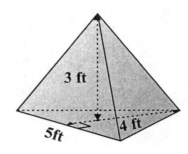

$V = \frac{1}{3}Bh \quad B = l \times w$

$V = \frac{1}{3} \times 4 \times 3 \times 5$

$V = 20 \text{ m}^3$

$B = \frac{1}{2} \times 5 \times 4 = 10 \text{ ft}^2$

$V = \frac{1}{3} \times 10 \times 3$

$V = 10 \text{ ft}^3$

Find the volume of the following shapes. Use π = 3.14.

1.

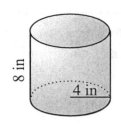

8 in
4 in

$V =$ _____

7.

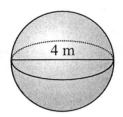

4 m

$V =$ _____

2.

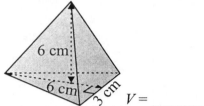

6 cm
6 cm
3 cm

$V =$ _____

8.

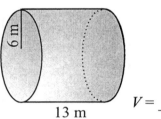

12 in
8 in
5 in

$V =$ _____

3.

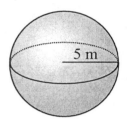

5 m

$V =$ _____

9.

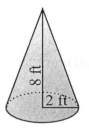

6 m
13 m

$V =$ _____

4.

8 ft
2 ft

$V =$ _____

10.

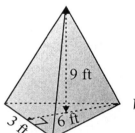

9 ft
3 ft
6 ft

$V =$ _____

5.

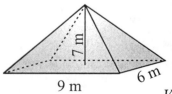

7 m
9 m
6 m

$V =$ _____

11.

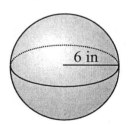

6 in

$V =$ _____

6.

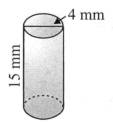

4 mm
15 mm

$V =$ _____

12.

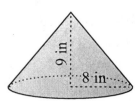

9 in
8 in

$V =$ _____

310

TWO-STEP VOLUME PROBLEMS

Some objects are made from two geometric figures, for example the tower below.

EXAMPLE: Find the maximum volume of the tower pictured at the right.

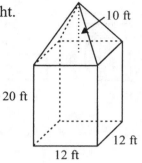

Step 1:   Determine which formulas you will need. The tower is made from a pyramid and a rectangular prism, so you will need the formulas for the volume of these two figures.

Step 2:   Find the volume of each part of the tower.
The bottom of the tower is a rectangular prism. $V = lwh$
$V = 12 \times 12 \times 20 = 2,880 \text{ ft}^3$

The top of the tower is a rectangular pyramid. $V = \frac{1}{3}Bh$
$V = \frac{1}{3} \times 12 \times 12 \times 10 = 480 \text{ ft}^3$

Step 3:   Add the two volumes together. $2880 \text{ ft}^3 + 480 \text{ ft}^3 = 3,360 \text{ ft}^3$

Find the volume of the geometric figures below. *Hint:* If part of a solid has been removed, find the volume of the missing part, and subtract it from the volume of the total object.

1.

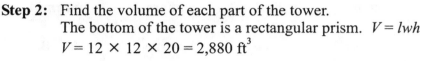
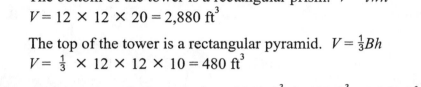

2.   Each edge of the cubes in the figure below measures 3 inches.

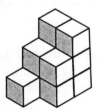

3.   A rectangular hole passes through the middle of the figure below. The hole measures 1 cm on each side.

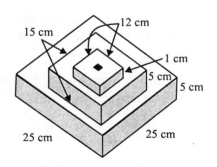

4.   In the figure below, 3 cylinders are stacked on top of one another. The radii of the cylinders are 2 inches, 4 inches, and 6 inches. The height of each cylinder is 1 inch.

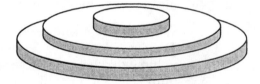

5.

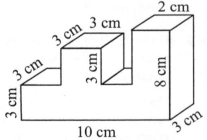

6.   A hole, 1 meter in diameter, has been cut through the cylinder below.

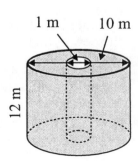

GEOMETRIC RELATIONSHIPS OF SOLIDS

The formulas for finding the volumes of geometric solids are given below.

cube
$V = s^3$

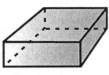
rectangular prism
$V = l\,w\,h$

cone
$V = \frac{1}{3}\pi r^2 h$

cylinder
$V = \pi r^2 h$

sphere
$V = \frac{4}{3}\pi r^3$

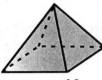
pyramid
$V = \frac{1}{3}Bh$

By studying each formula and by comparing formulas between different solids, you can determine general relationships.

EXAMPLE 1: How would doubling the radius of a sphere affect the volume?

The volume of a sphere is $V = \frac{4}{3}\pi r^3$. Just by looking at the formula, can you see that by doubling the radius, the volume would increase to 8 times the original volume? So, a sphere with a radius of 2 would have a volume 8 times greater than a sphere with a radius of 1.

EXAMPLE 2: A cylinder and a cone have the same radius and the same height. What is the difference between their volumes?

Compare the formulas for the volume of a cone and the volume of a cylinder. They are identical except that the cone is multiplied by $\frac{1}{3}$. Therefore, the volume of a cone with the same height and radius as a cylinder would be one-third less. Or, the volume of a cylinder with the same height and radius as a cone would be three times greater.

EXAMPLE 3: If you double one dimension of a rectangular prism, how will the volume be affected? How about doubling two dimensions? How about doubling all three dimensions?

Do you see that doubling just one of the dimensions of a rectangular prism will also double the volume? Doubling two of the dimensions will cause the volume to increase to 4 times the original volume. Doubling all three dimensions will cause the volume to increase to 8 times the original volume.

EXAMPLE 4: A cylinder holds 100 cubic centimeters of water. If you triple the radius of the cylinder but keep the height the same, how much water would you need to fill the new cylinder?

Tripling the radius of a cylinder causes the volume to increase by 3^2 or 9 times the original volume. The volume of the new cylinder would hold 9×100 or 900 cubic centimeters of water.

Answer the following questions by comparing the volumes of two solids that share some of the same dimensions.

1. If you have a cylinder with a height of 8 inches and a radius of 4 inches, and you have a cone with the same height and radius, how many times greater is the volume of the cylinder than the volume of the cone?

2.
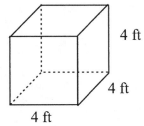 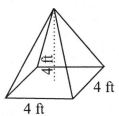

    In the two figures above, how many times larger is the volume of the cube than the volume of the pyramid?

3. How many times greater is the volume of a cylinder if you double the radius?

4. How many times greater is the volume of a cylinder if you double the height?

5. In a rectangular solid, how many times greater is the volume if you double the length?

6. In a rectangular solid, how many times greater is the volume if you double the length and the width?

7. In a rectangular solid, how many times greater is the volume if you double the length and the width and the height?

8. In the following two figures, how many cubes like Figure 1 will fit inside Figure 2?

    Figure 1   Figure 2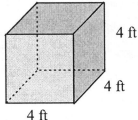

9. A sphere has a radius of 1. If the radius is increased to 3, how many times greater will the volume be?

10. It takes 2 liters of water to fill cone A below. If the cone is stretched so the radius is doubled, but the height stays the same, how much water is needed to fill the new cone, B?

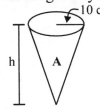 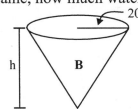

SURFACE AREA

The **surface area of a solid** is the total area of all the sides of a solid.

CUBE

There are six sides on a cube. To find the surface area of a cube, find the area of one side and multiply by 6.

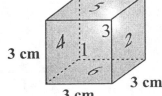

Area of each side of the cube:
$3 \times 3 = 9 \text{ cm}^2$

Total surface area: $9 \times 6 = 54 \text{ cm}^2$

RECTANGULAR PRISM

There are 6 sides on a rectangular prism. To find the surface area, add the areas of the six rectangular sides.

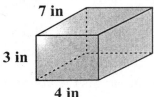

Top and Bottom	**Front and Back**	**Left and Right**
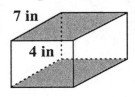	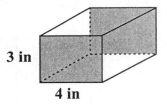	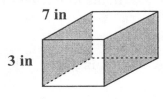
Area of top side:	Area of front:	Area of left side:
$7 \text{ in} \times 4 \text{ in} = 28 \text{ in}^2$	$3 \text{ in} \times 4 \text{ in} = 12 \text{ in}^2$	$3 \text{ in} \times 7 \text{ in} = 21 \text{ in}^2$
Area of top and bottom:	Area of front and back:	Area of left and right:
$28 \text{ in} \times 2 \text{ in} = 56 \text{ in}^2$	$12 \text{ in} \times 2 \text{ in} = 24 \text{ in}^2$	$21 \text{ in} \times 2 \text{ in} = 42 \text{ in}^2$

Total surface area: $56 \text{ in}^2 + 24 \text{ in}^2 + 42 \text{ in}^2 = 122 \text{ in}^2$

314

Find the surface area of the following cubes and prisms.

1.
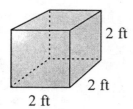
2 ft
2 ft
2 ft

SA = _____

2.
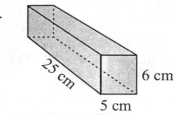
25 cm
6 cm
5 cm

SA = _____

3.
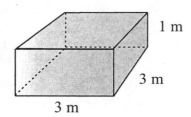
1 m
3 m
3 m

SA = _____

4.
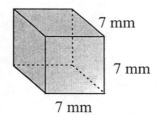
7 mm
7 mm
7 mm

SA = _____

5.
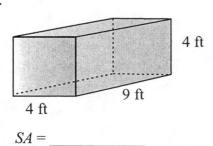
4 ft
9 ft
4 ft

SA = _____

6.
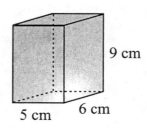
9 cm
5 cm   6 cm

SA = _____

7.
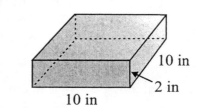
10 in
2 in
10 in

SA = _____

8.
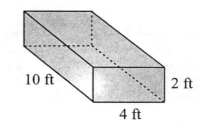
10 ft
2 ft
4 ft

SA = _____

9.
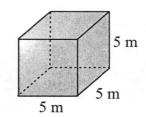
5 m
5 m
5 m

SA = _____

10.
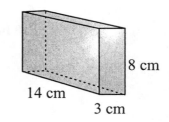
8 cm
14 cm
3 cm

SA = _____

PYRAMID

The pyramid below is made of a square base with 4 triangles on the sides.

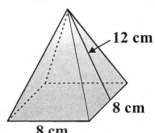

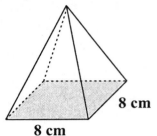

Area of square base:
$A = l \times w$
$A = 8 \times 8 = 64 \text{ cm}^2$

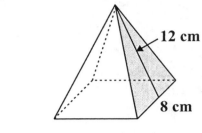

Area of sides:
Area of 1 side $= \frac{1}{2}bh$
$A = \frac{1}{2} \times 8 \times 12 = 48 \text{ cm}^2$
Area of 4 sides $= 48 \times 4 = 192 \text{ cm}^2$

Total surface area: $64 + 192 = 256 \text{ cm}^2$

Find the surface area of the following pyramids.

1.

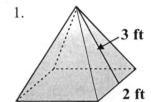

$SA =$ _____

4.

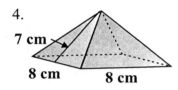

$SA =$ _____

7.

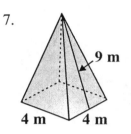

$SA =$ _____

2.

$SA =$ _____

5.

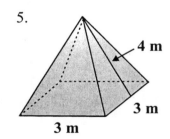

$SA =$ _____

8.

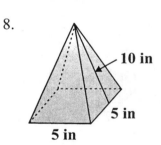

$SA =$ _____

3.

$SA =$ _____

6.

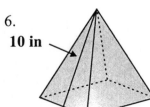
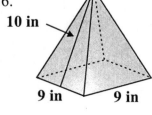

$SA =$ _____

9.

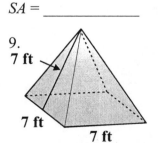

$SA =$ _____

CYLINDER

If the side of a cylinder was slit from top to bottom and laid flat, its shape would be a rectangle. The length of the rectangle is the same as the circumference of the circle that is the base of the cylinder. The width of the rectangle is the height of the cylinder.

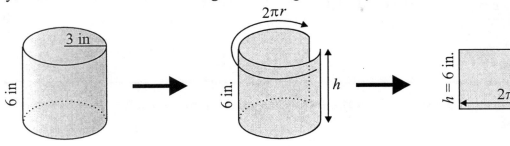

Total Surface Area of a Cylinder = $2\pi r^2 + 2\pi rh$

Area of top and bottom:
Area of a circle = πr^2
Area of top = $3.14 \times 3^2 = 28.26$ in^2
Area of top and bottom = $2 \times 28.26 = 56.52$ in^2

Area of side:
Area of rectangle = $l \times h$
$l = 2\pi r = 2 \times 3.14 \times 3 = 18.84$ in
Area of rectangle = $18.84 \times 6 = 113.04$ in^2

Total surface area = $56.52 + 113.04 = 169.56$ in^2

Find the surface area of the following cylinders. Use $\pi = 3.14$

1.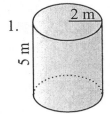

SA = _____

2.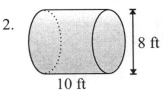

SA = _____

3.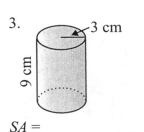

SA = _____

4.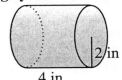

SA = _____

5.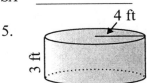

SA = _____

6.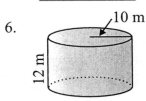

SA = _____

7.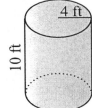

SA = _____

8.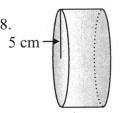

SA = _____

9.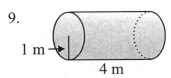

SA = _____

SPHERE

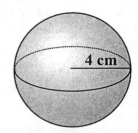

Surface area $= 4\pi r^2$

Surface area $= 4 \times 3.14 \times 4^2$

Surface area $= 200.96$ cm^2

Find the surface area of a sphere given the following measurements where r = radius and d = diameter. Use $\pi = 3.14$.

1. $r = 2$ in $SA =$ _____
2. $r = 6$ m $SA =$ _____
3. $r = \frac{3}{4}$ yd $SA =$ _____
4. $d = 8$ cm $SA =$ _____
5. $d = 50$ mm $SA =$ _____
6. $r = \frac{1}{4}$ ft $SA =$ _____

7. $d = 14$ cm $SA =$ _____
8. $r = \frac{1}{5}$ km $SA =$ _____
9. $d = 3$ in $SA =$ _____
10. $d = \frac{2}{3}$ ft $SA =$ _____
11. $r = 10$ mm $SA =$ _____
12. $d = 5$ yd $SA =$ _____

CONE

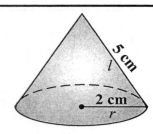

Total Surface Area $= \pi r^2 + \pi r l$

Area of circle $= \pi r^2$ Area of cone section $= \pi r l$

Area of base $= 3.14 \times 2^2$ Area$_{\text{cone section}} = 3.14 \times 2 \times 5$

Area of base $= 12.56$ cm^2 Area$_{\text{cone section}} = 31.40$ cm^2

Total Surface Area $= 12.56$ cm$^2 + 31.40$ cm$^2 = 43.96$ cm^2

Find the surface area of the following cones. Use $\pi = 3.14$.

1.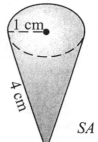

$SA =$ _____

3.

$SA =$ _____

5.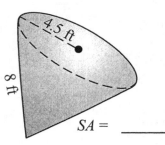

$SA =$ _____

2.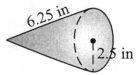

$SA =$ _____

4.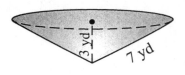

$SA =$ _____

6.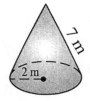

$SA =$ _____

318

NETS OF SOLID OBJECTS

Prisms

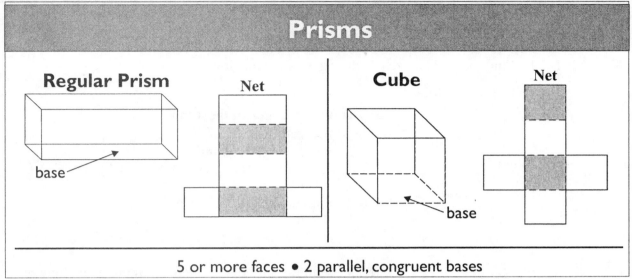

Regular Prism

Net

base

Cube

Net

base

5 or more faces • 2 parallel, congruent bases

Pyramid

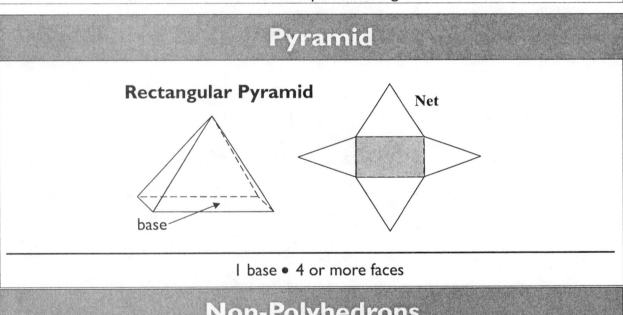

Rectangular Pyramid

Net

base

I base • 4 or more faces

Non-Polyhedrons

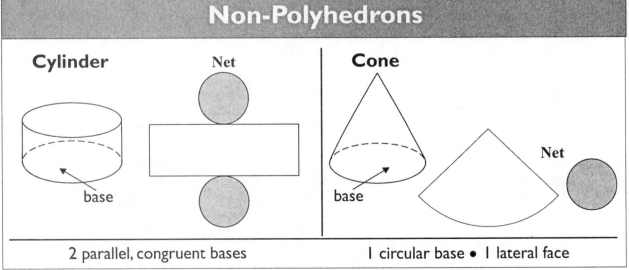

Cylinder

Net

base

Cone

Net

base

2 parallel, congruent bases

I circular base • I lateral face

USING NETS TO FIND SURFACE AREA

A **net** is a two dimensional representation of a three dimensional object. Nets clearly illustrate the plane figures that make up a solid.

EXAMPLE 1: Find the surface area of the figure shown below.

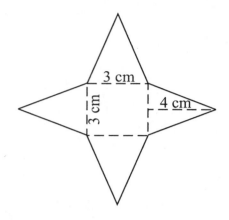

Step 1: Find the area of the 4 triangles.
$A = \frac{1}{2} bh$
$A = \frac{1}{2} \times 3 \times 4 = 6$ cm^2
Area of all 4 triangles $= 4 \times 6 = 24$ cm^2

Step 2: Find the area of the base.
$A = lw$
$A = 3 \times 3 = 9$ cm^2

Step 3: Find the sum of the areas of all the plane figures.
Surface Area $= 24$ cm^2 $+ 9$ cm^2
$SA = 33$ cm^2

EXAMPLE 2: A net for a cone is shown below. Find the surface area.

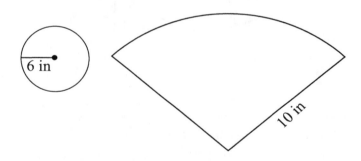

Step 1: Find the area of the base.
$A = \pi r^2$
$A = 3.14 \times 6^2 = 3.14 \times 36 = 113.04$ in^2

Step 2: Find the area of the cone section.
$A = \pi rl$
$A = 3.14 \times 6 \times 10$
$A = 188.40$ in^2

Step 3: Find the sum of the areas of the base and the cone section.
Surface area $= 113.04$ in^2 $+ 188.40$ in^2
$SA = 301.44$ in^2

The nets for various solids are given. Find the surface area of the objects. If needed, use π = 3.14.

1.

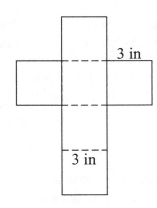

3 in

3 in

SA = _____

3.

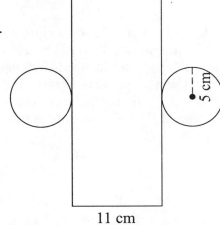

5 cm

11 cm

SA = _____

2.

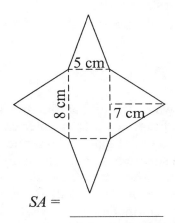

5 cm

8 cm

7 cm

SA = _____

4.

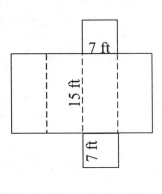

7 ft

15 ft

7 ft

SA = _____

Using a ruler, measure the dimensions of the following nets to the nearest tenth of a centimeter, and calculate the surface area of the object. If needed, use π = 3.14.

5.

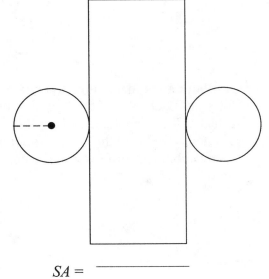

SA = _____

6.

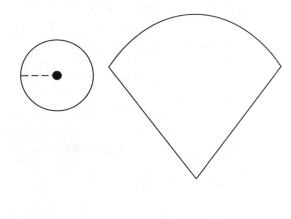

SA = _____

SOLID GEOMETRY WORD PROBLEMS

1. If an Egyptian pyramid has a square base that measures 500 yards by 500 yards, and the pyramid stands 300 yards tall, what would be the volume of the pyramid? Use the formula for volume of a pyramid, $V = \frac{1}{3}Bh$ where B is the area of the base.

    $V =$ _____

2. Robert is using a cylindrical barrel filled with water to flatten the sod in his yard. The circular ends have a radius of 1 foot. The barrel is 3 feet wide. How much water will the barrel hold? The formula for volume of a cylinder is $V = \pi r^2 h$. Use $\pi = 3.14$.

    $V =$ _____

3. If a basketball measures 24 centimeters in diameter, what volume of air will it hold? The formula for volume of a sphere is $V = \frac{4}{3}\pi r^3$. Use $\pi = 3.14$.

    $V =$ _____

4. What is the volume of a cone that is 2 inches in diameter and 5 inches tall? The formula for volume of a cone is $V = \frac{1}{3}\pi r^2 h$. Use $\pi = 3.14$.

    $V =$ _____

5. Kelly has a rectangular fish aquarium that measures 24 inches wide, 12 inches deep, and 18 inches tall. What is the maximum amount of water that the aquarium will hold?

    $V =$ _____

6. Jenny has a rectangular box that she wants to cover in decorative contact paper. The box is 10 cm long, 5 cm wide, and 5 cm high. How much paper will she need to cover all 6 sides?

    $SA =$ _____

7. Gasco needs to construct a cylindrical, steel gas tank that measures 6 feet in diameter and is 8 feet long. How many square feet of steel will be needed to construct the tank? Use the following formulas as needed: $A = l \times w$, $A = \pi r^2$, $C = 2\pi r$. Use $\pi = 3.14$.

    $SA =$ _____

8. Craig wants to build a miniature replica of San Francisco's Transamerica Pyramid out of glass. His replica will have a square base that measures 6 cm by 6 cm. The 4 triangular sides will be 6 cm wide and 60 cm tall. How many square centimeters of glass will he need to build his replica? Use the following formulas as needed: $A = l \times w$ and $A = \frac{1}{2}bh$.

    $SA =$ _____

9. Jeff built a wooden, cubic toy box for his son. Each side of the box measures 2 feet. How many square feet of wood did he use to build the toy box? How many cubic feet of toys will the box hold?

    $SA =$ _____

    $V =$ _____

322

CHAPTER 24 REVIEW

Find the volume and/or the surface area of the following solids.

1.

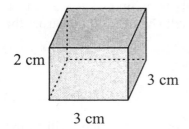

2 cm

3 cm

3 cm

V = _____

SA = _____

2.

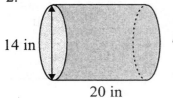

14 in

20 in

$V = \pi r^2 h$

$SA = 2\pi r^2 + 2\pi rh$

Use $\pi = \frac{22}{7}$

V = _____

SA = _____

3.

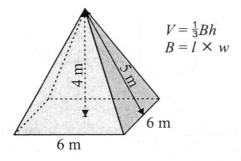

4 m

5 m

6 m

6 m

$V = \frac{1}{3}Bh$

$B = l \times w$

V = _____

SA = _____

4.

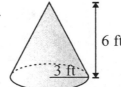

6 ft

3 ft

$V = \frac{1}{3}\pi r^2 h$

Use $\pi = 3.14$

V = _____

5.

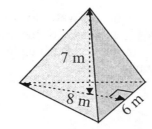

7 m

8 m

6 m

$V = \frac{1}{3}Bh$

B = area of the triangular base

V = _____

6.

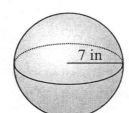

7 in

$V = \frac{4}{3}\pi r^3$

Use $\pi = \frac{22}{7}$

V = _____

7. The sandbox at the local elementary school is 60 inches wide and 100 inches long. The sand in the box is 6 inches deep. How many cubic inches of sand are in the sandbox?

_____

8. If you have cubes that are two inches on each edge, how many would fit in a cube that is 16 inches on each edge?

_____

9. If you double each edge of a cube, how many times larger is the volume?

_____

10. It takes 8 cubic inches of water to fill the cube below. If each side of the cube is doubled, how much water is needed to fill the new cube?

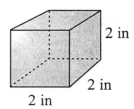

2 in

2 in

2 in

_____

11. If a ball is 4 inches in diameter, what is its surface area? Use π = 3.14

_____

12. A grain silo is in the shape of a cylinder. If the silo has an inside diameter of 10 feet and a height of 35 feet, what is the maximum volume inside the silo?

Use $\pi = \frac{22}{7}$

_____

13. A closed cardboard box is 30 centimeters long, 10 centimeters wide, and 20 centimeters high. What is the total surface area of the box?

14. Siena wants to build a wooden toy box with a lid. The dimensions of the toy box are 3 feet long, 4 feet wide, and 2 feet tall. How many square feet of wood will she need to construct the box?

_____

15. How many 1 inch cubes will fit inside a larger 1 foot cube? (Figures are not drawn to scale.)

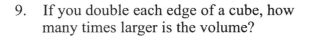

1 in

1 in   1 in

1 ft

1 ft

1 ft

_____

16. The cylinder below has a volume of 240 cubic inches. The cone below has the same radius and the same height as the cylinder. What is the volume of the cone?

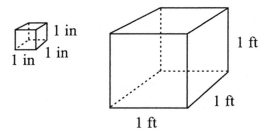

h

h

r

r

_____

17. Estimate the volume of the figure below.

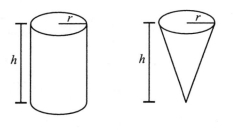

10 m

20 m

4 m

_____

18. Find the volume of the figure below.

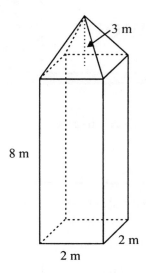

8 m

3 m

2 m

2 m

_____

19. Find the volume of the figure below.
Each edge of each cube measures 4 feet.

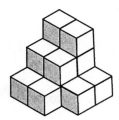

_____

20. The figure below is a net of a rectangular prism. Measure its dimensions to the nearest tenth of a centimeter and calculate its surface area.

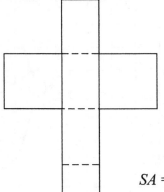

$SA =$ _____

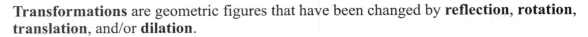

Chapter 25: Transformations

Transformations are geometric figures that have been changed by **reflection**, **rotation**, **translation**, and/or **dilation**.

REFLECTIONS

A **reflection** of a geometric figure is a mirror image of the object. Placing a mirror on the **line of reflection** will give you the position of the reflected image. On paper, folding an image across the line of reflection will give you the position of the reflected image.

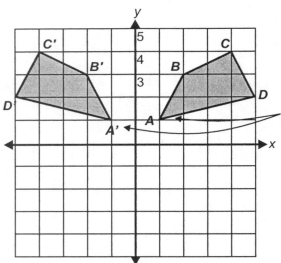

Quadrilateral *ABCD* is reflected across the *y*-axis to form quadrilateral *A'B'C'D'*. The *y*-axis is the line of reflection. Point *A'* is the reflection of point *A*, point *B'* corresponds to point *B*, *C'* to *C*, and *D'* to *D*.

Point *A* is +1 space from the *y*-axis. Point *A*'s mirror image, point *A'*, is −1 space from the *y*-axis.

Point *B* is +2 spaces from the *y*-axis. Point *B'* is −2 spaces from the *y*-axis.

Point *C* is +4 spaces from the *y*-axis and point *C'* is −4 spaces from the *y*-axis.

Point *D* is +5 spaces from the *y*-axis and point *D'* is −5 spaces from the *y*-axis.

Triangle *FGH* is reflected across the *x*-axis to form triangle *F'G'H'*. The *x*-axis is the line of reflection. Point *F'* reflects point *F*. Point *G'* corresponds to point *G*, and *H'* mirrors *H*.

Point *F* is +3 spaces from the *x*-axis. Likewise, point *F'* is −3 spaces from the *x*-axis.

Point *G* is +1 spaces from the *x*-axis, and point *G'* is −1 spaces from the *x*-axis.

Point *H* is 0 spaces from the *x*-axis, so point *H'* is also 0 spaces from the *x*-axis.

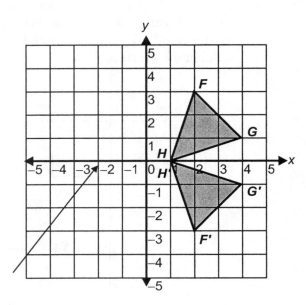

line of reflection: *x*-axis

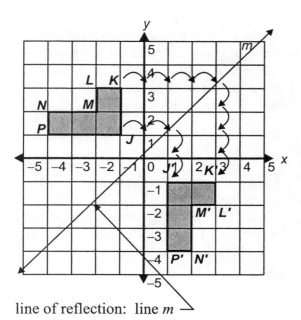

line of reflection: line *m*

Figure *JKLMNP* is reflected across line *m* to form figure *J'K'L'M'N'P'*. Line *m* is at a 45° angle. Point *J* corresponds to *J'*, *K* to *K'*, *L* to *L'*, *M* to *M'*, *N* to *N'* and *P* to *P'*. Line *m* is the line of reflection. **Pay close attention to how to determine the mirror image of figure *JKLMNP* across line *m* described below. This method only works when the line of reflection is at a 45° angle.**

Point *J* is 2 spaces over from line *m*, so *J'* must be 2 spaces down from line *m*.

Point *K* is 4 spaces over from line *m*, so *K'* is 4 spaces down from line *m*, and so on.

Draw the following reflections, and record the new coordinates of the reflection. The first problem is done for you.

1. Reflect figure *ABC* across the *x*-axis. Label vertices *A'B'C'* so that point *A'* is the reflection of point *A*, *B'* is the reflection of *B*, and *C'* is the reflection of *C*.

    A' = (–4, –2) *B'* = (–2, –4) *C'* = (0, –4)

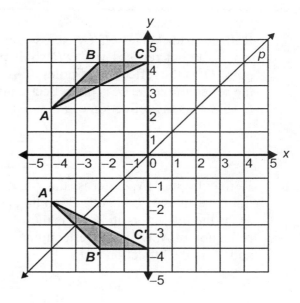

2. Reflect figure *ABC* across the *y*-axis. Label vertices *A"B"C"* so that point *A"* is the reflection of point *A*, *B"* is the reflection of *B*, and *C"* is the reflection of *C*.

    A" = _____ *B"* = _____ *C"* = _____

3. Reflect figure *ABC* across line *p*. Label vertices *A'''B'''C'''* so that point *A'''* is the reflection of point *A*, *B'''* is the reflection of *B*, and *C'''* is the reflection of *C*.

    A''' = _____ *B'''* = _____ *C'''* = _____

327

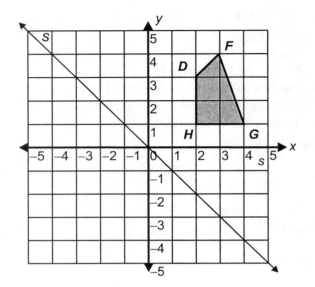

4. Reflect figure *DFGH* across the *y*-axis. Label vertices *D'F'G'H'* so that point *D'* is the reflection of point *D*, *F'* is the reflection of *F*, *G'* is the reflection of *G*, and *H'* is the reflection of *H*.

D' = _____   G' = _____

F' = _____   H' = _____

5. Reflect figure *DFGH* across the *x*-axis. Label vertices *D''*, *F''*, *G''*, *H''* so that point *D''* is the reflection of *D*, *F''* is the reflection of *F*, *G''* is the reflection of *G*, and *H''* is the reflection of *H*.

D'' = _____   G'' = _____

F'' = _____   H'' = _____

6. Reflect figure *DFGH* across line *s*. Label vertices *D'''F'''G'''H'''* so that point *D'''* is the reflection of *D*, *F'''* corresponds to *F*, *G'''* to *G*, and *H'''* to *H*.

D''' = _____   G''' = _____

F''' = _____   H''' = _____

---

7. Reflect quadrilateral *MNOP* across the *y*-axis. Label vertices *M'N'O'P'* so that point *M'* is the reflection of point *M*, *N'* is the reflection of *N*, *O'* is the reflection of *O*, and *P'* is the reflection of *P*.

M' = _____   O' = _____

N' = _____   P' = _____

8. Reflect figure *MNOP* across the *x*-axis. Label vertices *M''*, *N''*, *O''*, *P''* so that point *M''* is the reflection of *M*, *N''* is the reflection of *N*, *O''* is the reflection of *O*, and *P''* is the reflection of *P*.

M'' = _____   O'' = _____

N'' = _____   P'' = _____

9. Reflect figure *MNOP* across line *w*. Label vertices *M'''N'''O'''P'''* so that point *M'''* is the reflection of *M*, *N'''* corresponds to *N*, *O'''* to *O*, and *P'''* to *P*.

M''' = _____   O''' = _____

N''' = _____   P''' = _____

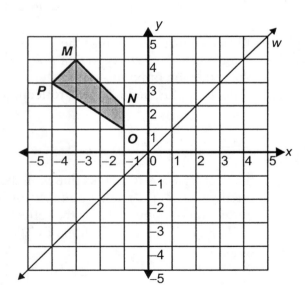

328

ROTATIONS

A **rotation** of a geometric figure shows motion around a point.

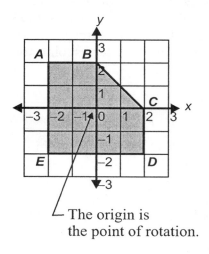

The origin is the point of rotation.

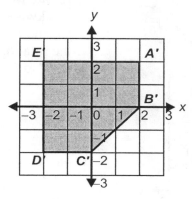

Figure *ABCDE* has been rotated $\frac{1}{4}$ of a turn clockwise around the origin to form *A'B'C'D'E'*.

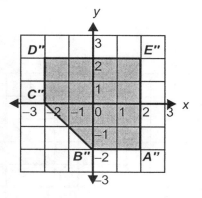

Figure *ABCDE* has been rotated $\frac{1}{2}$ of a turn around the origin to form *A"B"C"D"E"*.

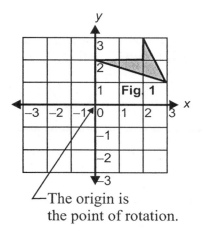

The origin is the point of rotation.

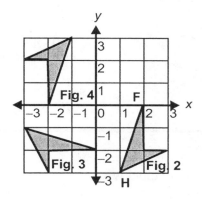

Figure 1 is rotated in $\frac{1}{4}$ turns around the origin. Figure 2 is a $\frac{1}{4}$ clockwise rotation of Figure 1. Figure 3 is a $\frac{1}{2}$ rotation of Figure 1. Figure 4 is a $\frac{3}{4}$ clockwise rotation of Figure 1.

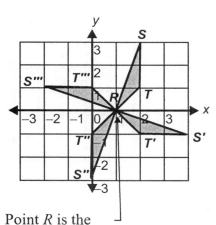

Point *R* is the point of rotation

Triangle *RST* is rotated around point *R*. Triangle *RS'T'* is a $\frac{1}{4}$ clockwise rotation of triangle *RST*. Triangle *RS"T"* is a $\frac{1}{2}$ rotation of triangle *RST*. Triangle *RS'''T'''* is a $\frac{3}{4}$ clockwise rotation of triangle *RST*.

Draw the following rotations, and record the new coordinates of the rotation. The figure for the first problem is drawn for you.

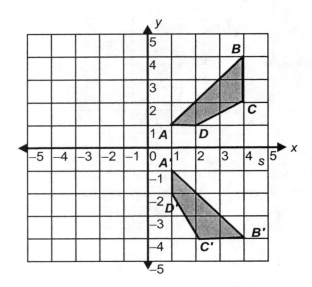

1. Rotate figure *ABCD* around the origin clockwise $\frac{1}{4}$ turn. Label the vertices *A'*, *B'*, *C'*, and *D'* so that point *A'* corresponds to the rotation of point *A*, *B'* corresponds to *B*, *C'* to *C*, and *D'* to *D*.

   A' = _____   *C'* = _____

   B' = _____   *D'* = _____

2. Rotate figure *ABCD* around the origin clockwise $\frac{1}{2}$ turn. Label the vertices *A"*, *B"*, *C"*, and *D"* so that point *A"* corresponds to the rotation of point *A*, *B"* corresponds to *B*, *C"* to *C*, and *D"* to *D*.

   A" = _____   *C"* = _____

   B" = _____   *D"* = _____

3. Rotate figure *ABCD* around the origin clockwise $\frac{3}{4}$ turn. Label the vertices *A'''*, *B'''*, *C'''*, and *D'''* so that point *A'''* corresponds to the rotation of point *A*, *B'''* corresponds to *B*, *C'''* to *C*, and *D'''* to *D*.

   A''' = _____   *C'''* = _____

   B''' = _____   *D'''* = _____

4. Rotate figure *MNO* around point *O* clockwise $\frac{1}{4}$ turn. Label the vertices *M'*, *N'*, and *O* so that point *M'* corresponds to the rotation of point *M* and *N'* corresponds to *N*.

   M' = _____   *N'* = _____

5. Rotate figure *MNO* around point *O* clockwise $\frac{1}{2}$ turn. Label the vertices *M"*, *N"*, and *O* so that point *M"* corresponds to the rotation of point *M*, and *N"* corresponds to *N*.

   M" = _____   *N"* = _____

6. Rotate figure *MNO* around point *O* clockwise $\frac{3}{4}$ turn. Label the vertices *M'''*, *N'''*, and *O* so that point *M'''* corresponds to the rotation of point *M*, and *N'''* corresponds to *N*.

   M''' = _____   *N'''* = _____

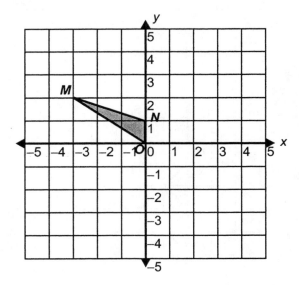

330   Copyright © American Book Company

TRANSLATIONS

A **translation** of a geometric figure is a duplicate of the figure slid along a path.

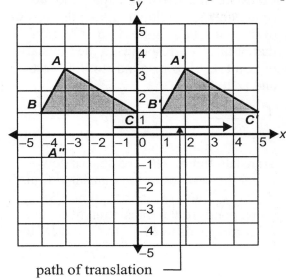

path of translation

Triangle $A'B'C'$ is a translation of triangle ABC. Each point is translated 5 spaces to the right. In other words, the triangle slid 5 spaces to the right. Look at the path of translation. It gives the same information as above. Count the number of spaces across given by the path of translation, and you will see it represents a move 5 spaces to the right. Each new point is found at $(x + 5, y)$.

Point A is at $(-3, 3)$. Therefore, A' is found at $(-3 + 5, 3)$ or $(2, 3)$.

B is at $(-4, 1)$ so B' is at $(-4 + 5, 1)$ or $(1, 1)$.

C is at $(0, 1)$ so C' is at $(0 + 5, 1)$ or $(5, 1)$.

Quadrilateral $FGHI$ is translated 5 spaces to the right and 3 spaces down. The path of translation shows the same information. It points right 5 spaces and down 3 spaces. Each new point is found at $(x + 5, y - 3)$.

Point F is located at $(-4, 3)$. Point F' is located at $(-4 + 5, 3 - 3)$ or $(1, 0)$.

Point G is at $(-2, 5)$. Point G' is at $(-2 + 5, 5 - 3)$ or $(3, 2)$.

Point H is at $(-1, 4)$. Point H' is at $(-1 + 5, 4 - 3)$ or $(4, 1)$.

Point I is at $(-1, 2)$. Point I' is at $(-1 + 5, 2 - 3)$ or $(4, -1)$.

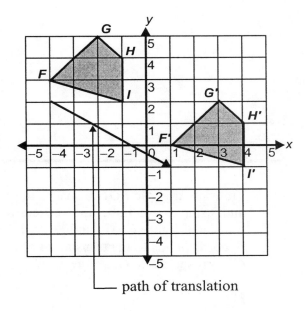

path of translation

Draw the following translations, and record the new coordinates of the translation. The figure for the first problem is drawn for you.

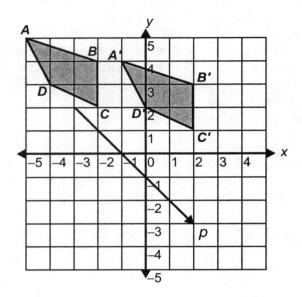

1. Translate figure *ABCD* 4 spaces to the right and 1 space down. Label the vertices of the translated figure *A'*, *B'*, *C'*, and *D'* so that point *A'* corresponds to the translation of point *A*, *B'* corresponds to *B*, *C'* to *C*, and *D'* to *D*.

   A' = _____   *C'* = _____

   B' = _____   *D'* = _____

2. Translate figure *ABCD* 5 spaces down. Label the vertices of the translated figure *A''*, *B''*, *C''*, and *D''* so that point *A''* corresponds to the translation of point *A*, *B''* corresponds to *B*, *C''* to *C*, and *D''* to *D*.

   A'' = _____   *C''* = _____

   B'' = _____   *D''* = _____

3. Translate figure *ABCD* along the path of translation, *p*. Label the vertices of the translated figure *A'''*, *B'''*, *C'''*, and *D'''* so that point *A'''* corresponds to the translation of point *A*, *B'''* corresponds to *B*, *C'''* to *C*, and *D'''* to *D*.

   A''' = _____   *C'''* = _____

   B''' = _____   *D'''* = _____

4. Translate triangle *FGH* 6 spaces to the left and 3 spaces up. Label the vertices of the translated figure *F'*, *G'*, and *H'* so that point *F'* corresponds to the translation of point *F*, *G'* corresponds to *G*, and *H'* to *H*.

   F' = _____ *G'* = _____ *H'* = _____

5. Translate triangle *FGH* 4 spaces up and 1 space to the left. Label the vertices of the translated triangle *F''G''H''* so that point *F''* corresponds to the translation of point *F*, *G''* corresponds to *G*, and *H''* to *H*.

   F'' = _____ *G''* = _____ *H''* = _____

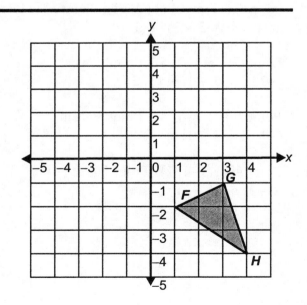

A point can undergo a translation as well.

EXAMPLE: A point at (1, 3) is moved to (0, 0). If a point at (−1, 2) is moved in the same way, what will its new coordinates be?

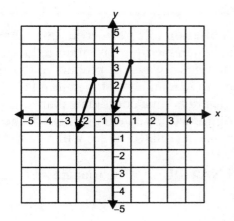

Step 1: Count how many lines down and over the original point is moving. In this problem, the point is moving down three places and then to the left one place.

Step 2: Find where point (−1, 2) is, and see where it would be when you move it in the same way–down 3 places and to the left 1 place. The new coordinates will be (−2, −1).

Use the grid to answer the questions that follow.

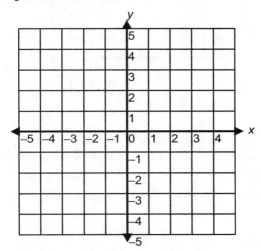

1. A point at (3, 4) is moved to (0, 0). If a point at (2, 2) is moved in the same way, what will its new coordinates be?

2. A point at (−3, 2) is moved to (0, 0). If a point at (−1, 2) is moved in the same way, what will its new coordinates be?

3. A point at (−4, 2) is moved to (0, 0). If a point at (−1, 1) is moved in the same way, what will its new coordinates be?

4. A point at (2, −4) is moved to (0, 0). If a point at (3, 1) is moved in the same way, what will its new coordinates be?

5. A point at (−2, −4) is moved to (0, 0). If a point at (−2, 1) is moved in the same way, what will its new coordinates be?

6. A point at (−3, 1) is moved to (0, 0). If a point at (1, 2) is moved in the same way, what will its new coordinates be?

333

DILATIONS

A **dilation** of a geometric figure is either an enlargement or a reduction of the figure. The point at which the figure is either reduced or enlarged is called the center of dilation. The dilation of a figure is always the product of the original and a **scale factor.** The scale factor is always a positive number that is multiplied by the coordinates of a shape's vertices, which is usually illustrated in a coordinate plane. If the scale factor is greater than one, then the resulting dilated figure will be an enlargement of the original figure. If the scale factor is less than one, then the resulting dilated figure will be a reduction of the original figure.

EXAMPLE: The triangle ABC has been dilated by a scale factor of $\frac{1}{4}$.

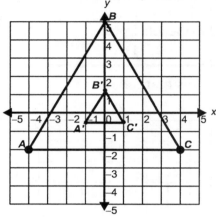

The first step in finding the dilated object is to list all the vertices of the original object, ABC. The next step is to multiply the coordinates of the vertices of ABC by the scale factor, $\frac{1}{4}$, to find the coordinates of the dilated figure. Lastly, draw the dilated object on the coordinate plane as shown above.

$A: (-4, -2)$ $A': (-4 \times \frac{1}{4}, -2 \times \frac{1}{4}) = (-1, -\frac{1}{2})$

$B: (0, 5)$ $B': (0 \times \frac{1}{4}, 5 \times \frac{1}{4}) = (0, \frac{5}{4})$

$C: (4, -2)$ $C': (4 \times \frac{1}{4}, -2 \times \frac{1}{4}) = (1, -\frac{1}{2})$

NOTE: Since the scale factor is less than one, the dilated figure $A'B'C'$ is a reduction of original triangle, ABC.

Circle the coordinate plane that contains the shape that has been dilated.

A.
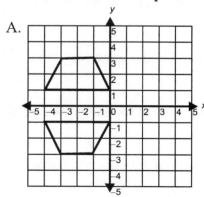

B.
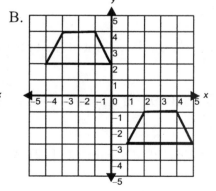

C.
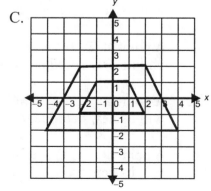

334

On your own graph paper, sketch the dilated and original figures.

For questions 1–6, find the coordinates of the vertices of the dilated figure.

For questions 7–10, find the scale factor.

1. A: $(-3, 1)$
   B: $(-1, 4)$
   C: $(1, 4)$
   D: $(3, 1)$
   Scale factor: 4

2. A: $(-6, 5)$
   B: $(3, 5)$
   C: $(3, -4)$
   D: $(-6, -4)$
   Scale factor: $\frac{1}{3}$

3. A: $(-10, 0)$
   B: $(0, 10)$
   C: $(8, 5)$
   Scale factor: $\frac{4}{5}$

4. A: $(1, -7)$
   B: $(1, 7)$
   C: $(5, 5)$
   D: $(5, \frac{1}{2})$
   E: $(1, -3)$
   F: $(-1, -3)$
   G: $(-5, -\frac{1}{2})$
   H: $(-5, 5)$
   Scale factor: 2

5. A: $(-8, 7)$
   B: $(-4, 7)$
   C: $(-2, 3)$
   D: $(-6, 3)$
   Scale factor: $\frac{3}{2}$

6. A: $(-4, 12)$
   B: $(6, -2)$
   C: $(-14, -2)$
   Scale factor: $\frac{1}{2}$

7. A: $(-3, 2)$ A': $(-10.5, 7)$
   B: $(1, 2)$ B': $(3.5, 7)$
   C: $(1, -3)$ C': $(3.5, -10.5)$
   D: $(-3, -3)$ D': $(-10.5, -10.5)$

8. A: $(-6, 9)$ A': $(-2, 3)$
   B: $(3, 12)$ B': $(1, 4)$
   C: $(6, 3)$ C': $(2, 1)$
   D: $(-9, 0)$ D': $(-3, 0)$

9. A: $(0, -3)$ A': $(0, -2)$
   B: $(6, 0)$ B': $(4, 0)$
   C: $(0, -3)$ C': $(0, -2)$

10. A: $(-2, 6)$ A': $(-10, 30)$
    B: $(2, 6)$ B': $(10, 30)$
    C: $(3, 3)$ C': $(15, 15)$
    D: $(2, 0)$ D': $(10, 0)$
    E: $(-2, 0)$ E': $(-10, 0)$
    F: $(-3, 3)$ F': $(-15, 15)$

For questions 11 and 12, determine whether or not $A'B'C'D'$ is a dilation of $ABCD$.

11. A: $(-2, 5)$ A': $(-1, 2)$
    B: $(8, 8)$ B': $(4, 4)$
    C: $(12, 0)$ C': $(6, 0)$
    D: $(2, -6)$ D': $(1, -3)$

12. A: $(0, 8)$ A': $(-2, 6)$
    B: $(5, 8)$ B': $(3, 6)$
    C: $(5, -3)$ C': $(3, -1)$
    D: $(0, -3)$ D': $(-2, -1)$

TRANSFORMATION PRACTICE

Answer the following questions regarding transformations.

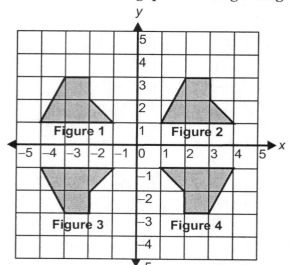

1. Which figure is a rotation of Figure 1? _____

   How far is it rotated? _____

2. Which figure is a translation of Figure 1? _____

   How far and in which direction(s) is it translated?

   _____

3. Which figure is a reflection of Figure 1? _____

4. Translate quadrilateral *ABCD* so that point *A'* which corresponds to point *A* is located at coordinates (−4, 3). Label the other vertices *B'* to correspond to *B*, *C'* to *C*, and *D'* to *D*. What are the coordinates of *B'*, *C'*, and *D'*?

   A' = _____   *C'* = _____

   B' = _____   *D'* = _____

5. Reflect quadrilateral *ABCD* across line *m*. Label the coordinates *A"*, *B"*, *C"*, *D"* so that point *A"* corresponds to the reflection of point *A*, *B"* corresponds to the reflection of *B*, and *C"* corresponds to the reflection of *C*. What are the coordinates of *A"*, *B"*, *C"*, and *D"*?

   A" = _____   *C"* = _____

   B" = _____   *D"* = _____

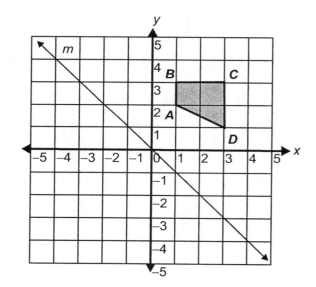

6. Rotate quadrilateral *ABCD* $\frac{1}{4}$ turn counterclockwise around point *D*. Label the points *A'''B'''C'''D'''* so that *A'''* corresponds to the rotation of point *A*, *B'''* corresponds to *B*, *C'''* to *C*, and *D'''* to *D*. What are the coordinates of *A'''*, *B'''*, *C'''* and *D'''*?

   A''' = _____   *C'''* = _____

   B''' = _____   *D'''* = _____

336

CHAPTER 25 REVIEW

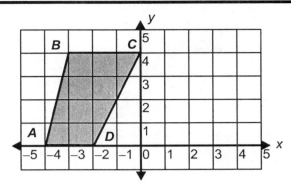

1. Draw the reflection of image *ABCD* over the *y*-axis. Label the points *A'*, *B'*, *C'*, and *D'*. List the coordinates of these points below.

2. *A'* _____   4. *C'* _____

3. *B'* _____   5. *D'* _____

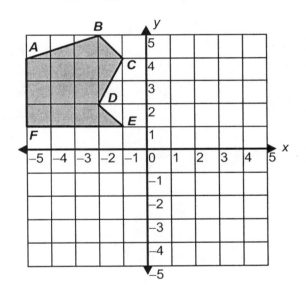

6. Rotate the figure above a $\frac{1}{2}$ turn about the origin, 0. Label the points *A'*, *B'*, *C'*, *D'*, *E'*, and *F'*. List the coordinates of these points below.

7. *A'* _____   10. *D'* _____

8. *B'* _____   11. *E'* _____

9. *C'* _____   12. *F'* _____

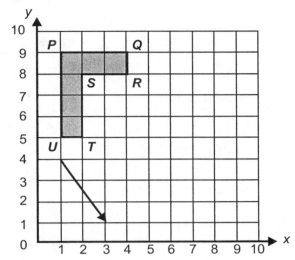

13. Use the translation described by the arrow to translate the polygon above. Label the points *P'*, *Q'*, *R'*, *S'*, *T'*, and *U'*. List the coordinates of each.

14. *P'* _____   17. *S'* _____

15. *Q'* _____   18. *T'* _____

16. *R'* _____   19. *U'* _____

Use the grid to answer the question that follows.

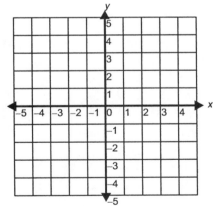

20. A point at $(-3, 2)$ is moved to $(0, 0)$. If a point at $(1, 1)$ is moved in the same way, what will its new coordinates be?

_____

For questions 21–23, graph the original and dilated figures.

21. *A*: (4, 0)
     B: (6, 3)
     C: (1, 3)
     D: (−1, 0)
     Scale factor: 2

22. *A*: (−6, −4)
     B: (2, 10)
     C: (10, −4)
     Scale factor: $\frac{1}{4}$

23. *A*: (−1, 5)   *A′*: (−3, 15)
     B: (1, 5)   *B′*: (3, 15)
     C: (3, 3)   *C′*: (9, 9)
     D: (3, 1)   *D′*: (9, 3)
     E: (1, −1)   *E′*: (3, −3)
     F: (−1, −1)   *F′*: (−3, −3)
     G: (−3, 1)   *G′*: (−9, 3)
     H: (−3, 3)   *H′*: (−9, 9)

Ohio Graduation Test Mathematics Review Sheet

Area (*A*) Formulas

parallelogram: $A = bh$

rectangle: $A = lw$

trapezoid: $A = \frac{1}{2}h(b_1 + b_2)$

triangle: $A = \frac{1}{2}bh$

Circle Formulas

$C = 2\pi r \qquad \pi \cong 3.14 \text{ or } \frac{22}{7}$

$A = \pi r^2$

Volume (*V*) Formulas

cone: $V = \frac{1}{3}\pi r^2 h$

cylinder: $V = \pi r^2 h$

pyramid: $V = \frac{1}{3}Bh \quad B = \text{area of base}$

rectangular prism: $V = lwh$

right prism: $V = Bh \quad B = \text{area of base}$

sphere: $V = \frac{4}{3}\pi r^3$

Combinations

$_nC_r = C(n,r) = \dfrac{n!}{r!(n-r)!}$

Permutations

$_nP_r = P(n,r) = \dfrac{n!}{(n-r)!}$

Distance Formula

$d = \sqrt{(x_1 - x_2)^2 + (y_1 - y_2)^2}$

Quadratic Formula

$x = \dfrac{{}^-b \pm \sqrt{b^2 - 4ac}}{2a}$

Trigonometry

$\sin A = \dfrac{opposite}{hypotenuse}$

$\cos A = \dfrac{adjacent}{hypotenuse}$

$\tan A = \dfrac{opposite}{adjacent}$

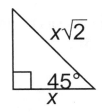

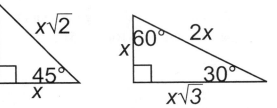

1. The sale price of a pair of sneakers at 25% off is $34.05. What was the regular price?

   A. $42.56
   B. $43.96
   C. $45.40
   D. $53.05

   1G

2. Which of the following is equal to 2.6×10^3?

   A. 0.0026
   B. 0.026
   C. 260
   D. 2,600

   1A

3. Which expression does not have the same value as the other three?

   A. $337\frac{1}{2}\%$

   B. $\frac{9}{6}$

   C. $125 \times .027$

   D. $\left(\frac{3}{2}\right)^3$

   1E

4. Which of the following numbers has the same value as $|-10| - (-5)^2$?

   A. -15
   B. 0
   C. 5
   D. 20

   1F

5. Using the Pythagorean theorem, what is the measure of side c of the triangle below? Round to the nearest tenth?

   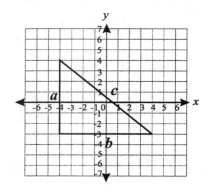

   A. 15
   B. 7.5
   C. 8
   D. 10.6

   3D

6. Which expression does not have the same value as the other three?

   A. 0.5^4
   B. 4^{-2}
   C. 6.25×10^2
   D. 0.25^2

   1E

7. An item is sold by a manufacturer to a wholesaler for $10. The wholesaler marks up the item 25% and sells it to a retail store. The retail storekeeper then marks up the item 50% of the wholesale price. What is the retail price of the item?
   What is the total markup percentage?

   1G

340

8. Abby received $16 for her 16th birthday. She spent one-fourth on treats for her friends. Then she put one-third of what was left in her savings account, and she kept the rest. What percentage of the $16 did Abby retain?

    A. 24%
    B. 25%
    C. $33\frac{1}{3}$%
    D. 50%

    1G

9. What is the approximate measure of angle *A*?

    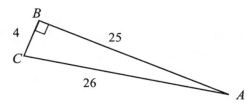

    A. 19°
    B. 81°
    C. 9°
    D. .003°

    3I

10. Mrs. Blake has 8 pairs of dress shoes. How many different ways can she arrange five pairs of her shoes in her closet?

    A. 40,320 ways
    B. 120 ways
    C. 8,000 ways
    D. 6,720 ways

    5H

11. Brice can type 22 pages in 3 hours. At this rate approximately how long would it take to type one page?

    A. 7.3 minutes
    B. 8.2 minutes
    C. 12.2 minutes
    D. 13.6 minutes

    1G

12. Below is scatterplot of 10 cars of same make and model that show the value of a car in thousands of dollars versus the age of the car.

    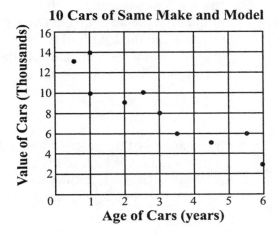

    What is the average age of the cars in years and the median value of cars in thousands of dollars?

    A. 2.95 years
        $8,400
    B. 2.75 years
        $9,000
    C. 3 years
        $8,000
    D. 6 years
        $3,000

    5A

13. The coordinates of three of the vertices of a rectangle are (−3, 1), (−3, −2), and (4, −2). Which of the following could be the coordinates of the fourth vertex of the rectangle?

   A. (−3, 1)
   B. (4, 1)
   C. (−4, −2)
   D. (−2, −2)

   3D

14. A rectangular garden measures 9 feet by 12 feet. Find the length of its diagonal.
   Draw a figure illustrating the problem, write an equation that can be used find the length of the diagonal of the garden, and calculate the length. Show your work.

   2C

15. The measures of the sides of triangles are given below. Which of the following triangles is similar to a triangle with sides 2.4, 7, and 7.4?

   A. 3, 8.75, 9
   B. 4, 8.4, 9.2
   C. 6, 17.5, 18.5
   D. 12, 14, 14.8

   2D, 3B

16. Consider a circle with diameter 5 inches and a square with sides measuring 10 inches each. How much smaller is the circle than the square?

   A. 21.5 square inches
   B. 78.5 square inches
   C. 80.4 square inches
   D. 214.2 square inches

   2C

17. Clark plots the point (2, 3) on a coordinate grid. Then, he reflects this point over the x-axis and translates it left 6 units.

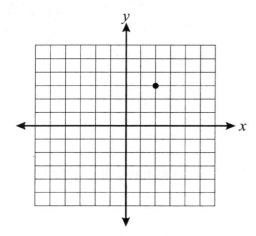

   What are the coordinates of the new point?

   A. (2, −3)
   B. (−4, −3)
   C. (−4, 3)
   D. (4, 3)

   3F

18. A cylindrical water tank with a diameter of 6 feet and a height of 10 feet is being replaced by a new tank with a diameter of 10 feet. If the two tanks have equal volume, what is the height of the new tank?

   A. 1.8 feet
   B. 2.5 feet
   C. 3 feet
   D. 3.6 feet

   2D

342

19. Beth wants to make a compost bin for leaves, grass clippings, and garden waste. She has a piece of stiff wire fencing material 4 feet high and 10 feet long which she forms into a cylindrical container with a circumference of 10 feet and a height of 4 feet. She wonders how many cubic feet of compost material her new container will hold. What is the volume of the cylindrical container?

2C

20. There are 6 red cards and 7 black cards in Laurie's hand. If two cards are selected at random (without replacement), what is the probability that the first card selected is red and the second is black?

A. $\frac{42}{169}$

B. $\frac{7}{26}$

C. $\frac{49}{156}$

D. $\frac{42}{144}$

5J

21. In a standard deck of 52 playing cards, there are 13 hearts. If 3 cards are drawn from the deck (without replacement), what is the probability that all 3 cards will be hearts?

A. $(13/52)^3$
B. $(13/52)(12/51)(11/50)$
C. $(13/52)(13/51)(13/50)$
D. $(13/52)(12/52)(11/52)$

5J

22. Dawn made a special deck of 12 playing cards for the math and science exhibit.

She shuffles the 12 cards and draws a card at random. What is the theoretical probability that the card she draws is a M, T, or H?

Next, she shuffles the 12 cards and draws three cards at random (without replacement). What is the probability that all three cards will be either a M, T, or H?

5I

23. A clown has 6 hats, 9 shirts, and 5 pairs of pants. How many outfits is that?

A. 20
B. 75
C. 84
D. 270

5H

24. The weights of six packages are 5 pounds, 7 pounds, 4 pounds, 18 pounds, 5 pounds, and 9 pounds. What are the mean, median, and mode of these weights?

	mean	median	mode
A.	6.0	5.5	7.0
B.	6.0	6.5	7.0
C.	8.0	5.0	5.0
D.	8.0	6.0	5.0

5D

25. Use indirect variation for the following. If $y = 12$ and $x = 3$, what is the value of y when $x = 7$?

A. 5.1
B. 28
C. 16
D. 22

4I

26. The volume of crystals in a jar triples every 5 minutes. The jar becomes completely full of crystals at 3:47 P.M. At what time was the jar only $\frac{1}{27}$ of the way full?

A. 3:20 P.M.
B. 3:22 P.M.
C. 3:32 P.M.
D. 3:37 P.M.

2E

27. Rebecca's scores on Spanish tests are 79, 84, 80, 76, and 83. What is the minimum score Rebecca can receive on the sixth test so that the average (mean) of the six tests will be 80 or above?

A. 75
B. 76
C. 77
D. 78

5D

28. Which equation represents the pattern shown in the table?

x	−5	−4	−3	−2	−1	0
y	6	2	0	0	2	6

A. $y = x^2 - x - 6$
B. $y = x^2 + 5x + 6$
C. $y = x^3 + 6x^2 + 11x + 6$
D. $y = x^3 + 9x^2 + 26x + 24$

4C

29. The scatter plot below shows the number of hours Emergency Medical Technician (EMT) trainees spent involved in TV and video games in the 16 hours between training and testing and the test scores of the trainees the following day.

The three points in the upper left hand corner of the graph below indicate that three of the trainees who were involved in TV or video games for 0 hours received a test score of 100.

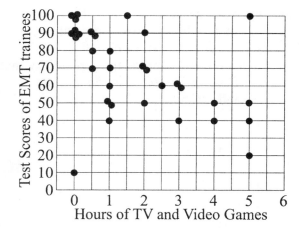

What is the mean test score of the 12 points which indicate less than one hour of TV and video games?

What is the mean test score of the 10 points which indicate more than 2 hours of TV and video games?

Which points appear to be outliers?

Does there appear to be a relationship between hours involved in TV and video games and the test scores of EMT trainees? If so, what type of relationship is it?

5D, 5F

30. At the Clothes Rack, the retail price (*r*) of an item is based on the wholesale cost (*w*) using the formula $r = 1.6w + 2$. The store policy allows employees to purchase items at wholesale cost. Which of the following formulas could be used to calculate the wholesale cost (*w*) of an item from the retail price (*r*)?

   A. $w = 1.6r - 3.2$
   B. $w = 1.6r - 2$
   C. $w = 0.625r - 2$
   D. $w = 0.625r - 1.25$

   4D

31. The Chamber of Commerce is preparing for the annual Renaissance Art and Music Festival. Spaces in the county park for exhibition, music workshops, performances, etc. are rented according to the formula
   $r = .50s^2 + 4s + 100$
   where *r* is the price of the rental and *s* is the longer side (feet) of the rectangular space rented.

   The Watercolor Society requires approximately 625 ft^2 for their workshop and exhibit area. What would be the rental fee for a square space 25 ft on a side?

   Jo-Jo the juggling clown rented a square space and was charged $142. Is Jo-Jo's square 6, 7, or 8 feet on a side?

   To simplify the fee information for prospective exhibitors, the following fee chart was posted.

Side in feet	10	20	30	40
Rental fee	$190	$380	$670	$1060

   What is the domain, and what is the range of the relation shown in the chart?

   4B, 4C, 4D

32. The functional relationship between altitude (*A*) above sea level (in feet) and the approximate boiling point (*B*) of water (in degrees Fahrenheit) may be expressed by the equation $B = -.00176A + 212$. What is the approximate boiling point of water at 2,500 feet?

   A. 194.4
   B. 207.6
   C. 208.3
   D. 216.4

   4F

33. What system of inequalities defines the shaded region below?

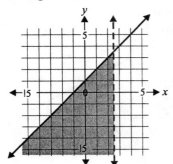

   A. $y \le x + 1$
      $x < 2.5$

   B. $y \ge x + 1$
      $x > 2.5$

   C. $y \le x + 1$
      $x > 2.5x$

   D. $y > x + 1$
      $x < 2.5y$

   4F

34. A dollar bill is approximately 2.5 inches in height by 6 inches in width. William is making a sign for the Dollar Store that is 10 feet in width. If the dimensions of the sign are proportionate to those of a dollar bill, what will be the approximate height of the sign?

A. 3 feet, 6 inches
B. 4 feet, 2 inches
C. 20 feet
D. 24 feet

2D

35. △ABC is similar to △DEF. What is the value of x?

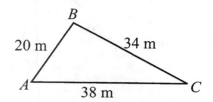

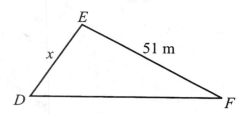

Note: The figures are not drawn to scale.

A. 17 m

B. 22 m

C. 30 m

D. 37 m

3B

36. Bob is buying frozen fruit juice bars for $1.00 each and ice cream bars for $1.20 each for a picnic. He has $40.00 to spend. Which of the following graphs models the possible number of fruit juice bars and the possible number of ice cream bars Bob can buy?

A.
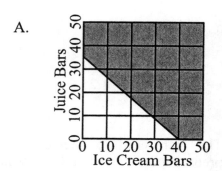

B.
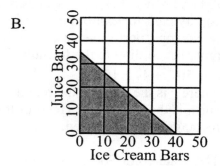

C.
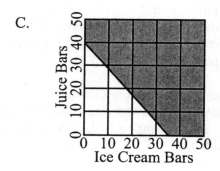

D.
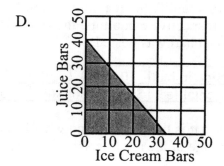

4C

346

37. If this shape's sides were folded upward at the dotted lines, what three-dimensional object would it make?

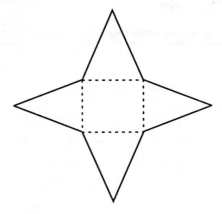

    A.   cube
    B.   cylinder
    C.   cone
    D.   pyramid

3E

38. All carnivores are meat eaters. Lions eat meat. Therefore, lions are carnivores. This kind of thinking is an example of _____ reasoning.

    A.   applied
    B.   inductive
    C.   qualitative
    D.   deductive

3H

1. Find A, when $\sin(A) = .5736$. Round to the nearest angle.

   A. $2°$
   B. $30°$
   C. $55°$
   D. $35°$

   3I

2. Which expression does not have the same value as the other?

   A. $\left(\frac{7}{50}\right)^2$

   B. 1.96×10^{-2}

   C. $\frac{49}{250}$

   D. 1.96%

   1E

3. Show the steps that you would use to find $(8.0 \times 10^9) \times (2.5 \times 10^5)$ without using a calculator. Write the answer in proper scientific notation.

   1I

4. Which of the following is equal to $-(-10)^{-3}$?

   A. -30
   B. $-.001$
   C. 3.0×10^1
   D. 1000^{-1}

   1E

5. The following two figures are similar.

   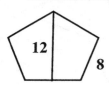
   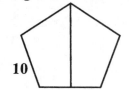

   What is the height of the second pentagon?

   A. 15
   B. 14
   C. 9.6
   D. 20

   3B

6. What type of transformation does the figure go through?

   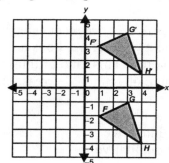

   A. dilation
   B. reflection
   C. translations
   D. rotation

   3F

348

7. During a 45-minute period, a math class spent 15 minutes going over homework, 5 minutes on a quiz, and 20 minutes taking notes on new material. What percentage of the 45-minute period remained for the students to begin work on the new material?

    A. $8\frac{1}{3}$ %

    B. $11\frac{1}{9}$ %

    C. 20%

    D. 25%

    1G

8. Approximately 15% of the shirts made at the Winsor and Best garment factory are labeled "irregular" and do not receive the Winsor and Best label. At this rate, how many shirts need to be made to produce approximately 500 Winsor and Best shirts which are not irregular?

    A. 515
    B. 575
    C. 590
    D. 605

    1G

9. The figure below is an isosceles triangle with two parallel lines within it. Find the measure of angle *FGC*.

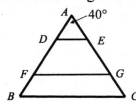

    A. 70°
    B. 140°
    C. 110°
    D. 290°

    3C

10. What is the area of the figure below?

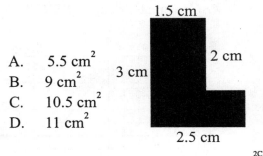

    A. 5.5 cm^2
    B. 9 cm^2
    C. 10.5 cm^2
    D. 11 cm^2

    2C

11. A 16 foot ramp is to be installed between a parking area and a 5 foot high loading dock as shown in the figure below.

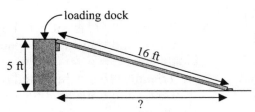

    How far will the end of the ramp be from the base of the loading dock?

    3I

12. The coordinates of three of the vertices of a square are (−2, −1), (−2, 4), and (3, 4). Which of the following could be the coordinates of the fourth vertex of the square?

    A. (−2, 2)
    B. (−1, 3)
    C. (−4, 0)
    D. (3, −1)

    3D

13. The measures of the sides of triangles are given below. Which of the following triangles is similar to a triangle with sides 18, 21, and 27?

    A. 12, 14, 20
    B. 15, 18, 24
    C. 20, 23, 29
    D. 24, 28, 36

    2D, 3B

14. What could have happened to triangle *ABC* to create triangle *A'B'C'*?

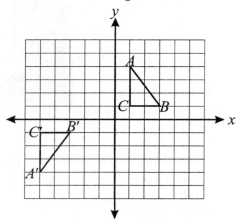

A. Triangle *ABC* is reflected over the *y*-axis and translated 2 spaces to the left.
B. Triangle *ABC* is reflected over the *x*-axis and translated 6 spaces to the left.
C. Triangle *ABC* is reflected over the *x*-axis and translated 2 spaces to the left.
D. Triangle *ABC* is reflected over the *y*-axis and translated 6 spaces to the left.

3F

15. An advertising sign is an equilateral triangle with sides 10 feet long.

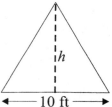

What is the approximate height of the sign?

A. 7 feet, 10 inches
B. 8 feet, 5 inches
C. 8 feet, 8 inches
D. 9 feet, 1 inch

2E

16. Derrell has made a cylinder using a 20-inch by 30-inch piece of poster board. The finished cylinder has a height of 30 inches. The top and bottom are closed with circular pieces of poster board to make a closed cylinder. What is the surface area of the entire closed cylinder?

2B

17. There are 10 boys and 12 girls in a classroom. If two students are selected at random from the class, what is the probability that the first student selected is a girl and the second is a boy?

A. $\frac{14}{55}$
B. $\frac{30}{121}$
C. $\frac{20}{77}$
D. $\frac{118}{231}$

5J

18. If 60 students eat 24 pizzas, which proportion below may be used to find the number of pizzas required to feed 15 students?

A. $\frac{60}{24} = \frac{15}{x}$
B. $\frac{60}{24} = \frac{x}{15}$
C. $\frac{60}{15} = \frac{x}{24}$
D. $\frac{60}{x} = \frac{15}{24}$

1G

350

19. In a standard deck of 52 playing cards there are 12 face cards (jack, queen, king). If 4 cards are drawn from the deck, without replacement, what is the probability that all 4 will be face cards?

A. $(12/52)^5$
B. $(12/52)(11/52)(10/52)(9/52)$
C. $(12/52)(12/51)(12/50)(12/49)$
D. $(12/52)(11/51)(10/50)(9/49)$

5J

20. A total of $30,000 will be required to complete the new playground in Greenville. A survey indicates that approximately 18% of the 5,975 residents of Greenville would be willing to contribute to a fund to complete the playground. Assuming that all donations were of equal amount, approximately how much money would each contributor need to donate to raise a total of $30,000?

A. $30
B. $50
C. $90
D. $100

4H

21. Which of the following is 4.9×10^{-4} equal to?

A. 0.00049
B. 0.0049
C. 4,900
D. 49,000

1A

22. A Republican politician running for mayor wants to take a poll to determine if he is the favored candidate in the upcoming election. The mayoral candidate is scheduled to give a speech not at all related to the election at an upcoming town celebration. For convenience sake, his staff polls all of the people in attendance at the speech as to who they are planning on voting for in the upcoming mayoral election. The staff reports to the candidate that, based on the recent poll, he is favored by the voters. Are the results of this poll most likely accurate or are they most likely misleading?

A. The results of the survey are accurate as long as at least 100 people were polled.
B. The results of the poll are most likely misleading because the sample of people surveyed were voluntarily attending a speech given by the candidate and do not necessarily represent the population of the town.
C. The results of the poll are most likely accurate because people are generally honest in declaring who they are going to vote for in elections.
D. The results of the poll are misleading because recent advertisements are encouraging people to vote, creating a more opinionated population than usual.

5G

23. The Coffee Cottage has various sizes of coffee mugs. The cost (c) of a mug of coffee is based on the equation $c = .15q + .25$, where q is the number of ounces of coffee the mug holds. What is the slope (m) of the equation $c = .15q + .25$?

   A. $m = .10$
   B. $m = .15$
   C. $m = .25$
   D. $m = .40$

   4E

24. Wade works at a men's clothing store. He also is studying statistics. He has collected the following set of data which shows the shoe size and the hat size of the 20 customers who bought shoes and hats last month.

Shoe Size	10	11	12	9	$9\frac{1}{2}$	10	13	$9\frac{1}{2}$	11	11
Hat Size	$7\frac{1}{4}$	$6\frac{3}{4}$	$7\frac{3}{4}$	$6\frac{3}{4}$	7	7	$7\frac{3}{4}$	$7\frac{1}{2}$	$7\frac{1}{2}$	7

Shoe Size	10	8	12	11	9	13	12	$10\frac{1}{2}$	12	10
Hat Size	7	$6\frac{1}{2}$	$7\frac{1}{2}$	$7\frac{3}{4}$	$6\frac{1}{2}$	$7\frac{1}{2}$	$7\frac{1}{4}$	$7\frac{1}{4}$	$7\frac{1}{2}$	$6\frac{3}{4}$

Use these data to make a scatter plot.

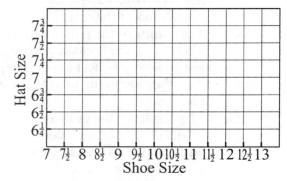

Sketch an approximate best-fit line through the data points on the scatter plot.
Based on the scatter plot and your best-fit line, does there appear to be a correlation between shoe size and hat size?
If a customer's shoe size measured 11, and the customer wanted to try on a hat, what size hat might Wade bring him? Use your scatter plot and your best-fit line to justify your answer.

5C, 5F

25. There are 44 students on the track team and 65 students on the swimming team. Of these students, 24 are on both teams. How many total students are there that are on the swimming team, track team or both teams?

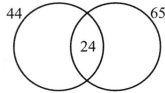

   A. 61
   B. 73
   C. 85
   D. 133

   1B

26. Juliette has a summer job as a camp counselor. Just for fun, she would like to wear a different combination of clothing items each day of the 28 days she will be at camp. She has three caps, five shirts, and two pairs of shorts.

Make a tree diagram to determine if she will have enough clothing combinations to make up 28 different outfits.

Next, imagine that Juliette has been hired for an additional 12 days, a total of 40 days. What could she add to her selection of clothing items to make exactly 40 distinct outfit combinations?

5H

27. Steven's scores on algebra tests are 91, 89, 86, and 93. What is the minimum score Steve can receive on the fifth test so that the average (mean) of the five tests will be 90 or above?

   A. 88
   B. 89
   C. 90
   D. 91

   5D

29. Both Robert and Carla are conducting surveys. They are selecting students from an alphabetical list of 974 students. Robert selects every 20th student beginning with student number 20, then number 40, etc. In a similar manner, Carla selects every 9th student, beginning with number 9. How many students will be interviewed by both Robert and Carla?

   A. 2
   B. 3
   C. 5
   D. 8

   4H

28. The Joyful Juice Co. sells 6 different fruit juices. The sales manager has decided to conduct a taste test on juice blends. Each blend will consist of equal parts of one of the 6 fruit juices and one other juice, producing blends such a apple-grape, cherry-orange, etc. Using the 6 fruit juices, how many two-juice mixes can be made?

   A. 12
   B. 15
   C. 30
   D. 36

   5H

30. The table below shows the estimated number of cases of a disease each year for 4 years.

Year	1	2	3	4	5	6
Total Cases	6,075	4,050	2,700	1,800	1,200	?

   If the pattern continues, what will be the estimated number of cases by the 6th year?

   A. 300
   B. 600
   C. 800
   D. 900

   4A

31. Solve the equation $3x^2 + 8x - 3 = 0$ using the quadratic equation. Show your work.

4G

32. Ken and Wilson are typing reports. Thus far Ken has typed 10 pages in 30 minutes. Wilson has typed 5 pages in 10 minutes. If Ken and Wilson continue typing at the same rates for 30 additional minutes, who will have typed the greatest <u>total</u> number of pages and by how much?

   A. Ken will have typed 5 more pages than Wilson.
   B. Wilson will have typed 5 more pages than Ken.
   C. Wilson will have typed 10 more pages than Ken.
   D. Ken and Wilson will have typed an equal number of pages.

4J

33. Which equation represents the pattern shown in the table?

x	−5	−4	−3	−2	−1	0	1
y	−24	−6	0	0	0	6	24

   A. $y = x^2 - x - 6$
   B. $y = x^2 + 5x + 6$
   C. $y = x^3 + 6x^2 + 11x + 6$
   D. $y = x^3 + 9x^2 + 26x + 24$

4C

34. Carl cut a 420-foot-long cable into two pieces. One piece is 5 times as long as the other. How long is the longer piece?

   A. 84 feet
   B. 168 feet
   C. 336 feet
   D. 350 feet

4F

35. At the Artists' Supply Center, the retail price of supplies is calculated using the formula $r = 1.75w + .25$. If the wholesale cost (w) of a paint set is $22.50, what would the retail price (r) be?

   A. $39.63
   B. $42.50
   C. $45.00
   D. $64.38

4D

36. Charlotte sketched a design for a sign board on a piece of paper $8\frac{1}{2}$ inches high and 11 inches wide. She wants to enlarge the design on a piece of plywood that is 4 feet high. If the dimensions of the sign are proportionate to those of the sketch, to the nearest inch, how wide will the sign be?

   A. 37 inches
   B. 41 inches
   C. 52 inches
   D. 62 inches

2D

37. At the amusement park, the Whirly Bird ride rotates at the rate of 15 revolutions per minute. How long does it take for the ride to make one complete revolution?

   A. .025 sec
   B. 4 sec
   C. 9 sec
   D. 90 sec

2F

354

38. Howard tossed a rubber ball into the air. The ball bounced three times and then dropped into a storm drain. Which of the following graphs best models this situation?

A.

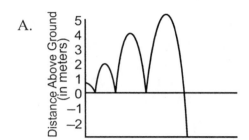

B.

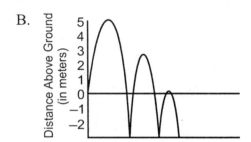

C.

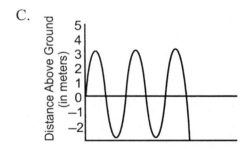

D.

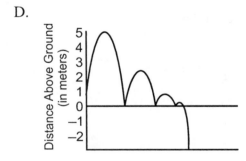

5B